Table of Contents

Foreword by

Hassan A. Tetteh MD

Multi Amazon Bestselling Author

Win the Wellness W.A.R.

We Are Responsible

for

All Things Wellness

More True Stories of the Heart, Spirit, Mind, and Body

Peggy Willms CHWLC   **Markus Wettstein MD**

Angi Currier	Renee Gideon	Alexxa Goodenough	Jesica Henderson
Christine Hersom	Evelyn Knight	Jacki Long	Sophia Long
Alysia Lyons	Faith Pearce	Lara Scriba	Tanner Willms
	Cyndi Wilkins		

Wellness Book Endeavors
c/o Authentic Endeavors Publishing
Clarks Summit, PA 18411

Book Interior and E-book Design by Amit Dey

Win The Wellness W.A.R.
ISBN: 978-1-955668-60-6 (Paperback)
ISBN: 978-1-955668-61-3 (EBook)
Library of Congress Control Number: 2023908943

AuthenticEndeavorsPublishing.com

To Our Contributing Authors

———— ★ ————

*W*e continue to believe storytelling changes and saves lives. Whether you are reading at night under the covers with a flashlight so you do not wake your spouse, sharing your thoughts in a church book club, or sharing a story with your grandson, stories provoke conversation and understanding.

As Contributing Authors, you were willing to get deep into the trenches of your lives and share personal battles within your heart, spirit, mind, and body. Your stories will change the lives of those holding this book in their hands.

You know how we feel about stories. They connect the world; they improve and save lives. Stories enhance perspectives and offer solutions; stories represent life.

Regardless of your geographic location, ethnicity, culture, or belief systems, you joined our All Things Wellness (ATW) Family, and we are honored. Thank you for sharing your light and love with the world. Revealing pieces of our past affect our present and future. Without sharing the morsels of our being, we cannot shift and align the energetic flow to One Love. We will *win the war* if we all show up for the battle.

Much Love and Peace,
Peggy & Markus

Acknowledgments

———— ★ ————

*M*arkus, my co-author, colleague, and friend, set off a year ago to write a trilogy about health and wellness with dozens of other contributing authors. We now have two books under our belt. We have stayed true to our mission of creating a platform for storytellers to dive deep and share their experiences with others. This journey would not be the same without you.

To Dr. Hassan Tetteh, thank you for writing our Foreword. Your experience, education, and passion align with our mission perfectly.

To our Media Partners, thank you for your continued support, and we look forward to the author interviews.

To Dana, what a ride this year has been. You're my pebble, rock, and boulder. To my oldest son, Shane, your support and insight are blessings. To my son, Tanner, who became a two-time author this past year, I am so proud of you for sharing with others.

Indebtedness to Cyndi for spiritually guiding me; Faith for being my verbal journal; Teresa for our Cawfee Tawks, and her team of experts, including, Aljon.

Peggy Willms, CFT, SPN, CHLWC, Co-Author

Peggy, my co-author, and friend, thanks for this amazing ride. You are the engine of this train.

We had to endure many battles to get here. But our personal transformation drives this second book in the *All Things Wellness* series. Yes, we are responsible for finding the punctures in our wellness wheel tires, and now we have the *ATW Wheel*^{TM} wheel to get the job done. Awareness creates the power to change, so thank you for giving us that power.

I also would like to thank my wife. Without you, none of this would be possible. Your patience and loving support help me through my personal battles with unhelpful programs. You are supportive of my wondrous journey to a joyful life. Thank you for being my one and only.

Thanks to everyone who have shared part of their lives with me. I am a successful, happy person because of you. You were instrumental in creating good. Thank you for that.

Finally, I want to thank all our Media Partners for their support. We know we have a game-changer in our hands. But you can help us spread the word so others can take responsibility and be confident to Win the Wellness War. Thank you for being you.

Dr. Markus Wettstein, MD

Foreword

By Hassan Tetteh, MD

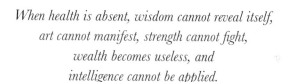

When health is absent, wisdom cannot reveal itself,
art cannot manifest, strength cannot fight,
wealth becomes useless, and
intelligence cannot be applied.

Herophilus of Chalcedon
(physician to Alexander the Great
and pupil of Hippocrates)

*W*hile training as a heart surgeon at the University of Minnesota and on my way to the infirmary, I stopped at a giant wall I had passed many times before. I was not well. I was very sick. The wall had the words above from Herophilus of Chalcedon. Despite passing the wall daily in transit to clinics and seeing patients, it was the first time I acknowledged the significant words boldly written there, which were both sobering and immediately relevant to my condition. My health and wellness were both absent. Long hours, poor diet, no sleep, and stress contributed to my ill state. Now, nothing else mattered. I visited the infirmary to restore my wellness so things would matter again. I also wanted to know who Herophilus was since he comprehensively described my condition in a way that made me fully appreciate my health and wellness once it returned.

Herophilus of Chalcedon (c. 335-280 BC) was a pioneering Greek physician and anatomist born in Chalcedon in Bithynia, Asia Minor. Within the context of the Hellenistic period, his life and work were vital at a time when the Macedonian king's conquests helped spread Greek culture and knowledge throughout the known world. Herophilus studied at the famed medical school of Cos under the tutelage of renowned physicians of his time, including Praxagoras and Hippocrates. Alexander the Great's conquests in this Hellenistic period, yielded significant advancements in various fields, including medicine, as scholars from different regions gained access to the accumulated knowledge of the time.

Herophilus would move to Alexandria, Egypt, where he worked under the patronage of the Ptolemaic Dynasty, established by one of Alexander's former generals, Ptolemy I Soter. The city of Alexandria became a leading center for research and learning, and its famed library and museum provided Herophilus with access to a wealth of knowledge. Herophilus is best known for his groundbreaking research in human anatomy, conducted through the systematic dissection of human cadavers, a revolutionary and controversial practice at that time. I learned that Herophilus' work laid the foundation for studying human anatomy and physiology, and his discoveries included detailed descriptions of the nervous system, circulatory system, and various internal organs. He contributed to our more profound understanding of the human body and its functions.

In *Win the Wellness W.A.R. (We Are Responsible)*, the authors build on *The Four-Fold Formula for All Things Wellness*. Not coincidentally, wellness is indeed a war story. As a physician, military surgeon, formally trained national security strategist, and student of Herophilus, I can draw the connection through events like the fall of Athens and COVID-19. During my studies in National Security Strategy at the National War College, I was the only physician in my graduating class of extraordinary leaders. In our seminars, my classmates appropriately lauded the generals and brilliant military minds endowed with the strategies and technologies to win the great wars of the past. In these conversations, my contributions generally centered on how viruses, disease, illness, and pandemics played an equally important role. At the War College, we studied war and national security. We went back to history to study wars like the Peloponnesian War and discussed modern campaigns.

In each of these campaigns, my colleagues talked about the brilliance of the strategist, the tactical advantages, and the weapons. I always looked for the health angle—and how, in every case, the health and wellness of the warriors was the decisive factor. True, the military strategies, technology, logistics, and leadership were influential and very powerful. However, health issues, and specifically war-fighter health, had the most significant impact on the outcomes of the campaigns we studied. How did Sparta defeat Athens? Think about it—a small nation versus the center of Greek civilization. It is the equivalent of a Caribbean island defeating the United States. I asked my classmates to "Consider reasons for why Athens was defeated. Before those decisive Spartan battles, if you recall, Athens experienced a devastating plague." The people of Athens lost the wellness war.

To deal with the plague, Athens closed its walls and kept its citizens inside. The disease spread like wildfire throughout the population. The disease impacted Athens' greatest politicians and leaders, even Pericles. Pericles was a tremendous force in Athenian civilization. He died. The plague wiped him out.

Consequently, Athens had inexperienced and unwise leaders who had lost their faith and moral compass due to the death and devastation they had witnessed. So, not surprisingly, Sparta defeated great Athens. The story is sensationalized in movies like *300: Rise of an Empire*. We praise the buff warriors and recount how they did it. However, the plague and the lost wellness war contributed to the defeat of Athens.

So, what is the connection to today? *Win the Wellness W.A.R.* connects to the present and brilliantly highlights how we are responsible for our wellness. The link is clear. Society fundamentally changes with global pandemic events. How you individually adapt, emerge, and how you evolve has consequences. You are responsible. Heart, spirit, mind, and body all contribute to wellness. How society collectively adapts, emerges, and grows from a pandemic will have global consequences and impact lives for generations.

In the following chapters, Peggy Willms, Dr. Markus Wettstein, and the authors invite you to reflect. They challenge you to work hard to improve your health, wellness, and life. They provide the tools and armor to face life's battles and challenges. Herophilus was a great teacher in his era and understood health and wellness. *Win the Wellness W.A.R.* is our battle plan for today. Take responsibility and study its lessons of health and wellness. With health and wellness, wisdom reveals itself; art becomes manifest; we have the strength to fight life's challenges; our wealth becomes useful; we may apply our intelligence and positively change the world for generations. To your wellness.

Preface

★

*Y*ou hold book two of the *All Things Wellness* series in your hands. *Win the Wellness W.A.R.* (We Are Responsible). If you haven't read book one, *The Four-Fold Formula for All Things Wellness*, grab it on Amazon or in a big box bookstore near you. The final book in the series, *Wellness G.P.S. (Get Prepared for Success)*, will be released in 2024.

Book one introduced you to the trademarked self-assessment tool, *ATW Wheel™*. It was developed a few years ago to help people determine the status of their health, wellness, and lifestyle. It is a real-time guide allowing you to design goals and reveal areas of improvement. With self-awareness and self-assessment, the tool identifies punctures or flats. Being armed with personalized knowledge enables one to live the highest-quality life. You get to meet yourself where you are.

As we discussed the weight of the world, we realized how the content of this book was aligned and timely. No coincidence. Over the past few years, we have been dodging a foray of bombs striking us from many directions. To name a few, the aftermath of the worldwide COVID-19 pandemic, government elections, struggling economies, battles in Ukraine and other countries, mass shootings, global warming, struggles to understand diversity in sexuality, culture, and religion, and the increased void in mental health support and stress awareness continually led us to one solution—we must take personal responsibility for what we can control and the steps necessary to find safe and healthy solutions. Most importantly, we must never give up, and we must band together.

Here are a few quotes that explain our thoughts:

Fear not the unseen.
Psalm 91:5-6

*The secret of health for both mind and body is not to
mourn for the past, nor to worry about the future,
but to live the present moment wisely and earnestly.*
Buddha

*It is only when you take responsibility for your life.
that you discover how truly powerful you are.*
Allanah Hunt

Responsibility Starts From Within

Can we solve the world's problems alone? No! Do we give up? No!!!
Can we create our best selves and at least show up—You bet!

How can we, as individuals and as a collective, improve this planet
and the humans and animals that live on it? What can we control versus what can we not control? How do we begin? Standing still or doing
nothing is no longer an option. Worse yet, complaining and not doing
anything should be punishable by law. Okay, that is a bit aggressive, but
you get the point.

We chose to hit the issues head-on. There are three steps to taking
responsibility. First, we must look inward, then we must look outward,
and finally, we must move forward. No step is an easy fix or a stand-
alone option. None of the three steps can be avoided. Determination,
consistency, and a desire to accomplish tasks are required for any goal in
life, such as graduating from college, raising a family, or nailing that promotion. And self-discovery and understanding others' perspectives are
priceless to facing and solving problems. We must prepare for and win the
battles, big and small, one or ten at a time. This brings us to the title of
this book. *Win the Wellness W.A.R.* (We Are Responsible).

Dr. Markus and I discussed the status of individuals and the world in general, and we decided to go big or go home when drafting this book. We chose to face a few words many people dislike. The words *hard, work,* and *war.* A few people hesitated to join this project because of the word "war." I can get a bit barky about this subject. Straight up, "Life is HARD. Life is WORK. Life is WAR." And the sooner we accept these "tough" words, the sooner we can create ways to conquer them." Reframing the true meaning of these words is a disservice. Reframing to make us feel more comfortable or less overwhelmed helps no one.

Improving your life and the world is not about sugar-coating. Having children is HARD. Owning and operating a farm is WORK. And if our soldiers are not trying to win a WAR, which by definition is an armed conflict between different nations, states, or groups, then what have our troops been fighting for? Having tea and crumpets? Tell that to the families who get a knock on their door from a military officer solemnly sharing that their son or daughter's life was lost while they fought for our freedom.

We chose to share our concepts, tools, and strategies within this book—based on the battles and hard knocks life throws our way. Over thirty contributing authors got down and dirty and dug deep into their souls to share their stories with you. We will leave you encouraged and armed with the knowledge you need to assess your battle cries and create your own treaty.

Win the Wellness W.A.R. by standing at attention and taking action. *We Are ALL Responsible.*

Peggy Willms and Dr. Markus Wettstein

Introduction

*Now more than ever, we need to
step back, step up, and show up.*

Peggy Willms

Wake up! We have work to do to Win the Wellness W.A.R.

Markus Wettstein, MD

There is no denying that we spin many plates simultaneously. As I thought about commitment, dedication, and emotional resiliency, a Toby Keith song played on the radio. We are currently staying at an extended-stay hotel which we now call our home away from home. Our "real" home is being restored from Hurricane Ian's destructive path last Fall. We survived a War. A life-changing battle for us, and we will win!

I am an early riser, so it is common to find me outside writing on my laptop and wearing a ball cap. As my fingers danced across the keys this morning, I paused to listen to the lyrics of a song I had never heard. The word "soldier" popped out. Wait for a second…I am writing a book about winning a war. I hurriedly researched the lyrics. The universe agreed with me…we are all spinning plates, wearing different hats, and trying to do our best in the process. It is a tricky balance, and Toby's song shared a compelling example. American Soldier is about an American in the Army Reserves. As he gets dressed and packs his bags for deployment, various video clips show soldiers from different wars throughout U.S. history. Although each soldier is in a different battle and time period (the American Civil War, World War I, World War II, the Vietnam War, and the Iraq War), they are all meant to exemplify the traits of an American soldier: loyalty, fearlessness, and bravery. The family gathers at a U.S. military base, where the protagonist will be flown off to a training camp. After saying goodbye to his wife and children, he boards a cargo plane, ready to serve his country.

We can become overwhelmed, defeated, and often give up when faced with adversity. The only way we can solve personal and worldly problems is to accept our responsibilities, live up to our integrity and promises, and take action.

Toby's song, *American Soldier*, tells of the many hats we wear and the struggles to balance it all. The song was written by Toby Keith And Chuck Cannon.

I'm just trying to be a father,
Raise a daughter and a son,
Be a lover to their mother,
Everything to everyone.
Up and at 'em bright and early,
I'm all business in my suit,
Yeah, I'm dressed up for success.
from my head down to my boots,
I don't do it for the money,
there's bills that I can't pay,
I don't do it for the
glory, I just do it anyway,
Providing for our future's
my responsibility,
Yeah I'm real good under pressure,
being all that I can be,
I can't call in sick on Mondays
when the weekend's been too strong,

I just work straight
through the holidays,
Sometimes all night long.
You can bet that I stand ready
when the wolf growls at the door.
Hey, I'm solid, hey, I'm steady,
hey, I'm true down to the core.

He recognizes the chase, the overload, but he takes responsibility. He is trained and stands ready to fight the wolf growling at the door. Having coffee with Toby would be insightful. First, I would give him a high-five and say, "Life is hard. It is work, and it is a war, huh, buddy?!" I would then ask, "Tell me the battles you have won, those you are still fighting, and how you plan to keep marching and become healthier and happier?" These are the same questions I ask you. What battles have you faced, and what have you learned, whether you won, were defeated, or surrendered? Dr. Markus, my co-author, and I will help you answer these questions and find solutions that work for you personally.

As the world spins, we will continually face challenges. Some will be expected, like a troop rushing over the field's knoll for the next attack; you know they are coming. Others catch us off guard, like an ambush from behind, and we find ourselves ill-prepared like your car engine blowing after you just paid all of your bills. Whether you give yourself credit or not, you have consciously or unconsciously faced several adversities.

So, together, let us gear up and trudge to the other side of that trench. You are about to gain control and arm yourself with strategies and tools to face the tough stuff…the battles. And, together, we will win the war. We will show you.

Self-awareness, self-discovery, communication, and collaboration improve every situation regardless of how dire your life or the world is. Using the recent global pandemic as an example, most people agree there were many positive learnings from such an unfortunate experience. We saw this in our own personal and professional practices serving our clients and patients. Everyone, everywhere, was affected by COVID-19 either physically, mentally, spiritually, or financially. The first "war," I am aware of, that affected every person on the planet simultaneously.

If you read the first book of our *All Things Wellness* series, *The Four-Fold Formula for All Things Wellness,* you became acquainted with the *ATW Wheel*^{TM}, which meets you right where you are and helps you take responsibility to improve 24 areas of your life. Whether you have been diagnosed with diabetes, want to purchase a house, or you are faced with surviving something as horrific as a pandemic or hurricane, this tool will help you win those battles and prepare for those ahead.

In this book, you will be primed to *Win the Wellness W.A.R.* (We Are Responsible). In each of the four chapters of this book, Heart, Spirit, Mind, and Body, you will learn definitions for each section of the *ATW Wheel*^{TM}, and you will become familiar with the *6Ws of Wellness*. In the back of the book, you will find *The Coach and The Doc Battle Tips,* which are recommendations or ideas we offer to guide you on a deeper path of self-discovery and growth. Ultimately, you can design an *ATW Improvement Plan* that aligns with your health, wellness, and lifestyle goals.

Additionally, we are proud to share personal and true stories written by our Contributing Authors. Their stories will motivate and inspire you. Stories about eating disorders, losing a family member, lies and deceit, motherhood, caring for the elderly, spiritual journeys, honoring beautiful memories, and more. Their bios and contact information are in the back of the book. Reach out to them. They would love to hear your stories, too. Stories connect everyone if we share them!

We're not done—you will also find a list of "Additional Reading" recommended by our Contributing Authors and "Questions for Your Book Club."

Our vision continues—storytelling can change and save lives. They prove we are not alone. We are not that special, meaning there isn't any single person on this planet that has experienced something someone else, somewhere, hasn't. Therefore, WE ARE CONNECTED. We are more similar than not!

This book is more than just an anthology or a doctor's office read. Sure, it is about learning, healing, and hope, but the content and tools help you feel the feels, analyze your history and habits, and launch you to success.

We believe in Real People with Real Problems finding Real Solutions, achieving Real Results, and ultimately sharing their Real Stories. Share the stories in this book with family, friends, co-workers, and even strangers. Create a book club at work, church, or school. Keep this treasure in mind when looking for a unique gift for a special someone.

Welcome to the All Things Wellness Family and Welcome to *Win the Wellness W.A.R. (We Are Responsible):* True Stories of the Heart, Spirit, Mind, and Body.

What is the All Things Wellness book series about?

———— ★ ————

*L*ast fall, book one, *The Four-Fold Formula for All Things Wellness*, kicked off the *All Things Wellness* trilogy. Metaphorically, we used a "formula." We took you through a cupcake recipe. If you miss one ingredient when baking, the result is less than optimal. Without all the necessary ingredients (pieces of the puzzle: the heart, spirit, mind, and body), we repeat the same mistakes resulting in many do-overs, and we often give up.

In the framework for each book in the series, we use three different metaphors. Book one, a recipe (*The Four-Fold Formula*). Book two, a war (*Win the Wellness W.A.R.*), and book three will help you design the path of your goals by using a global positioning system like in your car (*Wellness G.P.S.*).

Within each book, you will learn new content and tips on how to use Peggy's trademarked tool, the *All Things Wellness Wheel* (*ATW Wheel*^{TM}). Each book consists of four chapters representing the four quadrants of the wellness wheel: Heart, Spirit, Mind, and Body. Within the four quadrants of the wheel, there are six different spokes— 24 total. Each spoke represents a variety of lanes in your life. A few are…coping skills, emotions, creativity, habits, organization, nutrition, sleep, how you live your life at work, home, or play, and more. In each book, you will also enjoy personal stories from over 30 Contributing Authors.

In this book, *Win the Wellness W.A.R.* (We Are Responsible), we prepare you for life's battles, teach you how to take responsibility for your own health, and help you win the war. Building awareness, expanding your education, and creating a winning strategy, require diligence in training and a willingness to grow. It sounds like planning for a battle or a war, doesn't it? It is time to get tactical, more confident, and find peace.

We will tie up the trilogy in 2024, with the last book of the *All Things Wellness series*, *Wellness G.P.S.* (Get Prepared for Success). We will help you set destinations (goals) in your G.P.S. and show you how to align healthy habits as you design a "trip" (a goal). You will learn where, when, and how to get to that destination while maneuvering over speed bumps, shifting to a detour if necessary, and avoiding dead-ends. You will apply your learning styles, love languages, chronotype/bio-rhythms, right and left-brain approaches, review your habit history and more as you reach the "Land of Maintenance" and learn how to stay there. We are so excited to get that book in your hands.

Let's get started...welcome to book two of the *All Things Wellness* series.

What does
Win the Wellness W.A.R. Mean?
(We Are Responsible)

*To be prepared for war is one of the most
effective means of preserving peace.*

George Washington

$\mathcal{F}$ear, killing, and love are three of the most frequent words that soldiers refer to when asked what it feels like to be at war. However, after they are discharged and return home, they also state they miss being a part of a cause, a deep sense of family, and seeking justice.

Returning from duty can be extremely difficult for soldiers to acclimate back into their previous life. The world continued "without them," and creating a "new norm" can remain challenging throughout a soldier's lifetime.

Soldiers face consistent dopamine bumps when chasing the bad guys and fighting worldly causes. Returning to the "normal" cadence of the "real" world doesn't offer quite the hit for our soldiers. Conceptually, I can relate to fight or flight. As a self-professed dopamine junkie, I love the vibe of being under fire and the chase. It has taken me years to dial back the perceived notion that I need a rush. I continue to focus on unhealthy aspects of working excessively and chasing goals. I suspect many of you are similar.

The military bond is also like no other. A brotherhood and sisterhood fighting to save humankind are nearly impossible to match. "We are family!" I can speak to this union first-hand. While stationed in Heidelberg, Germany, I was married to an Army soldier, and I also worked for the U.S. Army as a civilian. You quickly connect with those in your like-minded circle and begin to pull away or find less in common with your old world, especially back in the day when there were no cell phones and an international landline call was about a dollar per minute. We military families spent holidays together, our children became best friends, and there was a shared level of secrecy, loyalty, and trust. Cults, activists, and certain religious groups operate very similarly. Save the world for "our" cause. We are THE one!

Though I have not personally fought in a war, many of my family members, friends, and clients have. Several generations in my family tree have served our country—my brother, cousins, father, grandfather, great-grandfather, and more. Over two hundred years ago, my great, great, great, great, great, great grandfather, Captain E.H. Mahurin commanded a troop in Stewartstown, New Hampshire, during the War of 1812. Go, #6xGrandpa.

Dr. Markus has also been affected by war. Hailing from Germany, he is the first generation to come to America. If you have read history books or have family or friends who lived through World War I, II, and the Depression era, you can understand how ghastly the experiences were. As a child, he felt fear, anxiety, anger, and a sense of scarcity or lack from his parents, who survived that era. To re-establish some sense of safety, many families rebuilt housing out of the rubble left behind after the "carpet bombings." Every household had reminders of the war, such as government-issued first aid kits, iodine pills, and gas masks.

We are living expressions of our environment. We learn by actions and words. Yet, they can haunt us for the rest of our lives unless we do the inner work to rewire unhealthy thoughts, emotions, and behavior. These emotions and physical experiences carried forward in Dr. Markus's backpack of life as he faced professional and personal obstacles. Our programming affects how we seek jobs, maintain relationships, and even how we approach a nutrition or exercise plan. And the programs are not always healthy or helpful.

In preparing for battle, organized military troops leave no stone unturned. Because of history, they know what to expect. A game of cat and mouse. There are prepared for two options: take the defense like a hunter patiently waiting for a five-point buck to meander over the hill, or you can take the offense like troops storming the barracks at dawn. Wellness is the same…be prepared for the what-ifs and be prepared to be the aggressor.

Being in tip-top shape, with weapons in hand, and ready for the unexpected is the most brilliant way to win any battle, large or small. Military soldiers are physically, psychologically, mentally, spiritually, technically, and financially torn down, rewired, and rebuilt. Sounds like parenting. But it also sounds like life in general. We can apply this principle to every negative program we identify with during our wellness wheel assessment which you will hear more about later.

For this book, as you walk through this war-like metaphoric world with us, note that we will conceptually compare a "real" war to a "wellness" war. Both involve "real" people seeking "real" solutions. Soldiers and their families are not the only ones affected by war. Wars affect everyone and everything, and this includes fighting the Wellness War. We are ALL affected. If you are not healthy, someone else is also affected. If you are not happy, someone else is also affected.

We are not minimizing or mocking the brave men and women who trained their asses off to provide the rest of us with the freedom to do anything we want. Fighting wars in the Middle East will never compare to battling with your CEO for a promotion, experiencing the trials of raising children, or losing one hundred pounds won't either. We get it. But we metaphorically compared soldiers to those of us trying to be healthy. Preparing for a military mission and strategizing approaches for our own health, wellness, and lifestyle goals are remarkably similar. You will soon sense the commonalities between a military battle and the one we all face in achieving optimal health and happiness.

Soldiers attend boot camp; we do, too (the gym, running at the track, etc.). They learn how to care for and wear their battle dress; we do, too (where are my running shoes?). They consume the same diet; we focus on nutrition, too. Troops keep the same sleep schedule, just as we should. There is a common kinship when the soldiers' goals align; just like us (support groups, walking groups, etc.). I could compare all day long.

A balanced wellness wheel keeps your Wellness Wagon on track, rolling along. You can avoid illness, injuries, and unexpected attacks by staying on course (just as our soldiers do). You can confidently control your health. You will learn to live, love, and laugh more deeply. The more resilient the wheel, the gentler the ride as you strive to reach your goals. The Wellness Wagon reference is similar to the military's APCs (armored personal carriers). APCs offer maximum protection by rolling over landmines and deflecting grenades and gun blasts. It is built to reach a desired location, all while performing at maximum capability. A smooth ride on your Wellness Wagon keeps you rolling along and achieving your goals.

You might not see it initially, but preparing for and fighting the battle on Culp's Hill at Gettysburg has similarities to balancing your *ATW Wheel*™. How can painting a seascape, buying a house, becoming pregnant, starting a new business, or getting off insulin be similar? Your goals affect every other area of your life and those around you...24 areas of your life. And remember, your wellness is not just a YOU. Your wellness affects all of those around you.

You might not see it now, but folding your laundry, opening your mail, and having a date night with your partner all require balance even if your health goal is to cross the finish line at the Boston Marathon. You get 168 hours a week to devise your nutrition and activity plan, embed new habits, and create a reliable support system. So balancing your time and energy is vital, which is precisely what our soldiers do when they prepare for a "real" war (goal). Is it clear and concise? How do we efficiently and effectively use our time to accomplish the goal? And are all troops on board?

It is time to take responsibility and balance your life. Becoming self-aware, finding solutions, and learning to pivot when necessary, by using our *ATW Wheel*™ tool. When you work through your *6Ws of Wellness* (the Who, What, Why, Where, When, and How), the process is further clarified. Knowing your target is better than throwing darts in the dark and hoping for the best.

Are you ready to gear up and fight? Let's *Win the Wellness W.A.R.*

Assess and Adjust Your
All Things Wellness Wheel
(*ATW Wheel*™)

★

*P*artying like a rock star every Friday night at Freddy's Bar and Grill may not seem like a big deal. Likewise, living in a cluttered home or not calling your sister for weeks might not seem like red flags. Likewise, flipping your sleep schedule or improving your coping skills might not seem related to vacationing in Australia.

EVERY SINGLE THING YOU DO OR DON'T DO determines how healthy and happy you are. You must take responsibility for balancing 24 areas of your life. Are you rolling your eyes right now?

The terms self-awareness, self-discovery, or inner work have been buzzwords for several years. Many books, videos, and experts "tell you" how to get there. Most of the time, they are excitedly sharing what works for THEM. We, in turn, grab onto their testimonies desperately, looking for another way to live our lives to the fullest. Rarely does someone else's self-help book, diet plan, or pill last forever, if they work at all. Why?

Because it is NOT about YOU.

It takes determination and diligence to master your "Real World." Only you know your health and wellness and your history and habits. So be honest; how often do you tell all your deepest darkest secrets to a coach or doctor? Do you share how many times you have started a diet just to keep failing repeatedly? How many people know you slam down five bottles of wine a week instead of the two you say you have? Ever told anyone how many days you have gone without a shower? We suppress or lie to ourselves half the time, so why would we share our truths with experts? You might share a certain level of your truths with someone, such as with a best friend over coffee, but only you know the "real" you. And we want you to get to know yourself even better.

Do you have a wellness plan designed specifically for you in your world? Have experts asked you personal questions when they tell you to lose weight or start taking 300 mg of the newest anti-depression pill? Do they know if you have kids, are employed, or live twenty miles from home? I doubt it. Why? Because generalities are easier. It is hard, takes work, and it feels like war to individualize your wellness. There are those three words again (hard, work, and war). Physicians and most health experts do not take or have the time to discuss your full spectrum of health; nonetheless offer strategies for you to balance home, work, or play.

You need to become the captain of your own troop.

It is time for your to call the shots. You will now be armed with a "personalized" tool, not a cookie-cutter plan designed for others.

If you haven't read book one of the *All Things Wellness* series, you will be unfamiliar with the birth and history of the *ATW Wheel*™. (Go grab a copy on Amazon and get caught up).

Dr. Markus and I use the wheel for our personal lives, and I use it with all of my clients. Our goal is for the self-assessment wheel to be used not only by individuals to balance their own health and wellness but for parents, teachers, and physicians to use it as a guide. So whether you are trying to work on your own goals or those of your children, students, clients, or patients, this tool will help you help yourself, and help them.

After decades in the health and wellness industry, I started to recognize that wellness wasn't that simple, and it certainly wasn't a cookie-cutter, one-size-fits-all program. After watching my clients and employees struggle, I knew there had to be a more efficient and uncomplicated method for them to become healthier, hit goals, and live out their dreams. People listened intently, and I started to identify answers. Since then, I have used my tool on hundreds of people.

All Things Wellness came to fruition after working with one of my mentors. "Peggy, you have been doing this wellness thing for a long time. Your personal and professional resume make you the All Things Wellness Coach." When I stepped into her belief in me, I began working on my imposter and perfection syndrome and confidently peeled back my huge onion. I created my business, All Things Wellness, and went to work helping others be "all things well." After lots of research, sticky notes, pounding on my keyboard, and scribbling on my whiteboard, the *ATW Wheel*^{TM} was born. The wheel is designed to help you identify small punctures, flats, or blow-outs in 24 areas of your life and to fix areas of improvement before your health and wellness fall completely off track. When the wheel is punctured in any one area, the risk of being catapulted off your Wellness Wagon altogether is inevitable. The wheel keeps the Wellness Wagon on track, and the Wellness G.P.S. dialed in.

Before you complete your own *ATW Wheel*^{TM} self-assessment worksheet, you will become familiar with the definitions of each quadrant and spoke. We will also give you prompts to guide you. Finally, you will identify your punctures within the full spectrum of your life.

Download the free *ATW Wheel*^{TM} worksheet right now. It will help you as you continue reading the book.

www.allthings.wellness.com/ATW-Wheel-Worksheet.

Suppose you run over a sharp object while backing out of the driveway. What happens? Either a slow leak or a blowout. As you complete the wellness wheel, think about the nail in your life. What is causing the slow leak, small puncture, or a full blowout? We use the concept of running over a nail (dot) as a place to start identifying where you stand in all areas of your life. To help you determine where your punctures are, consider the center of the wheel, the hub, as a zero and the outer end of that spoke, near the tread, as a 10. Those areas where your nail is closest to the hub (zero) require immediate attention. Punctures five and below require you to be honest with yourself, create healthy strategies, and take action now so you can get back on track.

You may need to pull in the troops for support or guidance—experts like coaches, teachers, physicians, and counselors. Maintaining an 80% (8/10; a "B") long-term also requires experts and a solid force. The stronger your support and accountability system is, the higher your success rate will be.

Thriving in Maintenance Land requires catching "slow leaks" early on. Maintenance Land is a great place to live. Yes, events will pop up, spinning you out of control, but if you have persistently focused on your wheel, your awareness, knowledge, coping skills, organization, and more will get you back on track in no time. You will not have to call a tow truck because you had a blowout! Those who recognize their red flags early on will more naturally default to healthy strategies, tools, and dedicated support systems.

Get a "B"— Break up with Perfection and Win.

This may be the first time you hear this—stop trying to get an A (10/10) in every lane of your life. It is not only impossible but unhealthy. In turn, you can only get a 4 out of 10 for so long before you crash and burn. Comparatively, you can only get an A for so long, but it eventually crashes and burns to an F. This rollercoaster is the culprit for yo-yo health and wellness. Staying the course at 80% is healthier than going from an A to an F and then starting over and improving from an F to an A. You know you relate! Go the speed limit, and you will safely and steadily get to your destination.

On the *ATW Wheel™* worksheet, about mid-wheel, you will see a white line that represents the 4/10 mark. If you are around this white line, you are below the 50% mark. You have entered *The Uh-Oh Zone*. Though your wellness wheel will still roll along with punctures at the four mark, it will roll more slowly and take you a bit longer to reach your goal—if you get there before the blowout.

The *Uh-Oh Zone* does not represent your best self. The further you place your nail out toward the wheel tread, the healthier, happier, and more harmonious your life is, whether at home, work, or play. Maintaining a B (8/10) long-term in all 24 spokes is challenging. Life happens. But early, slow-leak detection allows proactive intervention. This is where one develops the skill to maintain a healthy lifestyle, so I recommend filling out the tool regularly. I do it every two to three months.

We challenge you to remove "feelings" when you fill out your wheel worksheet. Think of this as data collection only. And data has no feelings. There are facts to review. How has your life been over the past two months? How did you get where you are? Did something catastrophic happen recently? Have you been busy, sick, injured, or battling a relationship, etc.? Something positive and extraordinary, like a new marriage or the birth of a child, can also cause a few punctures in some areas, like sleep or stress. The point is to identify some of your red flags. They will reveal themselves as you complete this wheel.

Below is an image of the *ATW Wheel*[TM] and *ATW Wheel*[TM] worksheet. The free downloadable worksheet shifts the spoke titles allowing you to rank the areas of your life more easily. The worksheet is the second image.

It is time to review the definitions of each of the spoke within each chapter (quadrant below) and the prompts will help you more accurately place your nail (dot); puncture. As you go, along, you can fill out each section of the *ATW Wheel*[TM]. You will then learn how to complete your *ATW Baseline Assessment,* and you can create an initial *ATW Improvement Plan* using the *6Ws of Wellness. The Coach and The Doc Battle Tip* sections will also help you devise a plan. Dr. Markus and I share two of our wheels later in the book and explain how we used the tool to get back on track and start rolling again.

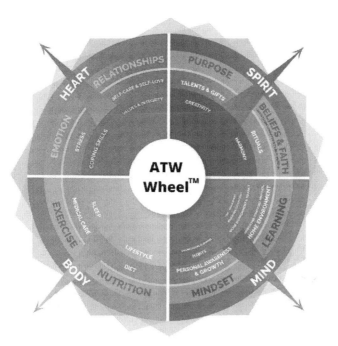

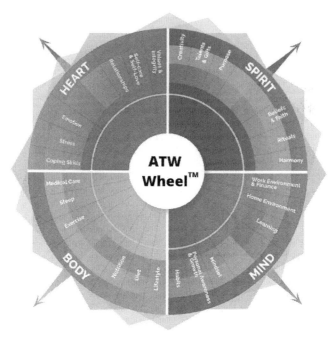

Quadrant Descriptions and Prompts

CHAPTER 1

HEART -
Live. Laugh. Love

*T*he color of the HEART quadrant is red. Duh. This section represents how the heart functions beyond simply pumping blood through our bodies. How does our heart feel as we cope with the difficulties on any given day? How does our heart react when stressed or full of emotion? How do our relationships with others and ourselves make us happy and healthy? Values and integrity also affect our hearts. The literal functions of the heart organ will be covered later in the BODY Chapter. For now, think about love and a sense of peace.

There are six HEART spokes: Coping Skills, Stress, Emotion, Relationships, Self-care and Self-Love, Integrity, and Values. You will find descriptions for each spoke below and prompts to help you determine where you sit on each spoke. At the end of this HEART chapter, you will place a nail (dot) on each of the six HEART quadrant spokes on your *ATW Wheel™* worksheet.

Coping Skills. *Feel the Feels. Respond Positively. Be a Resilience Warrior.*

> *If you don't like something, change it.*
> *If you can't change it, change your attitude.*
>
> Maya Angelou

This is one area that makes me a bit sad yet super excited. We can always improve our coping skills, and improving those skills changes and saves lives. Literally! We are not taught coping skills when we are young. They are developed (if at all) by trial and error. Without "trial," there is no "error," and without "error," there is no learning. So we are left to mimic what we have been exposed to. We then follow suit by watching our parents or mentors use their healthy or unhealthy coping skills. Being thrown into the trial and error fire, we can spend years trying to develop productive methods to manage stress and emotions. Enhancing this area will not only improve your personal and professional life but its overall quality.

Everyone's coping skills vary; what works in one area of your life may not work in others. Taking 10 deep breaths when trying to quiet a colicky infant might not work as well as deep breathing does when dealing with an insane neighbor. Learning to adapt is critical. For example, stepping outside for a walk because your boss embarrassed you at a team meeting is healthier than drinking a bottle of wine every night. Hiring a housekeeper once a month might stop you and your partner from screaming about chores. Now that sounds awesome.

Peggy: *Writing and walking in nature are my healthiest coping skills. Years ago, working out for two hours daily and painting scenes on rocks helped me cope. As I aged, my coping skills shape-shifted. It took experimenting to see what worked for me. If I cannot get out in nature, and I feel anxiety or fear pressing on my heart, I crank up the music or talk it out with someone I love and trust.*

Coping Skills Prompts:

- How do you respond, manage, and adjust your emotions and reactions when faced with stress, trauma, or difficult times?
- How do you cope with quick life changes or even differences of opinions with others?
- What emotion frequently pops us when you feel out of control? For example, you might rank lower on coping skills if your feelings are primarily negative.

- Think about the different coping methods, strategies, or tools you have used. Which ones have worked and which did not? And why? You might uncover a few nuggets to help you rate your coping skills' spoke.

Stress. *Balance of The Good. The Bad. The Ugly*.

> *The truth is that stress doesn't come from your boss,*
> *your kids, your spouse, traffic jams,*
> *health challenges, or other circumstances. It comes*
> *from your thought about your circumstances.*

Andrew Bernstein

There are three levels of stress: acute (events that happen urgently and pass relatively quickly), chronic (type of stress lasting weeks and begins to affect your health negatively, such as disrupted or lack of sleep, erratic emotions, reoccurring illness, etc.), and burnout stress (stress lasting months or years creating more severe problems such as diabetes, heart issues, weight gain, relationship demise, etc.).

Like all other spokes in the wheel, how we cope with stress is personal. I can find meditation stressful, whereas meditation, for Dr. Markus, is a go-to. He might find interviews stressful, but I do not. How we each define the three levels of stress (acute, chronic, and burnout) and our individualized solutions to manage them are unique to us. How do you respond if you are managing a massive project? What if you have been laid off, lost a pet, or your mom stops talking to you? How do you handle these situations?

There is an excellent stress exercise in *The Coach and The Doc Battle Tips* at the end of this book under the MIND Chapter.

Dr. Markus: *Stress management is a huge topic for me. It is safe to say I spent most of my life stressed out. Unfortunately, I pick up a lot of energy clues during social interactions; a disconnect between what people say and feel causes stress in my mind. If I ask a friend to help me move some furniture, and they respond with 'I am glad to,'*

I might feel their true desire is to find an excuse not to help me. In the past, it would be stressful to call people out on this, and I would usually reserve my thoughts for close friends and family. I have learned that it is not easy to convey a message without emotions to avoid a defensive response. It is usually stressful for both parties, but it results in honest communication, which will prevent stress in the future.

Stress Prompts:

- Who and what stresses you out?
- How many areas in your life cause you stress: work, kids, traffic, finances, etc.?
- In what ways does stress affect you—physically (rapid heart rate, increased blood pressure, sleep), emotionally (peaks and valleys, depression, etc.), spiritually (cease creativity, no longer attend church or connected to a higher power, etc.), financially (forget to pay bills, gamble, etc.)?
- How often and for how long do you feel stressed?

Emotion. *Live. Laugh. Love. Cry.*

Calmness is the cradle of power.

Josiah Gilbert Holland

We begin expressing emotions the second we enter this world. For example, babies cry when they are hungry, wet, tired, or afraid. As we learn to speak and express ourselves, we develop many emotions. With that, we must learn how to manage them maturely. Flailing into a temper tantrum does not work well in the boardroom. I've tried it. Fact!

Every single day we experience a wide variety of emotions, and you are no exception! Nothing is more frustrating than someone telling you how to feel or not validating your feelings. However, we can take responsibility for healthily expressing and managing our rollercoaster of emotions.

Emotions drive thoughts, beliefs, and behavior just as thoughts, beliefs, and behavior can spawn a stream of emotions.

Feeling the feels is healthy. The good, the bad, and the ugly. It is not just the dark side of emotions that requires attention. Managing elation and joyous feelings also requires healthy coping skills. Do not get me wrong, we all want to swallow a joy pill every morning. However, suppressing or ignoring the negative and pretending you are fine every day, all day, is as unhealthy as riding the negative train and never feeling true happiness.

Peggy: *The word FINE most accurately describes my grandmother, Mammie (R.I.P.). She was an extreme optimist. 'I am fine…everything is and will be fine.' I must have learned that behavior. However, in the 90s, a counselor smacked that word right out of my mouth. After telling her I was 'fine' a few too many times, she said, 'Peggy, do you know what the acronym FINE stands for?' (Waiting for no response, she said…) 'F'ing Insecure, Neurotic, and Emotional.' Okeedokee. Note to self. Learning to feel and share my full spectrum of emotions is something I still work on. I have learned that my counselor's acronym is okay as long as I am not avoiding my feelings.*

Emotion Prompts:

- How many emotions do you feel on any given day? Have you ever tried to list them? You will experience dozens. What are they? Happy, sad, angry, lonely…?

- How do you react when you receive positive or negative news?

- How long do your peaks and valleys last? Hours, days, weeks?

- How do you feel when you are not in control, such as being cut off on the interstate?

- How do your feelings and emotions show up physically, spiritually, emotionally, and financially?

- Do you *feel* your emotions or suppress them?

- What healthy and unhealthy coping mechanisms do you use to cope with emotions? For example, when you are highly emotional, do you grab comfort foods, go shopping, lock yourself in a room, work excessive hours, or reach for drugs or alcohol to numb you?

Relationships. *Communicate. Appreciate. Liberate.*

When we love, we always strive to become better than we are.
When we strive to become better than we are,
everything around us becomes better too.

Paulo Coelho

Most of us have three relationship zones: intimate/personal, extended (children and other relatives), and professional/ social (friends, co-workers, and collaborations). We communicate, act, and spend our time differently between the three categories of relationships. For example, you may be in a healthier relationship with your wife than you are with friends or co-workers. When completing the wellness wheel worksheet, you could make three relationship lines instead of using the one relationship spoke on the wheel. Make a line for 1) intimate/personal, 2) extended (children and other relatives), and 3) professional/social (friends, co-workers, and collaborations).

Dr. Markus and Peggy: *It was a game changer when we both realized every relationship is different and requires different communication and boundary setting. We are both in the service industry, and over the years, we have learned that we cannot please everyone. This requires practice, just like every other segment of our lives. So we now focus on quality peeps in our tribe. Quality over quantity, as they say.*

Relationship Prompts:

- How much quality time do you spend with your partner, children, parents, boss, and friends?
- How quickly do you respond when they reach out?
- Do you get positive or negative vibes after being with them or when you think about them?
- How does each of your relationships affect your overall quality of life?

- Do you feel happy, loved, and supported by certain people and not by others?
- Do you need to expand your circle and create new relationships?

Self-care/Self-love. *Me Time. Rest and Relaxation.*

Self-care is how you take your power back.

Lalah Delia

Self-care and self-love are terms that have been around for a while. The meanings are relative to each person. I may consider self-care a walk in nature, time alone, or binge-watching Netflix. Dr. Markus might consider self-care as gardening, dinner with his wife, or watching Gaia videos. We recommend trying several modalities. Determine how best to fill your cup. Experiment. I highly recommend you take Gary Chapman's *5 Love Languages* test to help you identify how to love yourself and others most naturally. You are responsible for how you fill your cup. No one else is. Also, consider that we change over time, so what works today may not work next year.

Dr. Markus: *One of the biggest self-care topics for me is sleep. Proper sleep is different for everyone, but a few principles are constant. I go to sleep at approximately the same time every night. I prepare for sleep without screen time for about one hour before lying down. I pay attention to humidity and clean air in the bedroom and strive for 6-8 hours every night. I use a sleep app for monitoring snoring, coughing, and deep sleep patterns. Once I started my sleep routine, I realized that some nights fall out of the pattern. I take this opportunity to ask myself why. This helps me understand, for instance, how stress at work affects my sleep.*

Self-care/Self-Love Prompts:
- How do you care for and love yourself?
- What feels relaxing or rejuvenating to you—fills your cup?

- Are you creative (tried multiple modalities), or do you keep trying the same ones repeatedly?

Values and Integrity. *Do or Die. What I Live By.*

> *We must adjust to changing times and*
> *still hold to unchanging principles.*

Jimmy Carter

Values are at the core of our being, character, and qualities. Integrity is the consistency between the values expressed verbally and the actions we display physically. Values are the backbone of our relationships with others and ourselves; how we show up in this world. To achieve goals, whether you want to lose weight or save money for a new camper, it takes integrity to stick to a plan.

So, when you get ready to mark your dot for this spoke on the wheel, do not just think about how you present yourself to your boss or spouse. How do you show up for yourself? Having a Values and Integrity score below seven puts a lot more into perspective than you might think. Words and actions are how we are judged and trusted, personally, and professionally. You got this.

Peggy: *So many clients have fibbed to me regarding their commitments. Not to be derogatory, but it is often like working with teenagers (which I have). As a team, we design steps to help them achieve their wellness goals. I do not 'tell' my clients what to do. The commitments are based on their goals. However, fibbing or straight-out lying helps no one, especially you. Taking responsibility for the execution of commitments lies on the individual. I have always said, 'You can lie to me, but please don't lie to yourself.' I have had clients tell me they checked in to the gym to work out, and when I confronted them and told them I had access to check-in data, they still came up with a reason. 'The machine must not have been working.' Seriously?! We are more honest about speeding when we are pulled over than we are about values and integrity when keeping our health and wellness promises. Fibbers not only hurt others but themselves.*

Your character, values, or integrity are on the line when you drop the ball or do not follow through. There is a reason you do this. Are you ready to figure it out?

Values and Integrity Prompts:

- How strong are your values and integrity? Do you keep promises and commitments to <u>yourself</u>? Before you make commitments, ask yourself if you can follow through. Can you stay committed if you declare you will go alcohol-free for a month or intend to walk three miles daily? Hint: tell a friend, and you are more likely to succeed) Actions. Actions. Actions. Honesty. Honesty. Honesty.

- Do you keep promises and commitments to others, or do you frequently cancel or break them?

- If you do not follow through, are you an excuse-monger who struggles to take ownership?

You have now read the spoke definitions and a few prompts for the HEART quadrant of the *ATW Wheel^TM*. On your blank worksheet, place your nails (dots) using a guideline of 1-10. The center of the wheel, the hub, is considered zero, and 10 is represented at the other end of the spoke on the outside rim of the wheel, the tire tread. PS: I have yet to find anyone who is a 10, so keep that in mind when you think that lane is "perfect." So, please remember, if you are a ten in any aspect, you may be spending too much energy in this category and neglecting others. Ultimately, we are shooting for 80% in all sectors.

CHAPTER 2

SPIRIT -
Inner or Outer Expansion

*T*he SPIRIT quadrant is represented by the color purple. The third eye, purple flame (St. Germain), and angelic hues are often light shades of purple. This color is about trust, loyalty, creativity, and fantasy—connecting to your physical and higher self and developing strong beliefs and faith.

Many of our spiritual beliefs are introduced to us when we are young. Did your family attend church, or was your grandma a medium and used crystals to connect with the Universe? Not mine. She connected with birds. (OMG, so do I. Whoa. I just figured that out.). For some, their faith and belief system may be strictly scientific, and they do not believe in a higher power at all.

However, I wanted to design the SPIRIT quadrant by reaching beyond conversations about quantum physics or Big Bang theories. So, Inner and Outer expansion was born.

There are six SPIRIT spokes: Creativity, Talents and Gifts, Purpose, Beliefs/Faith, Rituals, and Harmony. You will find descriptions for each spoke below and prompts to help you determine where you are on the appropriate location of each spoke. At the end of this SPIRIT chapter, you will go to your *ATW Wheel*^{TM} worksheet and place a nail (dot) on each of the six SPIRIT quadrant spokes.

Creativity. *Dig Deep. Hold onto your Seat.*

> *Every great dream begins with a dreamer. Always remember, you have within you the strength, the patience, and the passion to reach for the stars to change the world.*

Harriet Tubman

We are such creative and innovative little buggers as toddlers. I remember art and creative writing classes were requirements in high school. Home economics and physical education were, too. Wow, how times have changed. It has been shown that we are all more creative when we are in action. Getting to the "doing" part can be a challenge, but personally speaking, just "being" can also be helpful. Action and, conversely, meditation can be equally beneficial in improving your creativity.

Being innovative and imaginative should have no age limit. Adulting should not diminish our imagination. Our writing, drawing, and dancing should never die off. Yet as we age, blocking out time in our Google Calendar for stained glass classes or learning to paddle board becomes less likely.

Do the SPIRIT spokes come more naturally to creatives? Potentially. If you are "right-brain" dominant like Dr. Markus, you are led by intuition, feelings, and emotions. You connect to the development of a process versus the get-to-the-point thinking or actions of a left-brainer like me. Right-brainers will hang out more in the "To Be" land versus the "To Do" land.

That doesn't imply that we left-brainers, who are considered more verbal, analytical, and linear thinkers, are not creative. On the contrary, every person can be creative in every aspect of their lives; cooking, chores, decorating the baby's room, or creating a policy and procedure all count.

To be happier, healthier, and wiser, we must invoke creativity. It feeds our brain and body. Improving a puncture in this spoke can be very exciting if you set aside time and remove expectations and judgments.

Dr. Markus: *I have learned the importance of following my intuition over the years even when it comes to creativity. I believe there are multiple angles to improving my patients' health. Referring patients to counselors, yoga classes, or suggesting stress-reduction modalities is a far cry from the basic eat-better, move-more methods of improving diabetes. I now understand that creativity is necessary when individualizing patient protocols. Intuition plays a significant role in that. Suggesting treatments for my diabetic patients, for instance, involves a "buy-in" from the patient. I can tell if the patient will go along or if there is more work to do before they are willing to accept my suggestions. Sometimes, my intuition tells me to try a completely different approach for my patients or for myself. It all depends on the individual.*

Creativity Prompts:

- Do you find joy in accomplishing tasks and completing tangible projects, or do you find more joy in allowing things to ruminate and reveal themselves?

- What physical and creative activities did you participate in BEFORE age 18 and have left by the wayside as an adult?

- If you try new things, do you become stressed, or do negative emotions pop up? Dig into that history.

- Do you find daydreaming and creativity natural and enjoyable?

Talents and Gifts. *Don't be shy—just try.*

Every artist was first an amateur.

Ralph Waldo Emerson

We all have talents and gifts. You are not necessarily born with your gifts. Sometimes you must discover them. Being 7'6" tall gives you the advantage of playing center for the Lakers, but it doesn't guarantee you can shoot the ball into the hoop. Talents and gifts can be developed if you are willing to experiment and persist. Unfortunately, many are not ready to take a gamble and step outside their comfort zone.

Many people know their talents, but they get caught up in the daily grind, and their talents drift to the wayside. Were you a track star in college but have not run since? You are a star, so why have you let your sparkle fade? If you already know your talent, keep shining. Have you ever considered coaching? It is time to sit at that baby grand and start entertaining the family again. You are never too old to play the piano, become a chef, or become a florist. Hone in on those talents.

Start investigating. "You go, you!" You may need to try a dozen things before you find a connection. Using your talents and gifts will bring you and others joy. Warm up the spirit within. You might be well aware of your talents and gifts. You just need to dust them off. Come on, Grandma. If you have not quilted in years, get that sewing machine out and enter a quilt in the state fair. Get another Gold, girl.

Peggy: *Talents and gifts do not always fall into the musical, craft, or athletic realm. I have learned to capitalize and enjoy my 'spark' energy. I have little fear of being crazy in public, being on the stage, or in front of cameras. I learned to take 'me' wherever I go. Just say'n. Not everyone is comfortable being a whack job on TikTok or presenting what they really think in the boardroom. It is a gift.*

Talents and Gifts Prompts:

- Maybe you can dust off a hidden talent or gift you had growing up. Think back.
- When did you last spend time with your instrument, paint brushes, or writing skills?
- Do you feel you do not have a talent or gift? You do. This is a perfect time to experiment.

Purpose. *Desire on Fire. What makes you tick?*

> *Understanding purpose is one thing but recognizing*
> *the importance of having purpose is another.*
> *Everybody has a unique purpose in their life,*
> *whether to help others, provide for the family, or be free.*

Ben Gothard

What is your purpose? What is your why? These are two of the most frustrating questions we have been asked or have struggled to define ourselves. Maybe thinking about the word "passion" makes more sense to you. We all need a reason to get up in the morning, shower, and face the world. Why do you want to be happy, lose weight, help people, or buy a house? Think of the WHY. Think of PASSION.

Peggy: *I have said for decades that few people get a chance to earn a paycheck doing what aligns with their purpose and passion. But you can turn a desire or urge into a passion project or job and it can change your life. If you wake up in the middle of the night with an idea or you are excited about something, you are on your way to discovering a purpose! I call this the 3 AM Passion Message. What is your aha when you think of the word passion?*

Purpose Prompts:

- What is your underlying urge or lust for life? When you are 80 years old, I do not want you to look back and regret what you could have done or wanted to accomplish. What might those things be for you?

- You might uncover your purpose if you have volunteered at a school, an animal shelter, or a nursing home. Have you volunteered before?

- Spending time with a mentor or someone who inspires you can spark a purpose. Have you done that?

- Do you have a gratitude practice? When we are grateful, we can connect to things that make us joyous.

- Have you ever created a vision board? This tool is a great way to reveal your purpose or zest for life.

Beliefs and Faith. *The Connection Infection.*

Faith brings comfort and strength to all of us, but we must surrender to a higher power, and when we do, we are the most humble and the most powerful.

Mimi Novic

Our thoughts, behaviors, feelings, and actions around a faith-based practice are personal. You may connect by practicing a more institutionalized belief system, where others might sit on a mountaintop in a more "non-materialized" world to find theirs. Increasing your knowledge and participation in this area will improve your SPIRIT.

Dr. Markus: *In high school, I took a class in comparative religion. Later in life, I joined the Catholic Church. Now, I am looking into a scientific bridge to faith. It is universal energy. The universe can be described as frozen energy, and so can we. So, we are one expression of this huge spectrum of energy. As stated before, I keep marveling at our biological design. Beyond that, our consciousness has its origin in this energy. I call it cosmic consciousness (God). As a physician, I know how to alter the consciousness of patients with medication. As an example, anesthesia makes people unconscious. Most often, the basis for a patient who falls ill is a separation of individual consciousness from cosmic consciousness. However, following or living the ten commandments can give an enormous value to keep you on course.*

Belief and Faith Prompts:

- Do you have a regular faith practice? It might be reading the bible or, heck sitting on Machu Picchu.

- Do you participate consistently in your practice?

- Do you broaden your horizons by reading or talking with others about their connections to their beliefs and faith?

Rituals. *Deep Connection.*

This is the prevalence of ritual.
To remember something that cannot be forgotten.

Chris Abani

Several people get confused between the definitions of habits and rituals. Rituals have a deeper meaning than habits. Preparing your weekly meals every Sunday is a habit. Exercising before the kids get up is a habit. Attending church with your parents every Sunday is a ritual. Playing games with your parents before the annual Thanksgiving dinner is a ritual.

Peggy: *One of the best examples I can give for an old ritual of mine was walking and talking with my mom before she passed away. Sure, walking is a great habit, but my walks were connected to our time together. I rarely walked without talking to her on the phone.*

Rituals Prompts:

- Is there something you would feel upset or feel guilty about if you no longer participate?
- How important are traditions to you? Poker Night with the guys? Coffee every Friday with your neighbor? Lunch on Wednesdays with your dad?

Harmony. *Just Be & See. Stop/Look/Listen. Jive-Be Alive.*

*You are only afraid if you
are not in harmony with yourself.*

Herman Hesse

Over the years, work-life balance has become as overused as "I love you." When I worked on this spoke, I kept circling back to emotions. How do I feel when things feel balanced? Balance brings a sense of peace and harmony. So there it was. This spoke was named Harmony. Once you complete your wellness wheel, you will see how "balanced" your health and wellness are. You will clearly see where you need alignment.

Dr. Markus: *Harmony, in my mind, is linked to coherence as it pertains to the body. As I said before, in Book 1 of the wellness series, The Four-Fold Formula for All Things Wellness, we are a collective of roughly 30 trillion cells. As long as there is harmony, the body works well. Disease (dis-ease) represents a disruption of our harmony. But we can enhance our innate ability to return to peace by tapping into universal energy. I have had good results by working on heart/brain coherence. My tool of choice is called heart math. You purchase the ear lobe clip/sensor and connect it to your smartphone. The app will measure your heart rate variability (HRV). The higher the HRV, the more parasympathetic involvement. This translates into creative mode, not survival. Your smartphone will ping you if you don't remain at the minimum level of relaxation. On the other hand, sympathetic activation, as in fight or flight mode, is very regular with a very low HRV. So, it's not just the beats per minute, it's the variability between each beat. Once heart/mind coherence is established, universal energy becomes apparent. It pervades all of us, like everything seen and unseen.*

Harmony Prompts:

- Write down the emotions you feel when you think of the word harmony.

- What parts of your life feel in balance or out of balance?

- Accurately finding your nail (dot) on this spoke of the wheel is very important. It is a culmination of all other spokes.

You have now read the spoke definitions and a few prompts for the SPIRIT quadrant of the *ATW Wheel*™. On your blank worksheet, place your nails (dots) using a guideline of 1-10. The center of the wheel, the hub, is considered zero, and 10 is represented at the other end of the spoke on the outside rim of the wheel, the tire tread. PS: I have yet to find anyone who is a 10, so keep that in mind when you think that lane is "perfect." So, please remember, if you are a ten in any aspect, you may be spending too much energy in this category and neglecting others. Ultimately, we are shooting for 80% in all sectors.

CHAPTER 3

MIND -
Thoughts Become Things

The color of our MIND chapter is blue, which exudes calm, security, inspiration, and confidence. Think about the Mind quadrant as the Discover and Do section of the *ATW Wheel™*. Be patient and persistent when working through this section of the wheel. Do not get overwhelmed. Take a deep breath and remember you are trying to balance your life, not spin it out of control. I am beyond excited for you.

There are six MIND spokes in the wheel: Work Environment (time management, finance, education, and job satisfaction), Home Environment (organization and planning), Learning (intellectual), Mindset (thoughts and behaviors), Personal Awareness and Growth, and finally Habits (approaches, strategies, routines). You will find descriptions for each spoke below and prompts to help you determine where you are on the appropriate location of each spoke. At the end of this MIND chapter, you will go to your *ATW Wheel™* worksheet and place a nail (dot) on each of the six MIND quadrant spokes.

"Use it or lose it" doesn't just apply to our physical body.

As of 2022, according to the Education Data Initiative, over 20% of college enrollees were aged thirty and over. I am not an advocate that you must go to college to get a decent job or become financially free. However, I am a strong proponent that we should never stop learning. Improving knowledge will personally and professionally increase your confidence, enhance your relationships, improve your organization, and create a sense of belonging.

Your mind controls your thoughts, behavior, and actions. Use it to improve punctures in this section of your wheel.

Mindset. *Repetitive Actions = Habits. Calm the Chaos. Take Yucky to Yay. Breakdowns = Breakthroughs*

> *If you can't fly, then run. If you can't run, then walk.*
> *If you can't walk, then crawl. But whatever you do,*
> *you have to keep moving forward.*

Martin Luther King Jr.

Let me explain why this quadrant is called MIND, yet there is also a spoke called MINDSET. The "Mind" is the brain. It learns and helps you perform. Your "Mindset" controls the brain. Your feelings, thoughts, beliefs, and behaviors tell your "Mind" what to do. OMG. Look how much control you have. YOU are not the co-pilot of your brain. You are the pilot. You are on the frontline.

A positive Mindset will increase your happiness and health. We certainly would not want our soldiers facing enemy lines with a pessimistic mindset. Pessimism (a glass-half-empty mentality) causes isolation, mental health issues, lack of motivation, and lack of confidence.

Peggy: *Since our mindset is so malleable, whatever and whomever we expose ourselves to makes us susceptible to unhealthy habits and approaches. Keeping a gratitude practice is one way I stay on top of my game. When I feel like I keep getting fed a dish of crap or my workload has taken on a life of its own, I immediately compare my situation to those less fortunate. I also remind myself that I created or asked for most of my life path. I am where I am because of 'me.' Don't we all want to be happy and healthy? When I focus on gratitude, I am healthier AND happier. Period. I find a ray of sunshine in every cloud! The light brings the dark, and the dark brings the light. We learn from both. And both are inevitable.*

Mind/Mindset Prompts:

- Are you a pessimist, optimist, or realist? A balance between the latter two is the healthiest.
- Are you surrounded by more positive or negative people?
- Are you challenging your brain in new ways every day? Learning more and stepping outside your comfort zone will build character and confidence.
- Do you have a Can Do, or a Can't Do attitude?
- Is life happening To you or For you?

Work Environment. *Sense of value for the effort. Efficient. Satisfied. Builds independence and confidence.*

*Build your own dreams or someone else
will hire you to build theirs.*

Farrah Gray

Managing your economic life and performing a job you are proud of gives you purpose and freedom. We spend about one-third of our lives working; 90,000 hours. Overall, job satisfaction is typically a balance of what you do, whom you do it for and with, as well as being appropriately compensated.

Job satisfaction is a crucial component of overall life satisfaction. At the end of this book, you will find an exercise in *The Coach and The Doc Battle Tips* that will help you assess the pros and cons of your current job. As a result, you will decide whether it is time to move on or whether your current employment makes you happy.

"Bring home the bacon and fry it up in a pan." My grandfather used to sing that when he headed out the door for his shift at our town's paper mill. I suspect he didn't "love" every duty he performed each day, but I can assure you that he enjoyed those he interacted with, and for those tougher days, his positive attitude made the difference.

Believe it or not, you are not stuck. You may feel there are no other options than working for that crabby lawyer, a night-time shift at 7-Eleven, or building roofs in 90 degrees, but there are. You are in control. Take responsibility for your employment decisions, not just what you eat and whether you hop on the treadmill. Do you want to continue working for the person who signs your check?

During the COVID-19 pandemic, our work life changed dramatically. Most employees, other than the service, safety, and medical industries, were sent home to work remotely during the lockdown, or they lost their jobs entirely. Three years later, many are in the same situation.

For those who lost their jobs altogether, there has been an influx of self-employed entrepreneurs who were forced to find another source of income. According to NPR.org, 5.4 million new business applications were filed in 2021, smashing the record set in 2020 of 4.4 million. What are you doing now? If you are sick of working for someone else, then step outside the box. Get creative. Start writing a book, or build an Etsy store, or how about walking dogs?

I hear many grumbling business owners say they cannot find or retain workers. Maybe COVID helped us redefine the meaning of life. Has the definition of work-life harmony (balance) changed since COVID? We certainly adjusted financially and physically. Parents spent more time with their children, and many were forced to become their teachers. There was no choice but to step out of our comfort zones. If we were not forced to change in 2020, we would be doing the same things we did the year before. Tick tick tick. Repeating Groundhog Day over and over. Would you have whipped up new recipes, found exercise videos online, or started new hobbies if you weren't forced? And look how much time we saved by not ironing our suits, packing our lunches, or battling traffic.

As I thought about this further, curiosity drove me down a rabbit hole. I wanted to know how many hours the average American works. In 2014, the workweek averaged 47 hours per week. Pre-COVID, the average weekly hours were 43, and post-COVID, the average workweek has been about 40 hours. Salaried and hourly weekly averages vary, as they have for decades. Most salaried employees spend 50-60 hours working each week. If you ask a solopreneur, we work most every day that ends with a "y."

My curiosity continued, and I traveled back in time. In 1830, manufacturing was the only profession tracked. Labor employees averaged 70 hours per week. Once improvements and efficiencies entered the manufacturing world, the average hours worked dropped to about 60 per week.

In 1914, Henry Ford instituted a six-day, 48-hour workweek for male factory workers. In 1926, he changed the requirements for all employees, reducing the hours to a five-day, 40-hour workweek. In 1930, the U.S. Government recognized a few benefits of Ford's shorter workweek but it WASN'T driven by a self-care motive. The government realized it was an answer to combat the massive unemployment crisis. Requiring employees to work fewer hours each week, companies would need to hire more employees to get meet demands. By 1940, a series of U.S. laws made the 40-hour workweek the "norm," and it has been that way since, meaning you are supposed to be paid "extra" if you work over that allotment. The overtime rule began in 1938 when the first salary threshold was set at an annual income of $1,560. **WOW.**

We have come a long way, baby. In 1670 (yes, 1670) Massachusetts law demanding a minimum of a 10-hour workday. Sunup to Sundown!

Are idle hands really the devil's workshop?

Proverbs 16:27

I fell deeper into the rabbit hole. Can I fall any deeper? Yes! So, we have always complained about how long and hard we work. Well, how long have there been conversations about work-life balance? I spent decades in the worksite wellness world. For years it was touted as "breaking ground"—new conversations. NOPE! I would have guessed we started chatting about work-life balance in the 70s-80s. I was way off.

Interestingly enough, conversations are documented as far back as the Revolutionary War when Captain John Smith supported a shorter work week movement. He felt that three days of work satisfied the majority. It allowed balance and the job still got done. However, it did not take long for the government and businesses to realize that the longer and harder everyone worked, they made more cash, and, in turn, businesses AND people enjoyed spending that extra income. Capitalism was born.

We have the power; either improve what we dislike or stop complaining about it.

Peggy: *I like order but also adapt easily to change. Last fall, after Hurricane Ian damaged our home and we had to move out, one area of my life got turned on its head, throwing me for a loop. That was my work environment. I need a very orderly area to be efficient and creative. I also have a radio show requiring specific equipment and backdrops for the shows. Moving to a hotel caused me to regroup and find other ways to make my surroundings work for me, not against me. I set aside some goals, postponed my shows for a few months, and tackled my writing projects. Was it easy? No, not at first, but I have adjusted. And boy, did the hurricane and the move give me a lot of content to write about.*

Work Environment Prompts:

- How many hours a week do you work? Is your life balanced with a 30-hour week, or do you work 70 and your life is a mess? Time is money, and making money takes time; is it worth it?

- Are most of your conversations about your job negative or cause arguments at home?

- Do you love what you do? Are you living your dream?

- When you perform or think about your job, what adverse emotional, mental, or physical effects do you have?

- Are you aligned with the mission, vision, values, and integrity of the organization?

- Does your work environment embody effective communication between leadership and the employees?

- Do you feel in charge of your professional destiny?

Home Environment. *Safe. Loving. Organized. Without a Plan, Plan to Fail.*

The light is what guides you home,
the warmth is what keeps you there.

Ellie Rodriguez

Every single time you step over toys or piles of clothes, you may not realize it, but you are reminding yourself that you leave things incomplete or unfinished. An organized and clean environment not only improves your mental health but also improves your physical health (less dirt and dust, fewer falls, improved sleep, and more). You feel confident when you cross items off your To Do list, right? You would agree that staying organized reduces angst, frustration, and mental clutter. Decreasing external chaos lessens your internal chaos. Every piece of physical clutter, unopened mail, sink full of dishes, or piles of laundry stimulates and distracts your brain in an unhealthy way.

Being disorganized does not just affect your physical environment and mental state. It also affects your relationships and overall quality of life. A lack of planning causes past-due bills, family arguments, and missed doctor's visits, all causing undue stress. You know those soccer games when you forgot to bring a snack or when you forgot to show up altogether? You can really set yourself up for success by operating a smooth home environment.

Kids are watching. There is a huge opportunity to change generations by teaching our children to develop healthy habits. And it starts as home, as they say. Kids live in the moment. It takes years for brains to develop and become forward-thinking, therefore, teaching children to prepare for what-ifs or even to look ahead at next week's calendar can be life-changing for everyone. Organization doesn't come naturally to most.

Have a weekly family meeting. What is on the family calendar? If you are spreading yourselves too thin, planning out the week together will reveal that very quickly. You may even discover your son wants to play the drums instead of soccer.

Peggy: I remember when my youngest was about seven, and we chatted about why he couldn't sleep. After a conversation, he revealed that his anxiety was caused by hurried mornings. He was afraid he would forget something. We created a list to put on the refrigerator. It included all his tasks from preparing for bed to when he walked out the door each morning: brush teeth, help make lunch, put school work in backpack, and lay out clothes.

Home Environment Prompts:

- How long do you put off doing chores?

- How cluttered is your environment? Again, procrastination and disorganization lead to excessive busyness internally and externally.

- How smoothly does your household operate? Are your family members aware of each other's schedules? Do you talk about them or post them?

- Are there household repairs that could improve the safety of your home? Such as changing the locks, repairing windows, throwing away broken glasses or plates, etc.?

- Is your home a place of love, acceptance, and respect?

Learning. *Learn it - Master it - Live it.*

> *Education is the most powerful weapon*
> *which you can use to change the world.*
>
> Nelson Mandela

Do not stop learning! If you follow strict routines and are just ticking through life, these are signs that you aren't allowing time to learn new things. Continually forcing the brain to learn new things improves memory, mental health, and connections to a purpose or to others.

There are several things I wish we taught our children in school, such as healthy ways to communicate, nutrition, coping skills, and love languages.

Think back to being a child. It would be a gamechanger if you had discovered your learning style was auditory, visual, or kinesthetic/tactile at an early age. Knowing how you learn best makes learning more enjoyable!

There are many online tests to help you identify your learning style. Why it is so important? If you need to replace your toilet and are an auditory learner, you may absorb more information and be less frustrated by listening to someone talk you through the process. In contrast, a visual learner might prefer watching a YouTube video or reading the directions. It is the same with our children. Learning ABCs or biology does not just have to be done by watching a teacher draw on the chalkboard (visual). Determining whether you learn best by listening, watching, or doing changes every aspect of your life.

Ever wonder why some people love audible books, yet others want to hold the book in their hands? It is because of the ways we best absorb information.

Markus: *Most of you know by now that I was born in Germany and lived there for 20 years before coming to the U.S. Over there, schooling was and is practically free. As a trade-off, education was regulated very tightly by the government. Students were evaluated and pushed into what was regarded as the best schooling and job for you. If you were not applying yourself in high school, you were forced into the labor market, with no chance to enter college or university. When I came to the U.S. on a student visa, I did my pre-med courses. The amazing field of science generated a drive and hunger for more. This propelled me into medical school, where I dove deep into the awesome design of our human body. Over the years, I came to recognize how highly variable each person is. Every patient represents a new challenge, and no two individuals are the same. This is why part of the Hippocratic oath is to treat patients to the best of one's ability. This requires a commitment to a lifetime of learning. But this type of learning is not just benefiting but helping others. We are lucky to have a system in the US that allows us to learn what WE feel is appropriate for us. Unfortunately, this system is tied to money, so not everyone can afford formal, higher education. And with the development of the internet, we have the opportunity to learn whatever we want because a lot of information is free— if you are willing to spend the time to find it. Learning is a joy, not a chore, in my mind.*

Learning Prompts:

- Do you prefer to learn via workshops where you are more active? Do you bounce between reading and watching (flipping through TikTok or YouTube regularly but also reading articles)? (kinesthetic)

- Do you have an audible membership? Do you listen to podcasts in the car or on walks? (auditory)

- Do you read directions, follow recipes, take notes, and read maps well? (visual)

- Do you find yourself saying you want to take a course or go back to school, yet you have not taken steps to do so?

- Are you bored or find yourself having the same types of conversations over and over?

Personal Awareness and Growth. *Go Inside to Grow. Go Outside to Glow.*

> *I can't change the direction of the wind,*
> *but I can adjust my sails to always reach my destination.*

Jimmy Dean

Personal awareness requires constant check-ins. The *ATW Wheel*™ helps with this process. When you become aware, you can easily assess where you are in multiple areas of your life and create a plan to move forward. Most of us do not hear the squeaky wheel until there is a blowout, such as illness or injury. What happened before you ruptured your Achilles tendon? Six months of running 10 miles a day? You should have heard "that squeaky wheel" coming.

Self-awareness includes internal and external observations. Without not awareness, we cannot utilize our knowledge, and without knowledge, we have no awareness. Hmm. Self-awareness incorporates learning to understand and control your actions and emotions. This builds your emotional intelligence.

Self-discovery can be exciting or painful—likely both. Every time I complete my *ATW Wheel*^{TM}, I become aware of areas requiring my focus. The self-care, self-love, self-discovery spoke is usually an area requiring improvement. This allows me to dial in my coordinates and stay on track to happiness and health. It shows me data, not emotion.

There are several modalities to help you "discover" more about yourself. Time in nature, meditation, learning, and conversations all lead to unveiling who you are and what you want to do or be. What are your values, dreams, favorite foods, activities, skills, etc.? And more importantly, how will you improve your education and expand your tools to grow? Only you know you, boo.

Peggy: *Many of you are in the 'other people' business. You take care of family, friends, co-workers, neighbors, and even strangers. In the 'other people' business, I lost myself. After decades and decades of injuries and illness, I realized that I better get into the 'me' business. Experts in any field walk a fine line between sharing that they have their crap together yet wanting to walk the talk and be transparent. 'I am not doing well. I don't know what I am doing. And I am exhausted.' I didn't learn my 'me' business by reading books, going to the doctor, or swallowing pills. I learned it in the hard-knock school of life, which, by the way, is not the smartest or easiest route. But I am on board now. Phew. Not the brightest light in the campsite, Coach.*

Personal Awareness and Growth Prompts:

- Do you take responsibility and own up to your mistakes?
- Are your values aligned with your actions? Do you keep commitments and promises?

- Do you know your strengths and weaknesses?
- Are you aware when you are hungry, tired, or unhappy?
- Are you having deep conversations? By chatting with others, we become more aware and expand our perceptions. Life is not just about those repetitive conversations about the weather, traffic, and how your arthritis is acting up.
- Are you aware of how you present yourself to others? More often than not, do you present your utmost, best self?

Habits, Approaches, Strategies, and Routines. *Experiment. Measure Outcomes. Modify. Repeat.*

> *Your beliefs become your thoughts,*
> *Your thoughts become your words,*
> *Your words become your actions,*
> *Your actions become your habits,*
> *Your habits become your values,*
> *Your values become your destiny.*

Gandhi

Routines are manifestations of habits. Habits are healthiest when you have created solid approaches and strategies. Take charge, become your very own scientist, and experiment over and over again. What works and what does not? Finding what best suits you comes from measuring the results, modifying, and repeating. It is like a fine-oiled cog. To keep rolling along, teach your brain habits that benefit the goals you want to achieve. And put them on repeat until you decide they no longer serve you.

How do you approach life and create habits and routines? Some of your habits were stolen from your parents. You watched their performance and routines for decades. Whether positive or negative, healthy, or unhealthy, we have mimicked mentors and society. Are your wellness wheels going in a different direction than you desire? Why?

Life happens for me, not to me.

The majority of us are sad, frustrated, or angry when our habits are disrupted. We create and follow our habits. If you are stressed out each morning, you may have a habit you can quickly modify. The result: you are no longer late. Do you hit the alarm clock three times before you get up? If so, why do you continually say the traffic "makes you" late for work? You are the reason you are late! Change your habit. Figure out a way to get up earlier.

Your habits do not have to be identical to others. And remember, even healthy habits have room for improvement. If you struggle to embed new behaviors, don't think of them as failures. Just find a new way that suits you. Breakdowns become breakthroughs. Realizing there is a learning opportunity in every struggle can shift your thinking, especially when striving to embed something new. You don't need a complete overhaul or a drop-dead action to force you to make a change. Some habits can be modified easily. Sometimes, quick action is necessary, such as changing eating and exercise habits if you had a heart attack. On the contrary, if you are gaining 10 pounds a year, you can improve your health by making slow modifications. What about stopping the evening snack? You do not need to wait until New Year's Eve to start a goal... baby steps matter.

Here is a Clue...What is your Cue?

Actors, teachers, and parents give and receive cues and create looping. Cues prompt action. Actions are repeated steps that loop until they are automated. And your brain loves repetition because it wants to do the same things repeatedly. Your brain is very happy when you begin to embed habits because it no longer needs to think on its feet. When an actor learns his lines and the scene plays out, he is prepared for what comes next. Cues. Teachers and parents are fantastic at teaching cues which ultimately lead to habits and looping patterns. From when the alarm rings on your nightstand until you turn out the lights before bed, you receive cues that drive action. What cues are prompting your brain to act?

You will learn how to identify your cues in *The Coach and The Doc Battle Tips* at the back of the book. In the Reference section, you will find a link for *100 Ways to Slightly Improve your Life.*

You have now read the spoke definitions and a few prompts for the MIND quadrant of the *ATW Wheel*[TM]. On your blank worksheet, place your nails (dots) using a guideline of 1-10. The center of the wheel is considered zero, and 10 is represented at the other end of the spoke on the outside rim of the wheel, the tire tread. PS: I have yet to find anyone who is a 10, so keep that in mind when you think that lane is "perfect." So, please remember, if you are a ten in any aspect, you may be spending too much energy in this category and neglecting others. Ultimately, we are shooting for 80% in all sectors.

CHAPTER 4

BODY -
Your Vessel

*T*he Body chapter is represented by the color green. When I thought of the color green, I felt vitality (growth, rest, and high energy), saw nature, and could taste healthy foods (kale, lol). Maintaining a vibrant, strong, and mobile vessel (body) also requires regular visits with your physician, dentist, eye-care specialist, or therapy visits.

You have now completed three of the four quadrants: heart, spirit, and mind. You should now have 18 nails (dots) on your *ATW Wheel*™. After you complete this chapter, you will have 24.

Let us bring it all together. Each spoke in each quadrant affects the others. You cannot ignore one without affecting the other.

Improvements in the HEART quadrant spokes might involve marriage counseling, stress-reduction classes, and establishing an effective self-care practice, all of which could lower blood pressure and improve the quality of your sleep, which are BODY quadrant spokes. Some spokes in the SPIRIT quadrant, like becoming more creative or embedding meditation practices, might improve your personal awareness, growth, and learning, which are MIND quadrant spokes. Finding another job, creating a family calendar, or a habit of prepping foods on Sunday, which sit in the MIND chapter, might help lower your cholesterol or encourage you to start playing pickleball. Everything you do or don't do affects every other area of your life. You get the point.

Our final quadrant: there are six BODY spokes in the wheel: Lifestyle, Diet, Nutrition, Exercise, Sleep, and Medical Care. You will find descriptions for each spoke below and prompts to help you determine where you are on the appropriate location of each spoke. At the end of this BODY chapter, you will go to your *ATW Wheel*^{TM} worksheet and place a nail (dot) on each of the six BODY quadrant spokes.

Lifestyle. *Who? What? Where? Why? When? How?*

> *Live in the sunshine, swim the sea, drink the wild air.*

> Ralph Waldo Emerson

Your lifestyle is the culmination of all the choices you make in all areas of your life: heart, spirit, mind, and body. How you live. I am not just talking about if you live in Manhattan and drive a Benz or if you sleep in a tent in your parents' backyard. Your lifestyle is broader than that. It is the culmination of where and how deep your punctures are in 24 spokes of your life. The wheel is a visual representation of your life and lifestyle. If your tread runs thin, you break a lug nut, or your wheel falls off the axle, you will be placing a call to the tow man. Why wait until your wheel falls off to take charge of your life?

How you live physically, emotionally, financially, and spiritually is your lifestyle. As we have said in this entire book, if you desire to become healthier and live a different lifestyle, the responsibility sits on you.

If you attend college five days a week, party every weekend, homeschool your children, or are a vegan, you have a particular lifestyle. Working fifty hours a week might not give you the energy to socialize. Partying every Friday and Saturday might lead to health issues. Working with five-year-old's all day may affect your mental health. And being the only vegan in the family can be challenging if they all want to barbecue burgers every weekend. Again, what you do and don't do creates who and what you are, providing a glimpse into where you are headed. Create your own lifestyle.

Before you continue, take a peek at the three quadrants of the worksheet you completed earlier. If you have more nails (dots) towards the center (the hub), it is a sign that you can improve your lifestyle.

Dr. Markus: *Most of us struggle with the financial aspect of our lifestyle. The stress imposed by the monthly bills is sizable. On the other hand, there are wants we cannot fulfill due to the constant financial burdens. This causes frustration and even anger issues. So, I decided to dive deep into my wants. It was a big surprise to discover that most of my wants were programs instilled by society. Looking further, I found these programs to be snares that lead to enslavement. Taking out a loan for a house requires us to work to pay it back. Now work becomes a requirement, not a joyful expression of your talents. I fell into this trap, and maybe you are also living in Slavedom. Try to analyze what is truly a necessity and what is a want. Get away from the programmed "Keep up with the Joneses." There was a time in my life when enough was never enough, and because of that, my happiness suffered. Now I live a modest lifestyle in happiness.*

Lifestyle Prompts:

- Do you feel optimistic about the direction of your life?
- Are you spontaneous? Do you try new things?
- Which do you choose more often, healthy, or unhealthy choices?
- Do you surround yourself with people who lift you up?
- Do you watch the news frequently?
- Do you participate in anything you consider excessive such as gambling, shopping, drinking, smoking, the gym, working, etc.?
- Do you spend time weekly with family and friends?
- Do you use a smart or fitness watch to measure your sleep, heart rate, activity, and more?
- Do you have a will or medical power of attorney?
- Think about your average week. Is your house mostly organized, bills paid on time, your hygiene on point, you eat at least 80% nutritionally, and move most days of the week? Depending on your answers, you might be a 9 on the wheel or maybe a 5.

Diet. *Just go step by step - no bets!*

Your diet is a bank account.
Good food choices are good investments.

Bethenny Frankel

There is a difference between diet and nutrition. A diet is a step-by-step plan intended to improve nutrition and overall health. Being on a diet does not automatically translate to a calorie-restricted meal plan or trying to lose weight. You might be Vitamin D or B deficient or have chronic inflammation; therefore, you may choose a different diet plan than others. You should adopt a diet plan that helps you maintain or improve your health.

There are over ONE HUNDRED diet plans to try. No joke! Maybe you have already tried a dozen of them. Find what works for you. Perhaps you have tried the juicing diet or a keto plan but ultimately landed on the Diabetic Diet your physician recommended. How you feel, move, and your overall quality of life are often directly linked to your diet.

Nancy Henderson reported in Parade magazine a summary of the following studies. The goal for these study participants was to lose weight.

The Journal of Clinical Nutrition reported the following data from a registry of volunteers:

- After one year of dieting, 35% regain at least five pounds.
- 59% maintained their weight.
- Only 6% continued to lose weight.

Medical Clinics of North America analyzed dozens of diet groups, spanning thousands of participants.

- More than half of all weight lost in diets is regained within two years.
- By year five, more than 80% of all weight lost is regained.

Another set of studies quoted by UCLA found that:

- In less than two years, 23% of people gain more weight than they lost.
- More than two years after dieting, 83% gained more than they lost.
- A final study followed up on dieters after five years, and 50% of them were 11 pounds over their initial weight.

Most weight-loss diets are not successful long term because they are either the latest fad or based on strict black-and-white rules. The Mediterranean Diet is still considered a plan that meets nutritional needs. It is colorful and satisfies most lifestyles and financial means.

You can look up most meal plans and see the short-term and long-term success rates. Unfortunately, most people struggle to maintain someone else's rules or plans. Remember, they are not personalized for you, your health and wellness goals, lifestyle, or finances. They won't work for you long term unless they meet your personal requirements.

Peggy: *In 1989, when I started my health and wellness career, I decided that I would never endorse a specific diet plan for me or for my clients long-term. It was often met with mixed emotions. Why won't you tell me what to eat? Because we are all different, and we need to adjust our diet ("rules") based on our goals and nutritional needs. When considering a meal plan, take into account the time you can commit to it (prepping food can take a while), if you can afford the foods on the plan, your habit history (how long can you commit to the plan), and your support system. After meeting with your health experts (doctor, trainer, nutritionist, counselors, family, and friends), you may choose to become a vegan, vegetarian, pescatarian, or adhere to the Mediterranean diet. Whichever plan you follow, make sure your nutritional needs are met, and you feel stronger and more vibrant.*

Diet Prompts:

- How many different diet plans have you tried? Which ones have been relatively successful?

- With your diet plan, do you feel more energetic or groggy and off your game?
- Do you dive in headfirst or take smaller steps to embed healthy food habits?
- Is your meal plan full of nutrients, varies in color, and contains fewer chemicals?
- Do you know how many macronutrients you need to meet your wellness goals? For example, you may need more protein and fewer carbohydrates if you are a bodybuilder.

Nutrition. *Food is Fuel. Fad or Ironclad. Become a Food Snob,* and *Experiment. Do You!*

> *Came from a plant, eat it; was made in a plant, don't.*
>
> Michael Pollan

I said it in our last book, and I will repeat it. You are what you eat from your head down to your feet.

Healthy *nutrition* provides the necessary "nutrients" for full-body maintenance, growth, and reproduction. In addition, proper nutrition helps prevent disease. To maintain proper health, each person must meet nutrient requirements such as calories, macronutrients (proteins, carbohydrates, and fats), and micronutrients (vitamins and minerals).

According to American Dietary Guidelines, four main nutrition components are missing in our diets today: calcium, potassium, dietary fiber, and vitamin D. Of course, eating nutrient-filled foods is preferred. However, you may need supplementation. In many cases, a blood draw might be the best way to see where your nutrient level lies.

A growing body of evidence shows that an increase in carbon dioxide worldwide is negatively affecting the levels of nutrients in our foods. Though plants need CO_2 to grow, an abundance of it is like junk food to them.

For years we have understood that the overuse of soil is depleting the nutrients in our fruits and vegetables. This includes the lack of nutrients in the grains animals consume. Depending on where animals graze, you may be more nutritionally drained than you think. Interestingly poor air quality and malnourished soil affect the protein levels in pollen and plant nectar. Uh, Oh, honey lovers.

Eating a healthy diet is no longer about simply choosing the right foods and adequate quantities based on your health goals. Even healthy foods are lacking essential nutrients, where the products grow and what the animals eat (if you eat meat). Look at the resources of the products you consume. Yes, more nutritious foods can be more expensive such as grass-fed beef versus open range, but in the long run, it is wise to spend your money on nutrition than to spend it on medication because you have become unhealthy.

Nutrition Prompts:

- Is your diet plan at least 80% free of trans fats, preservatives, and colorings?

- Have you learned to read nutrition labels? If you cannot pronounce the ingredients, they are primarily synthetic and not nutritious. Do you pay attention to the first five ingredients? The order determines the highest ingredient content down to the least.

- Do you eat meals and snacks regularly to avoid binge-eating episodes? If you space your meals or snacks longer than six hours, you might be at risk for unhealthy cravings and binge eating.

- Do you have energy during the day, or do you chase excessive caffeine and sugar?

- Do you measure your food portions?

- Are you a condiment king or queen (do you smother your food in "something")?

- Do you enjoy your food, or are you constantly feeling guilty or thinking about not eating it?

Exercise. *Use it or lose it. Find Your Fun. Strong is the new Sexy.*

Good things come to those who sweat.

Anonymous

We are healthier the more we move. How many more decades do we have to say that?

The U.S. Department of Health and Human Services recommends these exercise guidelines: at least 150 minutes of moderate aerobic activity per week or 75 minutes of vigorous aerobic activity. Preferably a goal of 300 minutes. Five 60-minute Zumba classes might work for you, or 45-minute walks daily. It is also recommended to strength train various muscles with 12-15 repetitions at least two times a week. We should also stretch at least 5-10 minutes each day. Flexibility improves mobility and range of motion, increases blood flow, and lowers injury risk.

What happens to your body when you move more?

When you move, your heart races, improving oxygen and blood flow to your muscles and organs. Movement elevates your body temperature aiding in burning calories and fat. Improved strength protects your bones and organs. Your brain sends signals increasing communication between mind and body. Mental health improves due to the release of endorphins and an increase in blood flow. And we all know how important mental health is. A good night's sleep is more likely if you move throughout the day.

So why aren't we healthier when we have all of this information? Isn't knowledge everything? The benefits of moving are well known. Yet, on some days, exercise feels like terribly hard work. Starting a new 30-minute walking routine might feel like you enlisted in the U.S. Army and are required to complete 1000 push-ups a day and run 10 miles. And each time you fall off your Wellness Wagon, it will be a struggle to start again.

A movement plan affects many aspects of your life, including physical, mental, emotional, and financial. And it has been drilled into us for decades that exercise sucks. But does it? Not everyone likes to go to the gym to work out. It can be tedious, and it can be expensive. How many of you pay the monthly dues for the remainder of your contract, and you don't even go? Not many people are successful in exercising in a home gym. How many of you have seen treadmills in yard sales? The most successful, long-term movement plans are those you enjoy. It is tough to continue doing things you hate. You would not go to lunch every day with a boss you cannot stand. If you love hiking in nature or kayaking on the lake, go. If you hate the elliptical machine or hot yoga, do not do it. If you adopt the motto, *Fitness is Fun*, you will be more successful. We do not have to be miserable to get our hearts pumping.

Starting anything is a challenge. Becoming more active can be as tricky as improving your diet. If it was not hard, we would all ride off into the sunset, loving vegetables, doing crunches, and drinking 64 oz. of water. Embedding and maintaining habits are the most challenging. Compare nutrition and physical activity for a second. Break up your movement throughout the day just as you should with snacks—a fifteen-minute walk in the morning counts. You do not have to reach 160 beats per minute every time you work out. Add diversity to your exercise just as you would vary your nutrition. Take different exercise classes, work out indoors and outdoors, and try cardiovascular, strength, and flexibility training just as you would try to eat various vegetables and fruits. Treat yourself. Take a paddleboard class instead of another night of eating out.

Dr. Markus: *As mentioned in our first book, The Four-Fold Formula for All Things Wellness, I was turned off to exercise by my endeavors to become an Olympian at age 18. At that time, it was impossible to win without doping. The use of hormones to help improve performance completely turned me off. I struggle with "exercise" to this day. But my lifestyle and genetics unmasked a pre-diabetes health condition. I adjusted my diet to lose weight, knowing this would reverse my condition.*

Then I realized that a significant portion of my weight loss came from losing muscle mass, not fat. Exercise is vital while eating correctly to ensure you are eating enough protein and maintaining muscle mass. So, I decided to vary my exercise routine daily. Sometimes it is walking, gardening, and most recently, I started Tai Chi, a low-impact martial art. Now I maintain my lean muscle mass and melt away the fat, normalizing my blood sugar. The sense of accomplishment was a huge boost to my sense of wellbeing. This recognition drives me to continue what I categorically rejected in the past.

Exercise Prompts:

- Do you move more days of the week than not?
- Are you active for at least 50 minutes a week with moderate intensity?
- Is your exercise regimen fun or dreadful?
- Do you move throughout your workday? An upset tummy, tiredness, cognitive struggles, or fluctuating emotions could indicate that you need to move.
- Do you stretch regularly?
- Are you frequently stiff and sore?

Sleep. *Count Sheep and Sleep - and the benefits you shall reap.*

> *The minute anyone's getting anxious, I say,*
> *You must eat, and you must sleep.*
> *They're the two vital elements for a healthy life.*

Francesca Annis

I have more conversations these days with people about sleep than I do about nutrition and exercise. Unless you have a suspected medical condition, you do not have to see a sleep expert or be strapped to a device to determine if you are getting the quality or quantity of sleep you need.

Feeling tired isn't the only hint that you should improve your sleep. Your body is likely telling you. Sleep deprivation causes brain fog, irritability, and increased illness.

For many, falling asleep is a struggle, or if they wake up in the middle of the night, they struggle to fall back asleep. (On another note, for those who believe alcohol helps you sleep. It does not. It may help you fall asleep, but for the rest of the night, you will stir.).

Sleep and sleep patterns are unique for everyone. For example, if you work nights and need to sleep during the daytime, you may need to use blackout curtains, an eye mask, ear plugs, and a fan for white noise. At the same time, a nighttime sleeper may sleep well by leaving their phone outside the bedroom.

Thousands of sleep studies prove we need adequate sleep and there are dozens of ideas to improve our sleep quality. If you are still struggling to sleep even if you have tried a dozen methods, keep trying—you haven't found the best methods for YOU. When trying a new solution, don't give up on day three. Give it a few weeks before you quit or move on to another idea.

To mention again, if you have struggled with sleep for years or, conversely, sleep has suddenly become an issue, you may need a sleep study to rule out a medical problem.

The bottom line, when the sun goes down, our body begins releasing a natural hormone called melatonin which is intended to help you sleep. The body then begins to prepare you for sunup by releasing another hormone called cortisol. The imbalance of these two hormones will affect your quality and quantity of sleep.

Peggy: *My oldest son has struggled with his sleep for 20 years. It is about experimenting. He became stressed out and anxious that he couldn't sleep. After years of working on the road and staying in hotels, he had learned to sleep with one eye open, waiting for the phone to ring. He also struggled with decompressing from the day's work and not being anxious about the next. He eventually left that job, but it took months to improve his sleep behavior.*

Sleep Prompts:

- Do you take a sleep aid most nights of the week?

- Do you sleep consistently between 6-9 hours most nights?

- Do you have a good nighttime routine? Such as winding down about an hour before bed, no screen time, dark room, etc.?

- Do you drink alcohol to "help you" sleep?

- How does sleep affect you personally and professionally?

- Do you stress or feel hyper-focused about sleep?

- Are you chasing caffeine all day to "wake" up?

Medical Care. *Prevention and Compliance, NOT Defiance. Take Care of Yourself, or Someone Else Will Have To.*

> *Take care of your body. It's the only place you have to live.*
>
> Jim Rohn

Prevention and compliance are vital whether you follow Western, Eastern, or holistic medical practices. However, a combination of all three is the best prescription for overall health.

Lack of prevention or compliance is selfish.

If you do not follow a pro-active versus reactive medical plan, do not check in regularly with experts regarding your health status, and do not take your prescribed medications regularly, you are potentially hurting yourself and your family and friends. Who is going to take care of you if you are sick? How will your illnesses or diagnoses affect your caregiver's life? If you have a family cardiac history, continue to smoke, or ignore other ways to improve your health, who do your behaviors affect now or in the future when something happens to you? Your healthy or unhealthy choices will make you more susceptible to certain health conditions. How you care for yourself today will impact your care down the road.

Dr. Markus: *Most of us heard the saying: 'Physician heal thyself.' Yes, I have deep knowledge about the workings of the human body, and I can assess my health status better than most. But there are limits, and I need to employ colleagues to help me. For instance, dental checkups, eye exams, and colonoscopies are necessary for the early detection of problems, and I cannot perform these services myself. Furthermore, yearly visits with my Primary Care Physician uncover potential issues like diabetes, hypertension, and hypercholesterolemia, to mention only a few. Therefore, health maintenance requires a group effort. As a result of this understanding, access to health care must be universal if we want to maintain a healthy society.*

Medical Care Prompts:

- Do you visit your health providers regularly (primary care, dental, eye care, or therapists)?

- Do you follow through with recommended screenings (mammograms, colon, or prostate screenings)?

- Do you take your prescribed medications properly?

- Do you have medical care or a backup plan if you become ill?

You have now read the spoke definitions and a few prompts for the BODY quadrant of the *ATW Wheel*™. On your blank worksheet, place your nails (dots) using a guideline of 1-10. The center of the wheel, the hub, is considered zero, and 10 is represented at the other end of the spoke on the outside rim of the wheel, the tire tread. PS: I have yet to find anyone who is a 10, so keep that in mind when you think that lane is "perfect." So, please remember, if you are a ten in any aspect, you may be spending too much energy in this category and neglecting others. Ultimately, we are shooting for 80% in all sectors.

Once you have placed your dots on each spoke, it is time to connect the nails (dots) between each of the quadrants of your wheel. Draw a line connecting each nail (dot), making a circle. Sit back. What does your wellness wheel look like? Is the wheel symmetrical or jagged? Can you back the wagon out of the garage, or are you looking for the tire jack?

Look at you. You just created your baseline health and wellness assessment by using the *ATW Wheel*™ 24-spoke descriptions and prompts. You should have a nail (dot) on every spoke—24 in total. You may have 26 if you created a few extra lines on the relationship spoke of the HEART quadrant. This may be the first time you have ever dissected every nook and cranny of your existence. But guess what? Now you have no excuses.

Before we share a few tips and tricks to get you on track to achieving great things, we want you to double-check your nail (dot) locations. Is your self-assessment as accurate as possible? Are your nails really where they should be? People often fill out the wheel quickly without fully absorbing the spoke descriptions or utilizing some of the prompts we have provided.

In the next chapter, you will find the *6Ws of Wellness*. These are steps to help you adjust your nails (dots) if necessary. No guessing. Your baseline needs to be as accurate as possible.

Here is an example of why. If you decided to lose 10 pounds, and one month later, you have not lost an ounce, you might start waving the white flag of defeat. Stop before you quit. Complete a new wheel worksheet and compare it to your previous wheel. You may find a few leaks to help you understand why such as you are working more, haven't been sleeping, etc. Or you may find improvements in four or five spokes, such as relationships, organization, creativity, or medical care, have improved. By filling out the wheel, you might find data to keep you motivated and on track. The tool allows you to remove your emotion, and it will continually remind you that being healthy is NOT just about the scale.

By regularly completing the wheel and adjusting your health, wellness, and lifestyle plan, you will stay on top of your wellness instead of repeatedly quitting and wasting energy digging yourself out of the ditch.

6Ws of Wellness

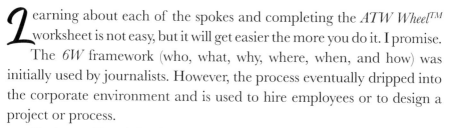

*L*earning about each of the spokes and completing the *ATW Wheel*™ worksheet is not easy, but it will get easier the more you do it. I promise.

The *6W* framework (who, what, why, where, when, and how) was initially used by journalists. However, the process eventually dripped into the corporate environment and is used to hire employees or to design a project or process.

Grab a coffee, sit back, and take a peek at your wellness wheel while we dive a bit deeper. Are you ready to bring it all home?

Like frosting on a cupcake, the *6Ws of Wellness* add to the prompts and definitions we shared above. This chapter will help you place those nails (dots) even more accurately than you already have. And will help you find solutions.

A cupcake is fantastic, but the frosting takes it to another level. Sprinkles level up that treat even more. The *6Ws* are your sprinkles. Many of you will shift a few nails (dots) higher or lower on several spokes. Let's sprinkle some finishing touches on your *ATW Wheel*™ baseline assessment worksheet.

Here is why it is important. What if, before reviewing the *6Ws of Wellness* below, you placed a dot in the seven-ish area on your Coping Skill spoke? Then you work through the who, what, why, where, when, and how, and realize it should be about a five. That "slight" difference will affect the "urgency" of creating strategies and embedding healthier habits to keep your Wellness Wagon rolling along. Trust me.

In addition, the *6Ws of Wellness* as they relate to each spoke of your wellness wheel, will help you create strategies and tools that work for you personally. This is your *ATW Improvement Plan*.

I used the *6Ws* when designing the *ATW Wheel*^{TM} itself. It helped me refine the tool over and over again. Who needs the tool? What would the tool look like, and what were the main pain points (problems) to solve? Why weren't my clients achieving their health, wellness, and lifestyle goals? Where, when, and how could the tool be used? The *ATW Wheel*^{TM} was born after I worked through the *6Ws*.

Who: Any human being can use it. We can all improve the quality of our lives at work, home, and play. (I also created a wheel to introduce life balance to pre-teens.)

What: Create a visual self-assessment tool (worksheet) using a metaphor so people can relate to it (wellness wheel). Within four macro components (heart, spirit, mind, and body quadrants), drill down to micro areas in one's life (including coping skills, habits, lifestyle, etc.; 24 spokes). Create descriptions for each area, assisting people in assessing their life at any given moment and thus designing personal strategies that work for them.

Why: For years, we have set goals; some we achieve, many we do not. Why do we keep giving up? How many years have we set the same New Year's Resolution? I had a client once who joked (funny, not funny), "I have lost the same 50 pounds 20 times, so I have lost and gained 1000 pounds."

According to Inc.com, over 40% of Americans set a New Year's Resolution, and 91% give up. Resolutions, on average, fall apart within four-six weeks.

It is no shock that we "fail."

However, I am on your side. I will go down with the battleship saying the same thing for the rest of my life—"Your wellness needs to be designed FOR YOU." If most tools focus on only three or four areas of your wellness and the experts' recommendations are generalized for the mainstream, no wonder you struggle to hit your personal goals. Being healthy and happy transcends beyond how long you sleep, how many veggies you eat, and your Nautilus program at the gym. That is why it was vital for me to create a self-assessment tool that could be used in real-time based on current health status, beliefs, patterns of behavior, and lifestyle.

Where: They say wherever you go, you are. I wanted you to have data at your fingertips at any point in your life. Ultimately, the onus rests with you. No more blaming a nutritionist, trainer, or doctor. No more pointing fingers. However, you cannot improve your health and wellness without a strong support team and experts when you need them.

When: Offer a real-time tool people can use to self-assess and create strategies to design their own health plan. For example, if you want to run a marathon and train six days a week, the tool will reveal areas where you need support, such as home and work organization, meals for the family, etc. In addition, if urgent issues pop up, such as a medical condition or the loss of a family member, you can fill out your wheel and make a real-time plan.

How: Use the results from the assessment tool to design personal strategies and identify other tools to improve life at work, home, or play.

Now you can see how the *6Ws* helped me create the *ATW Wheel*^{TM}.

Ready to have some fun? The content of this book thus far might feel a bit heavy or overwhelming, so let's lighten the tone.

We are about to bring peace to the North Pole using the *6Ws*. A war just broke out, and the elves are revolting against Santa's labor laws!

Below you will see how we can use the *6W* process to win a battle raging at the North Pole AND how you can use the *6Ws* to win a Wellness War. There are two scenarios for each of the *6Ws*. The North Pole battle is first followed by how you might find gaps to adjust any nails (dots) on the *ATW Wheel*^{TM} you just completed.

Who is involved in the North Pole War: The elves, Santa, Mrs. Clause, reindeer, government, and security organizations.

Who is part of your *ATW Wheel*^{TM}: You, your family, friends, co-workers, organizations, and experts such as your physicians, trainers, nutritionists, counselors, etc.

What is the issue at the North Pole: Get the elves back to work.

Looking back at your completed *ATW Wheel*^{TM}, **what** should be your wellness focus? Is it to improve your lab results, spend more time on self-awareness or creativity, repair a relationship with your father, or maybe to decrease your blood pressure, blood sugar, or cholesterol? Have you figured out your "what?"

Why is there a war at the North Pole: Santa's elves are revolting against current labor-law policies, which require 15-hour days, and they only have Christmas Day off. They are responsible for helping Santa prepare for his annual gift-giving ritual, and without resolution, the holiday season will forever change for children worldwide.

Why are you trying to get healthier, happier, wiser, and wealthier? Do you know what your answers are? In my experience, people struggle the most to answer this part of the *6Ws*. Being hyper-focused on your why or your purpose in life can cause frustration, depression, anxiety, and even rigor mortis, ultimately preventing you from taking any steps at all. Some think, "Why bother if I don't know my why?" Determining why you are on the planet is more challenging than deciding why you need to lose weight, why you want to start your own business, or why you want a divorce.

Your passion and life purpose might be right in front of you. Your why may reveal itself while you focus on something else or while reading this book. You might uncover a hidden "why" when you complete your wheel.

You can also dig deeper by asking yourself why, why, why??? You may have heard the process described as "peeling back the onion." The conversation might go like this: I ask, "Why do you want to lose weight?" You respond, "Because I have no energy, and nothing fits." I bounce back with, "Why do you want more energy?" You answer, "So I can play on the floor with my grandchildren?" I keep going, "Why do you want to play on the ground and have fun with them?" You roll your eyes but keep responding. "Because my grandparents were unhealthy and never played with us." Now we are getting there. Find an emotional connection to "why" you want to do something. Explore deeper and deeper until you find a reason so personal that you can grab onto it when those challenging days pop up and you want to quit.

The **where** is easy for the North Pole war. Duh, it's taking place in Santa's workshop.

Where. We are constantly surrounded by potential wellness battles. Every location and aspect of your life is an opportunity for a struggle with wellness, whether you are at home, work, a restaurant, a store, a gym, a doctor's appointment, etc. This is why you need to be on your toes. There are opportunities around every corner to make healthy or unhealthy choices.

The **when** for the North Pole is tomorrow. Troops leave at dawn. The toys are not going to build themselves.

The **when** for your Wellness War varies. We should focus on our health every day. Do not wait until Monday. However, some goals require preparation. Diving unprepared into large-scale goals often backfires. Ensure your goals are clear and concise, and determine what you have and what you need before you kick off your goal. Each step you take either moves you toward or away from your goal. Winning even minor battles builds confidence. But beware of procrastination. That bugger can be a killer.

How will we win the North Pole War? Every country across the globe will deploy a battalion. They are physically trained for cold-weather acclimation, armed with battle gear, and prepared to surround Santa's workshop by land, air, and sea. As part of a peace treaty, they will create a communication center, take two daily breaks, have a 30-minute lunch, and have weekends off—oh, and unlimited cookies.

The **how** of a Wellness War stumps almost everyone. **How** in the hell are you going to win the wellness war if you don't know **how**? Identifying strategies that work for every one of the 24 spokes of the *ATW Wheel*™ takes time. The how is the most ambiguous and frustrating, but if you keep experimenting, gathering data, and assessing your outcomes, you will keep moving forward. Utilizing medical reports and lab results might help you determine why and how. Meeting with health and wellness experts can help you create the "how." We all need a physical, mental, emotional, spiritual, and financial plan to map out goals. Smartwatches, nutrition and meditation apps, body measurements, and more can help you stay on track. Vision boards are a tool many use to manifest goals and dreams; colorfully decorated boards or a wall with cut-out magazine pictures of a car, a fit body, or buying a beach home can give you focus and help you design a path to making things become reality. My son, Shane, has said for years, "Hopes and dreams do not come true unless you take steps in their direction. Keeping your hopes and dreams in your mind is not enough to make sure they come to fruition." Smart dude, eh!

There is no magic pill, however...

We have the tools. We have experience. You have learned many steps to get you started. If you do the work, you will succeed. Why are we so confident? Because we believe in you. We all want to live our best life. We know you want to sleep better, take walks in the park, pay your bills, travel, and more.

Your willingness to dig deep and discover where you are and where you want to go is up to you. Whenever you feel you are falling off track, use our *ATW Wheel*™ and the *6Ws of Wellness*. Don't you love it when you have control, and things just seem to fall into line?

Improving your life is not a quick fix.

As we have said, it is hard, it is work, and it is war. However, as long as you remain focused, diligent, and consistently take action, you will see improvements. You could see improvements as soon as today.

It is time to take responsibility for our role in the world and not just as it stands today, but where it is going in the future. We have learned from our past. Haven't we? If so, why do we keep repeating the same mistakes? Most of us have a long history with Western medicine, physicians, their staff, insurance companies, and policies and procedures. Collectively, we believe the world is taking steps in a positive direction by improving and expanding the current version of itself through internal and external expansion, prayer, meditation, and other self-discovery modalities. We all have successes or failures in our past. Own the experience. Use them to your benefit. And move the troops forward.

ATW Wheel™ Baseline Assessment

*I*f you have printed off the wheel and followed along throughout the book, you are on your way to improving your health. Again, the free downloadable can be found at:

www.allthings.wellness.com/ATW-Wheel-Worksheet.

You can purchase the *ATW Wheel*™ *Assessment and Improvement Plan* (link below), or you can take notes as we finish up.

www.allthings.wellness.com/ATW-Wheel-Assessment-Improvement-Plan.

The *Baseline Assessment Review* is used to analyze how balanced your Wellness Wheel is based on where you put your nails (dots) in each of the 24 spokes of the wheel.

If you have chosen not to use the improvement plan document available, grab your paper and pen. Make three columns. Title them: *Doing Well* (spoke eight and above), *Doing OK* (spokes at six or seven), and *Not Doing So Well* (spokes at five and below). In the appropriate column, write the spoke titles into one of the above three categories. You may have a dozen spokes in your *Doing Well* category, eight in *Doing OK* and four in the *Uh-Oh Zone.* You must have all 24 spokes assigned.

The main focus right now is to take a peek at your *Uh-Oh Zone.* How can you use the prompts Dr. Markus and I gave you in each of the previous spoke descriptions, and how can you use the *6Ws of Wellness* above to create strategies to fix the punctures you have in your *Uh-Oh Zone?*

The Coach and The Doc Battle Tips below may also give you ideas to create your *ATW Wheel*™ *Assessment and Improvement Plan.* Feel free to research other ideas as well. You do not need significant shifts to keep your wheel on track. The goal is to achieve 80% across all spokes, but shifting a three to a six can change your life.

Continue to gather data, experiment, build your troop (support system), pick your weapons (knowledge, tools, and strategies), and be ready to fire (take action with healthy habits and routines).

Reminders: 1) Set your emotions aside every time you complete the *ATW Wheel*[TM] 2) Be aware of any red flags 3) Complete your wheel worksheet every few months (set a calendar alarm) or anytime you experience an immediate health or lifestyle change, and 4) Continue to adjust *ATW Wheel*[TM] *Improvement Plan.*

At any point in time, you may be hit with a piece of shrapnel causing a minor lifestyle hiccup like an illness. Or you may step on a landmine, which is a more significant lifestyle blowout, such as bankruptcy or the birth of your twins. Remember, no matter how small or large your battles are, they all require you to take responsibility in order to *Win the Wellness W.A.R. (We Are Responsible).* Any spoke that is five out of 10 or less are brewing battles and may have already disrupted your health and lifestyle. Now that you have the *ATW Wheel*[TM] at your fingertips, you can identify your *Uh-Ohs* and be healthier and happier.

Coach Peggy's *ATW Wheel*[TM]

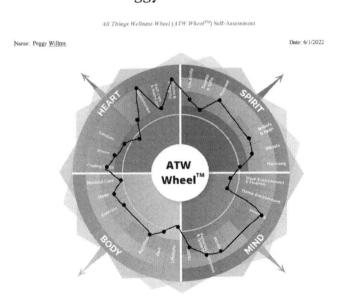

All Things Wellness Wheel (ATW Wheel[TM]*) Self-Assessment*

Name: Peggy Wilms   Date: 6/1/2022

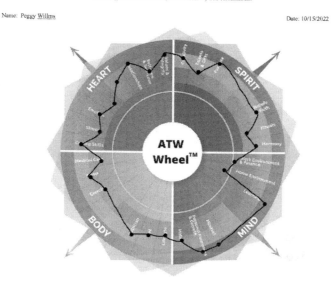

All Things Wellness Wheel (ATW Wheel™) Self-Assessment

Name: Peggy Willms

Date: 10/15/2022

Peggy: *Most of my punctures typically fall in the Spiritual or Body quadrant. I usually excel in the Heart and Mind quadrants. I am 70% left-brained and am blessed that my purpose and passion align with my profession. That is, it is a blessing until it isn't. We all need balance. Most people fall at 50/50 right and left-brained. When I am avoiding (intentionally or otherwise) my "feels" or fighting a sense of just "being," it is because I am hanging out too much in my "doing" world. I get busy working long hours and feel the rush to accomplish my To Do list. Going for the Dopamine Fix. I have had the fight or flight repeated programming in my life forever. My high is tangible, almost edible. When I am hyper-focused on my work (Mind quadrant), I neglect to eat, exercise, sleep, see a doctor, or check in with my loved ones. My stress levels and time with the people in my life also suffer (Heart Quadrant). Lack of sleep, increased migraines, and obsessive-compulsive behavior reveal their ugly head, and then anxiety joins the whole mix (Body Quadrant).*

Note: you can see in my wheel above that I intentionally split the "relationship" spoke into three separate spokes, as I have mentioned before. It allows me to dissect how I am doing my intimate, external (children, family) and social (co-workers, friends) relationships.

Last summer, I used the worksheet to see where I was instead of guessing. My Devil and Angel were fighting. My mind and body were at war. And frankly, running to trim the tree limbs because they were not perfect was getting to my boyfriend. I was off-kilter.

A few significant events affected my wheel last summer. My mother died 10 months earlier, and my five-month-old grandson had open-heart surgery. Both of which I had not dealt with. I had written a book, bought a house, and moved. I had seen several red flags waving. I was hardly eating, racing around 15 hours a day, and my OCD and anxiety were running rampant. I had nearly half the 24 spokes of the wheel below six. I started meditating, walking, focusing on my nutrition, and went to the doctor. Thank God I was already trying to patch a few punctures because Hurricane Ian hit our home just a few weeks later.

Comparing my October (post-hurricane) wheel to my June wheel, you can see that I had made several improvements. In fact, it was one of my healthiest wheels of all time, and I just spent 9 hours in the eye of the storm, and it ruined the house I had only lived in for two months! So how was my wheel so strong when I was just hit with a tragedy?

Because I have been using the wheel for years, I know those areas where I need to focus. Before I get a flat in my tire, I can now recognize my large waving red flags much earlier than I did before. For decades I lived a busier-than-normal life. I raised two competitive moto crossers, was married, worked full-time for Corporate America, and was a trainer and coach. I was constantly sick and injured. I did not address my wellness until the ship went down, causing me to plant my white flag and surrender.

Developing this wheel and completing it regularly has given me the necessary infor-mation to build my own personalized health plan. I let off the gas in my typically hyper-focused areas, such as work and my obsession with organization and efficiency. I started spending time writing and being with my flowers and trees. I knew where my attention needed to shift. I focused on my self-love and self-care spokes, AND I reached out to a support system to hold me accountable.

Dr. Markus's *ATW Wheel*^{TM}

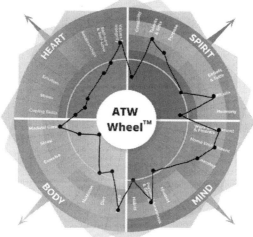

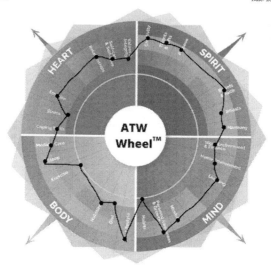

Markus: *Looking back at 2016, prior to completing the first wheel above, my divorce after 25 years of marriage took a significant toll on my wellness. It reminded me of my move from Germany to the U.S. in 1980. Back then, the move was my own decision, so I had a better mindset going into a new beginning. But I was unprepared for the loneliness. This time, I was broadsided by the event. Still, I was familiar with the survival aspects. I set up my home environment within walking distance of my work. My mind was focused on survival aspects for about two years. Then, I decided to take my alone time to begin the journey inwards. Learning was concentrating on personal growth.*

I expressed my talents and gifts in my work and explored meditation as a new ritual. My portal into this new world of discovery was Gaia, a subscription channel.

My heart was busy expressing my values and integrity, and there was not much energy for anything else. When you carry the title M.D. integrity is inherent. My value to society was the gauge of my self-worth. It still plays a big role.

In 2018, with Peggy's help, I took a comprehensive "deep dive." She introduced me to her wellness wheel. I had never looked at health and wellness this comprehensively. Looking at my first image above, I noticed the staggering lack of energy overall. My research into the topic of the energy content of the body led to the study of subtle energy. I was amazed at how research into quantum physics developed new measurement devices.

This is when I started observing my energy content with Bio-Well. My total energy content measured around 0.45 Joules. Not bad for a range of 0.40-0.60. A Joule is 0.7377 foot-pounds. A foot pound is the amount of energy it takes to move one pound by one foot in one direction. This amount of metabolic energy creates electromagnetism which can be measured via electro photonic imaging (EPI) captured by the Bio-Well device.

The hunt for ways to improve my energy content led me to HeartMath. This is when I started nurturing the connection between mind and heart. This intervention resulted in stress reduction of a considerable magnitude. I was quite surprised at how stressed I was. And I did not even know it. Retrospectively speaking, 90% of my time was spent in a stressed-out survival mode.

As you can see in image two, I am in a much better place today. There are still bad habits and poor exercise to work on. Then again, we are all sinners. And the punctures in the wheel tend to shift. As a result, I go over the wheel regularly. Persistent trends need attention. A big rewire for me was thinking I needed a trainer or a gym membership in order to exercise regularly. When I shifted to functional movement, it was a big help. Gardening is hard work, after all!

HEART CHAPTER STORIES

True beauty is a warm heart, a kind soul,
and an attentive ear.

Ken Poirot

Rest In Peace, Ms. Beverly

By Peggy Willms

*Ms. Beverly gave me the confidence to paint
with words and to never veer from my
"invoking worth math," as she called it.
She taught me that stories connect us.
Her angel wings brush by from time to time
when I am throwing my thoughts and feelings on paper.*

Peggy Willms
(author, coach, host, and motivational speaker)

*I*t is such a ride when you are a writer. Especially if you honor the process and let your passion and thoughts guide you versus writing through sheer force to drive an end product. And if you let go of the mindset that there is a "perfect" way to express your thoughts, feelings, beliefs, or behaviors, you are in for quite the ride, my friend.

For years, I have thrown my words on paper. I have learned not to fight the process. Stories tend to vessel through me rapidly. I do not fight the GPS of my creativity. There may be detours or roadblocks, but I tag along for the ride. My fingers do the walking.

My story starts with three words, *Green Ink, Inc.*, and the unfolding of a lifelong dream I shared with a 71-year-old lady decades ago. Every single relationship we have presents lessons. Ms. Beverly's physical imprint on me lasted only a year, but she has been guiding me for decades. People are in your life for a reason, a season, or a lifetime. She has held all three titles.

It feels like magic when I write. It is like taking a vision to a destination. When I am done, there is an overwhelming feeling of—we arrived! At times, aspects of my writing are driven by images bouncing around in a psychedelic rain dance in my head, and I have been caught a time or two jotting notes on gum wrappers.

A year ago, I stumbled onto a pile of old journals, blogs, college papers, and more while packing to move. One piece stood out. It was a blank piece of letterhead I had created back in 2001 with the words I said above, *Green Ink, Inc.* I laughed out loud. At the top of the letterhead was my AOL email address—good ole America Online. The edges are now yellowed. In the back of a weathered, green notebook, written in green ink, there was a poem I had written to Ms. Beverly, my English professor. It was dated October 2001.

In 2000, I decided to attend night school at Colorado Christian University. I was a 35-year-old wife working full-time and raising two sons. I had declined many scholarships after high school to follow the small, papermill town "dream." Get married to your High School sweetheart and get to hell out of Dodge. College can wait, I thought, and it did for 18 years.

I have always loved English. I fancied creative writing. Painting with words...paint paint paint. I tend to be an overly rambunctious compound-complex sentence fan, and who doesn't love a good modifier? I adore punctuation driving my overuse of ellipses, dashes, and semicolons. I can nail a dozen adverbs in a single bound. We could play indirect and direct pronouns all day. I can rearrange a story framework like I am walking in the park on a blissful Sunday stroll with a pungent scent of jasmine filling my soul. Words and imagery flow easily. Painting with words is a passion. What a tangent that was.

I took five English classes in my first year. Yes, five! Simply put, I was in Heaven. During this time, *Green Ink, Inc.* was born. There were essays, poetry, and a children's book with illustrations. My first book, *The Boy with the Broken Nose*, when taking Ms. Beverly's class. I sent it off to publishers the old fashion way. Shove it into brightly colored green or red envelopes, so the publisher's eyes would gravitate toward my manuscript when it was thrown on her desk. Time and time again, I insured and certified my precious book and accompanied it with a return postage-paid envelope. Trusting companies to send my passion project back was a risk. Denial after denial arrived. I still have all of them. My confidence level was stabbed more deeply with every trip to the mailbox, and the cycle continued for months.

Ms. Beverly repeatedly checked in with me.

She taught all but one of my English classes. She made me promise to never stop writing, never give up, and make sure I got published. She loved writing, too, and it was evident after teaching English for nearly 50 years. We had a special bond. She said I looked like Nicole Kidman in Moulin Rouge and always told me I sparked like a diamond. "You have a spark, Miss Peggy" … "You are sparking, Miss Peggy." Our relationship was priceless, and I think the other students knew it.

She ALWAYS carried a green pen and repeated time and again, "I use a green pen when I write. It reminds me of money. Making money and being financially independent is not bad as long as you do good things with it." I attended a Christian university, so I took her word for it.

She told me to dream big. Picture it. Touch it. After months of writing and submitting the children's books, she encouraged me to go into manifestation overdrive. "I am a successful publishing company." I started using green pens, green notebooks, and green suede journals, and I even created letterhead and named my "publishing company" *Green Ink, Inc.* This shit was coming true if I had to force it down my own throat.

Ms. Beverly never gave up on me. Maybe I did, or perhaps life just got in the way. Yes, I continued to write over the decades, but my "green ink" had dried up other than professional content and blogging. After I left college, I wrote a novel I have yet to publish, and after several months of writing and submitting my children's book, I gave up. That is until I found my English school work and submission denial letters tucked away in a Tupperware bin last year, and I was "sparked" to write again. *The Boy with the Broken Nose* will become the first book I will publish with my son, Tanner. We are creating a children's book series called *Tanner's T.A.L.E.S.* (Truth. Accountability. Love. Emotion. Support.). How fun is that? The first one is halfway through the process and in "colorization." I also co-authored a book with 39 contributing authors, The *Four-Fold Formula for All Things Wellness,* launched in 2022. And you are now reading book two of the three-book series. I have also created a wellness series for children that is in the making.

**Relationships matter whether they are
for a reason, a season, or a lifetime.**

We learn from healthy relationships, but we also learn from unhealthy relationships. And we often forget that others are learning from us as well. Diversity in age, culture, views, and opinions shape the world. Be patient in creating and maintaining your connections. Debate and dialogue in a healthy fashion. One love.

Ms. Beverly, I am still writing. Still sparking.

I found this poem in the back of my old green notebook. I gave it to Ms. Beverly 22 years ago.

> *When I see green, I think of you.*
> *When I see a child giggle and dance, I think of you, too.*
> *Do not separate church and state, you teach.*
> *You brought me to Calvary Chapel to hear Jeff preach.*
> *For when I see a morsel of nature bloom,*
> *Do you know how your spirit fills the room?*
> *Wisdom and age are no limits to you.*
> *Your heart is as gentle as the skies are blue.*
> *Beautiful, velvet skin so ivory and pure.*

Your being permeates an infectious lure.
You believe in me, push me, and inspire me.
You Let Me Be Me.
Can a day go by that I don't mention your name?
Nope, it simply wouldn't be the same.
"You Spark, Miss Peggy," you frequently said.
I thought, "This lady is cuckoo in the head."
Why did we hit it off? You are my age, times two.
Will you be settled in Heaven the next time I see you?
If so, you'll see me sparking through the clouds.
And I hope you tell me you are so very proud.

One of Peggy's Favorite Quotes

Writing is the only thing that when I do it,
I don't feel I should be doing something else.

Gloria Steinem

From Behind the Gaming Chair

By Keith Zygland, aka Ziggy Salvation

Having just one person genuinely listen to you and engage means the absolute most.

Ziggy Salvation (author, master barber)

*I*f you read my story. Behind the Barber Chair, in book one of the All Things Wellness series called, *The Four-Fold Formula*, I shared a few stories from my clients over the years. I was inspired to write in this book because of its title: *Win the Wellness W.A.R.*—WE ARE RESPONSIBLE! The word "responsibility" really hit home.

Before I share a few experiences from sitting in my gaming chair, a few more popped into my head as a Master Barber as it relates to things conquering the battles in life. I have learned that everyone, and I mean EVERYONE, is at war with themselves to some degree. Whether it's personal issues, problems at work, trouble with a friend or spouse, or the occasional argumentative child, there is always something we all strive to improve.

Our wellness and growth are hard to talk about because, at the end of the day, it is our responsibility to take action to try to improve it. One would think these interactions are only shared in close quarters; how wrong we are.

Since as early on in cutting hair as I can remember, people often and easily open up about things that bother them, knowing full well that they're in a place of confidentiality. An even more rewarding part of that process is seeing how those individuals overcome and grow from each situation.

The first example that comes to mind is one of my regular customers. He came in for a cut and talked about a difficult day he had been having. He would use his time in the barber's chair to relax, reflect on the work week, and recalibrate for the next. The most interesting thing we talked about was that his favorite bait shop didn't have the regular type of bait he used on his weekly fishing excursion, yet something was different this time. He asked for my phone number before leaving.

I had a gut feeling that it was the right thing to do.

The next evening, I received a call from him. His mindset had darkened considerably as his wife had informed him that she had been unfaithful. It rocked him to the point that he admitted at that exact moment that he didn't even want to live. My heart broke for him as I heard the unimaginable pain coming through the phone.

You can't really prepare for hearing something like that, so I sprung into the action of reassurance and quickly reminded him of all the positive things he had accomplished for himself in the last couple of years. I reminded him of finding his faith and being baptized, switching companies for the better in his professional life, finally obtaining a vehicle he'd always sought, and through the church, finding a group of supportive friends who love him no matter what he is going through.

He unnecessarily thanked me for listening to him. Listening is simply all it takes to help someone. We live in such a fast-paced world; it's easy to feel unseen or forgotten. Having just one person genuinely listen to you and engage means the absolute most. Since that heart-wrenching conversation, he still comes in for his weekly cut.

He is not embarrassed to vocalize his trials that the emotional distress his wife's infidelity put him through.

Something has changed, however. He not only shares the detriments he feels but now includes what he does to prepare himself, protect himself, and improve himself daily. You can tell he quickly realizes his worth and no longer wants to give up. Instead, he is learning through his experiences how his mindset can further improve his wellness.

When I had my little barbershop in western New York, a gentleman stumbled across our shop and came in for a cut.

It was a relatively quiet first interaction, yet it was enough to uncover that the guy was going through some personal stuff. He had admitted without details that times were trying.

When he left, I remember thinking, I sure hope shit turns around for that guy.

About five or six weeks passed, and he came back. He told me that he felt compelled to come back because I was the first person who asked him how he was in a very long time, and it made an impression on him. Something so easy to ask yet wasn't, profoundly impacted him.

During that second haircut, the guy opened up significantly, admitting to his past struggles with addiction, going to prison, finally being released, and facing the temptation to use again without any support system to help.

He was trying to stay motivated to improve, as he promised the mother of his children he would, but he was struggling with the temptation of falling off the wagon. Over the course of about a year, during every haircut, we would discuss goals because I told him that having a goal in any aspect would help him focus on something to keep himself distracted from wanting to fall into bad habits.

My way of engaging in that type of conversation was always started by asking, "So what's the plan, Stan?" He always found the phrase lighthearted because it wasn't even his name, but he knew it was how I opened dialog to check in with his wellness and where he was trying to go with it.

Through his own will and goal orientation, I was privileged to watch him get his G.E.D., plan, and manifest his goals by becoming a licensed electrician. Watching someone battle their way to the top was empowering because he finally recognized his worth and went for it!

It still blows my mind that I may have helped someone by simply asking how they were doing and genuinely caring about the response.

One of the most positive experiences I've had behind the chair came from a 19-year-old kid who had been medically discharged from the Navy due to multiple strokes, leaving him with many physical challenges.

This time, I was the one that took something away.

This heroic defender of our country always, and I mean ALWAYS, came into the shop smiling. He was continually pushing himself to improve and accomplish more.

A friendship bloomed between us, and meeting him taught me to appreciate my life in a new way.

We were quite different from one another regarding interests and goals, which made it awesome to bounce ideas about them back and forth. Someone with a different mindset and approach can help you see your roadblocks.

He taught me that whatever is blocking your path, aggressively face it and catch it. This allowed us to witness each other's progress, keep each other motivated, offer support for setbacks, and celebrations with successes.

My friendship with him proved to me how vital receiving support from those we trust is. I have embedded the practice of supporting others and asking for help.

When I'm not spending time behind the barber chair or with my wife and kids, I submerge in another aspect of my life that has been there even longer than barbering.

I am an avid video game enthusiast and dearly love all aspects of the culture. Not only have my experiences from behind the barber chair taught me about recognizing our struggles and how we can improve them, but with the explosion of live streaming, the same can be said in the virtual gaming world.

It may even be more accessible for people to express what is bothering them in the gaming realm, as there is no face-to-face interaction. At any given second, they can either eject themselves from the conversation or share what's ailing them.

Online gaming changed in the early 2000s.

Today, gaming is recognized and normalized across the world.

For many, it is such a routine part of their life that it is as ordinary as grabbing a drink after a hard day at work or school.

Throughout the decades of watching the gaming industry change, I have also watched the players themselves evolve.

I have decade-old friendships with people that have never been more than pixels on my computer monitor, yet with the power of voice chat, I consider them some of my closest friends. These relationships, oddly enough, come from spending time in a reality some people use to get away to become someone they could never be in "IRL" (in real life). A place where a brow-beaten accountant can become a powerful Troll Mage, using his knowledge of Ice and Fire Magic to overcome enemies big and small. Where a 9 to 5 factory worker with an abusive supervisor can be a renowned Goblin Shaman using his relationships with the primal elements to slay enemies and heal their friends.

I have been the funny, chubby guy for most of my life. However, I've never been one to be reclusive or shy away from social situations.

Making more friends was a natural fit because, in the game, I wasn't judged as the overweight guy.

I allowed others to get to know me for me.

I was the brunt of jokes by guys trying to look cool in front of others as they casually poked fun at my labored breathing. I didn't have anyone laugh at the expense of my asthma or my eczema breakouts.

In the digital world, I could slap on the persona of an Orc Warrior, and my actions in the game were praised and met with kindness and friendships rather than ridicule. Naturally, for me, that "reality" was very attractive.

The craziest part was that the people I met and got to know empowered me to become healthy by supporting a new workout idea. This community truly became a family to me over time.

Through the years of playing, you learn qualities about yourself you didn't know you had. You learn to stand up for yourself when someone questions your play style. The confidence you gain allows you to give and receive smart Alec comments.

I learned some of my best tools for problem-solving, setting goals, meeting adversity, and dealing with combative people via gaming. A big part of whom I've become and how I've become so malleable and relatable is from that reality.

As a barber and gamer, I have learned you HAVE TO set aside time from yourself, no matter how that time is spent.

Alone time allows you to reflect and reevaluate your feelings, goals, and appreciation, ultimately becoming more productive and healthier.

Gaming allows me to sit back, reflect on my life mentally, and weigh things out. During this time, I can also recognize how vital my overall wellness is. Whether it's emotional, mental, physical, or spiritual, it matters. I have learned to take responsibility for my health; only I can make changes and stay motivated to overcome and improve my own life.

One of my biggest struggles has been admitting what I need for my own wellness. I would distract facing those sometimes harsh truths by focusing on anything I could to deter myself from facing it. We all eventually realize that we need to face it, and what I felt most important in discovering my wellness was that the sting of being honest with yourself gets easier.

Just hit your first small goal, and boom, your journey begins.

I track my goals in a very special notebook. It's red with a gold embossed sword and shield on the cover. With my nerdy background, I don't call my next goal a goal. I refer to them as "Quests." I have a quest with an objective, and as the adventurer in my own story, I slowly work to complete them. With every significant milestone or "Boss Fight" I surpass, I refer to them as "Leveling Up." In the game world, leveling up means your character gets a little wiser and stronger with each win. It's quite similar throughout life.

Whether I am behind the barber chair and physically bonding with my clients or when I participate with others I literally cannot see, both have taught me how we collectively can prepare for and, more importantly, overcome battles in relationships, mental health, and more. We are all facing the war on health and wellness.

I always encourage anyone distressed or exhausted to find time for themselves, recharge their batteries, and remind themselves not to ignore their wellness. Take charge, or it will take charge of you.

Ziggy Salvation ~ A million thanks to my beautiful wife for always loving and encouraging me to achieve my goals and to my amazing parents who gave me so much enough confidence and love throughout my entire life.

One of Ziggy's Favorite Quotes

Don't judge each day by the harvest you reap
but by the seeds you plant.

Robert Louis Stevenson

My Daughter the Drug Addict

By Christine Hersom

She kicked and thrashed, screamed that she hated us,
and called the police "Pigs."

Christine Hersom (author, daycare owner)

*D*rug addiction is a prevalent disease in this society. We all read about it and watch it on television. But unless it hits you up close and personal, you cannot imagine the destruction it causes. I speak from experience here.

Every parent dreams of the blessed event of the birth of their child. Nobody spends their pregnancy thinking their child will grow up to be a drug addict. It certainly isn't a child's dream, either. But it appears our story isn't that uncommon.

My daughter was born on December 21, 1990. She was a beautiful baby with a head full of hair. She was happy and vivacious, and her attitude continued until middle school. My daughter was an A student and didn't have to work hard to get high grades. As her mood changed from a loving child to more of a rabid dog, we weren't too concerned. She was still an A student, but most often, offensive attitudes come along with being a teenager.

After graduating high school, she started at New Hampshire Technical Institute (NHTI). She wanted to become a dental hygienist. Again, she excelled at school. She only struggled with anatomy and physiology. This confused us because she had a natural ability to memorize. But again, we passed it off to the pressures of college.

She had moved out of the house and into an apartment with her boyfriend. Like many parents, we worried that falling in "love" would cause her to neglect her schoolwork.

Looking back now,
I wish love had caused the problems.

While in middle school, our daughter started to exhibit bursts of rage. She became such a mean girl. She would order, push people around, and instigate fights with anybody who looked at her. I spent more time at the principal's office than I did at home. Again, we couldn't believe what was going on with our daughter. But again, like naïve parents, we assumed her behavior was hormonal.

When she was nineteen, her boyfriend finally told us, "Holly is a drug addict." I couldn't believe what I was hearing. How was this possible? How come he didn't tell us before? She was still excelling in school. Was this all a bad dream?

We moved her back into our house and admitted her to a thirty-day rehab program. The entire ride to the program, she screamed about how much she hated us and that she would run away. I thought, "This has to be the worst day of my life." However, once we arrived at rehab, she nodded off and passed out on the couch. Unbeknownst to us, she had shot up before she got in the car.

This kind of behavior continued for two years. She was in and out of rehab, drugging whenever she could. To finance her habit, she began stealing from our friends and us. Finally, she was so desperate for drugs that she stole my cremains necklace and sold it in a pawn shop. Her addiction had such a firm hold on her that she had lost her values and integrity. At the time, she could not recognize its importance and was unaware we would realize the necklace was missing. My father's life and the memory of his death were nothing but a melted piece of silver. Our lives had reached an all-time low.

I begged social workers, police, and anyone who would listen and help. I didn't want to lose my daughter forever to drugs. But unfortunately, the police told us that the only way they could do anything was if charges were pressed against her. Desperately, we asked everybody she had stolen from to file charges, but they all refused. Either they couldn't prove it, or they weren't willing to put her in jail.

Press charges or watch her die.

My husband and I faced one of the most difficult decisions we have ever made. Were we willing to press charges against our daughter to try and save her life? After many conversations and many tears, we came to a decision. Unfortunately, we made a terrible decision. We would save her life now and worry about her future when the time comes.

If you had told me two decades earlier when I held my precious newborn baby in my arms that two decades later, I would put her in jail, I would have found that unfathomable. We thought she would face one felony, but more importantly, jail time would allow her to dry up a bit, and she would be alive and safe. As a parent, I shifted from wanting my little girl to be happy and healthy to desperately trying to keep her alive.

When someone you love becomes an addict, you watch the phases of their addiction escalate. The symptoms and actions are often gradual, and for someone who has never had drug issues, they can go on for years. It usually begins with signs you might miss, like increased irritability, and they begin to lie and steal. As they begin to take higher risks to support their habit, petty theft escalates to higher levels of breaking the law. Their friends change, and often they become physically unrecognizable.

Not only had the drug scene been foreign to us, but not understanding the Justice System soon followed. Authorities like to press many charges in the hopes that one charge sticks. We went from trying to dry our child up and save her life with one charge we pressed to sixteen felonies. SIXTEEN. We were shocked and no longer in control of her future. While trying to save her life, we also took away any chances of her working in the medical field. Conceptually, we realized she had caused her future to melt in her hands. With each needle she used, she stepped further away from a promising future. But as a parent, you never give up. You know who your "previous" child was. Deep down inside, their values and positive character traits are dormant, but they are there.

The police arrested her at our home the same day we pressed charges. I worked from home as an in-home childcare provider, which I still do to this day. I asked for the arrest to happen after hours. But, again, crime is not very accommodating. I know that the police do their best, but they arrested her on my back lawn in front of six little kids. She kicked and thrashed, screamed that she hated us, and called the police "Pigs." It was very traumatic for everyone.

Her first stint in jail lasted nine months. By the end of her stay, she was starting to look alive again. Holly was alert, healthy, and happy to be alive for the first time in years. She came to live with us when she was released from jail. Her boyfriend had broken up with her after telling us she was an addict. She had nowhere else to go, and I needed to be able to keep an eye on her. I still couldn't believe I had been so naïve and missed all the signs of drug use. We figured she was cured. Not so fast. She was right back on the drug wagon within two months of being released from jail. She would disappear for days at a time, and again we had no help as she had served her time in jail. Because her time served was less than a year, she was released unconditionally. She had no probation or parole. In other words, she was totally unsupervised unless she was with us. The police couldn't return her to jail unless new charges were pressed against her.

While breaking into somebody's home, the police caught her.

She received another year in jail for this offense. We were heartbroken by this continuing cycle. She was assigned another parole officer at the end of her sentence. This woman became her guardian angel. She convinced us that Holly would never break the cycle if she didn't do live-in rehab. So she got a bed at a rehab center in Franconia, New Hampshire. Holly was admitted that same day. The first day or two was difficult, but she loved it. She took all the classes, worked on her health, and lived there for sixty days. When she came home, she was a new person.

Holly will be the first to admit that it hasn't always been easy, but the tools she received in rehab have kept her successful. She hasn't used drugs since walking out of that door. She has been clean and sober for ten-plus years.

She had a boyfriend for about two years that started using heroin. While recognizing the signs, she ignored them because she thought she was in love. Though you cannot see it at the time, bad situations often end up being for the good.

The police stopped her boyfriend while he was driving my vehicle. Because he had a needle with heroin in his pocket, they wanted to prove that he was dealing drugs, so they impounded my vehicle and tore it apart. It would be too kind to say that I lost my mind.

I pressed charges against my daughter and the boyfriend. The charges were that they did not have permission to use the vehicle. They were charged with grand theft auto. The boyfriend was sentenced to one to three years. Since Holly was on parole, she was immediately lugged back to jail for ninety days. I was so angry. We had been dealing with drug addiction for four years now. Once I had calmed down, I visited my daughter in jail. She apologized and swore that she was clean. She admitted ignoring the signs of her boyfriend's drug use because she thought she was in love. After speaking with her parole officer, I found that she was telling the truth and was not using it again. While I felt terrible getting her thrown back into jail, I told her it was an invaluable learning experience for her. She needed to learn to make better decisions.

It was time for another difficult but critical decision. We forbid the boyfriend from ever coming to our house again.

She can never work in the medical field because of her criminal record. However, she has embraced her decisions and past life and become a very successful server. She has financial freedom because of her personality and work ethic. She is confident and has applied the hard lessons from her difficult journey. She is open and honest with everybody about her past drug use and now never hesitates to call someone out for it.

Her father and I have never given up on her. However, tough love is real. It is difficult, in the moment, for the one you love to understand why you are doing what you are doing to support them.

Holly is now married and has a twenty-month-old daughter. She is happy, vibrant, healthy, and safe. She currently volunteers to help other drug addicts get the help that they need.

The drug problem in this country is ruining an entire generation. It is sad, scary, and deadly. Holly was the lucky one…she lived. Every day she thanks God for our decision to have her arrested and charged with felonies. Without that, she swears she would be dead now.

Christine Hersom ~ *I would like to thank Peggy Willms for pushing me to keep writing and encouraging me to continuously improve.*

One of Christine's Favorite Quotes

Today is only one day in all the days that will ever be.
But what will happen in all the other days
that ever come can depend on what you do today.

Ernest Hemingway

I'm Not a Good Mom

By Alysia Lyons

I'm not a good mom.
Good moms don't almost drop their babies.

Alysia Lyons (author, coach, host)

$\mathcal{S}$omeone once asked me, "What's the best compliment you've ever been given?"

It didn't take long for one to come to mind. "You're such a great mom."

To a mother, there are no sweeter words to hear, but for years, it was hard to believe this was true about me. I would never take credit for how amazing my son, Zander, is. There may be a slight bias here; he is freaking amazing, with confidence that outshines my own. I know I can't take all the credit. He is wise beyond his years, and at just eleven years of age, he has the kindest soul I have ever met.

I see other moms in my life and on social media killing it as mothers. They make homemade meals every night. Their kids aren't allowed screen time, or it is significantly limited. They read a bedtime story every night and have a great nighttime routine. I hardly ever cook, dinner is never at the same time, Zander's screen time is rarely limited, our bedtime routine is non-existent, and it never includes reading.

To think back on how far we both have come brings back some painful thoughts and areas of extreme negativity and dysconnectivity. The first time I questioned if I *was* even close to being a good mom was when he was six months old. We were heading down the stairs to take him to his six-month checkup, and I slipped on the last step and landed hard on my bum. The thought of what could have happened caused me to burst into tears. The negative thoughts started clouding my brain.

I'm not a good mom.
Good moms don't almost drop their babies.

At the appointment, I filled out the necessary forms and asked questions related to my son's development, but one question caught me off guard: "Are you getting the support you need at home?" I stared at the question and held back the tears as I checked "yes" when I wanted to check "no."

I wasn't clear on what it would mean to get the support I needed at home, but I knew I wanted his dad at the appointment. He had some excuse for not coming. There seemed to always be an excuse.

I went home that night and picked a fight with my husband. I don't remember what it was about. It was just another fight in a long stream of arguments we'd been having since he came home from deployment, but I remember how it ended.

"I want a divorce," he said.

This seemed to come out of the blue and was a complete shock to my system. Sure, we fought more than we used to before Zander was born, but divorce? We'd *just* started our family.

Again, negative thoughts flooded my brain. The thought of being a single mom terrified me to my core. What I didn't realize at the time was that my postpartum hormones took that fear, magnified it, and threw me into a pit I didn't know how to climb out of.

Death seemed less scary than being thirty and a single mom.

I am not a good mom.
Good moms don't think about suicide.

If that sounds like a huge leap from the mention of a divorce to suicidal thoughts, believe me, it was. I spent the next two hours in that pit with my closest friend filling my ears with the truth: I was going to be okay. I don't remember any other details of that time, but eventually, the overwhelming emotions subsided, and I took steps toward getting back to healthier and more rational thoughts.

Although it took another eight months to admit, our marriage was over that day.

Zander and I moved in with my dad and stepmom for the next year, and in a matter of months, I lost everything that had been bolstering my self-esteem. I was a grown-ass woman with a one-year-old mooching off her parents. I lost my position with my direct sales company and had to return the company car I'd been leasing. This was my second divorce, and I struggled with that reality as a pastor's daughter.

Mostly, I felt isolated, alone, and unsupported in my situation. I found myself just going through the motions.

My son was (for the most part) a very happy kid. However, he would sometimes lose his shit over a toy falling off the table onto the floor or scream bloody murder when it was time to leave the park. In those moments, I would think to myself, "What is wrong with this kid? Why is he behaving like this?" and then there was the time I said, "I don't want to be a mom anymore."

I am not a good mom.
Good moms don't think about quitting motherhood.

When he was sixteen months old, my sister suggested I talk to his pediatrician about getting him evaluated for autism. At the time, she was in school to get her master's degree and thought he might benefit from some early intervention.

He qualified for services, and over the next four years, they taught him (and me) how to manage his emotions, communicate his needs and interact with others in a healthy way. They taught him things I believed were my job to teach, but I hadn't a clue how to do it, so I was always very grateful for them.

They are also part of the reason I told myself I could not take credit for what an amazing kid he was.

I am not a good mom.
Good moms don't need help raising amazing kids.

My best friend and I lived together for four years. She never had any biological kids, but she loved Zander as if he were her own, and he loved her back. When she died, he grieved her loss like he had lost a mom. One day, he said, "I loved Chellie more than I love you, Mom." I didn't take offense to those words. I knew exactly what he meant.

At times, I had been jealous of the connection they had. I didn't know how to connect with him. I was stuck in an old story that I never felt a connection with my dad, so it seemed logical that a mother/son connection wasn't possible.

Part of me was glad he had her. He was better off having an amazing surrogate mom because that would save him from the pain of my emotional deficiencies.

I am not a good mom.
Good moms don't struggle to connect to their children.

Her death was a wake-up call. I was the only mom he had, and damn it, he deserved to have a great mom.

About a year before my friend passed away, I hired a coach to help me succeed in my direct sales business, although we had never talked about business for the first six months. Instead, we focused on healing the emotional traumas I was carrying around. We shifted old thought patterns that no longer served me and dismantled limiting beliefs about who I was and what I could do. She helped me peel back the protective layers I'd put on over the years.

She helped me heal my relationship with my dad by helping me rewrite the stories I'd been telling myself for years. The more stories I reframed, the more I emotionally connected to my dad and son.

My coach reminded me of *The Five Love Languages*, a book by Gary Chapman that I had purchased to help me in my marriage but never got around to reading while in that relationship. However, I was able to apply the concepts to my relationship with my dad. It profoundly affected how I viewed my connection with him, so I asked Zander how he felt most loved by me.

By asking him that question, I realized that the thing that helped him feel connected to me was something I wasn't doing very often. In the past, I would have gone down a negative thought spiral and beat myself up for not showing him enough love, but instead, I decided to make filling his love bucket a priority every day.

I'm not such a bad mom. I take action to relieve my guilt instead of using it to punish myself for not knowing better.

My coach suggested I take a coaching certification program because it would help me in my business. During the weeklong training, I learned to love myself even deeper and open myself up to receiving love from others - especially my son.

I forgave myself for the pain I felt throughout his life. I used to be so hard on myself for spending so much time mourning the life I thought I was building with my son's dad. Learning to love myself opened me up for a relationship I could never have imagined before and gave Zander an example of a healthy relationship.

I am a good mom. I look for ways to improve myself, and as I become a better person, I become a better parent.

When I think about the journey I have been on as a mother and a woman, I can definitely say it didn't go as I expected, but I am grateful for it because it's made me the woman I am today. I am continuing to learn better ways to talk to myself, and I am healing the generational harm that comes from a lack of love and empathy for oneself.

Every day, I spend time working on our connection. I am open with him about how I feel. When I lose my temper, something that happens significantly less as I've spent countless hours understanding myself and what makes me tick, I explain to him what was happening in my mind and my emotions. As a result, he does the same to me when he loses his temper.

Our open communication helps us understand one another better and deepens our connection. He knows he can tell me anything without fear of punishment or shame. I talk to him the way I wish my dad would have talked to me to help him know that I am not perfect and that we all make mistakes.

Every day, I spend time learning more about him. I continue to ask him what I do to make him feel the most loved. It has evolved as he's gotten older. He still enjoys his daily snuggles, but he also likes it when I jump on the trampoline, and he loves our talks.

Every day, we make each other laugh. The funny things he says usually end up on Facebook under the hashtag Zandersations because his wit needs to be shared with the world.

I am a great mom.

Alysia Lyons ~ *Thank you, Zander, for being my beautiful course corrector.*

One of Alysia's Personal Quotes

Wake up, do epic shit, change the world, repeat.

Two Sisters' Perspectives

By Angi Currier and Peggy Willms

―――――― ★ ――――――

*I was in shock. I had no idea. Again, I felt alone, and
I soon realized I was just an inconvenience to my parents.*

Angi Currier (author, patient access rep)

*Digging up the past is always challenging.
But we have come a long way, baby girl.*

Peggy Willms
(author, coach, speaker, radio and retreat host)

*N*o two people experience the exact cookie-cutter feelings, thoughts, and behaviors even if they descend from the same family tree and experience many of the same events simultaneously. We are proof of that. Our memories of childhood, holidays, illnesses, addictions, and more are not the same. We wrote this story together as sisters showing how we respect each other's perspectives.

The Little Sister (Angi)

While scanning the items on the fireplace mantel, I focus on a delicate pearl butterfly figurine filled with some of my mother's ashes. She passed away in August of 2021 from Multiple Sclerosis. On either side of the butterfly sit photos of her. The images take me back to my youth.

These photos show my beautiful, slender, got-it-together mom. Memories start to stir, and I think of my sister. At times, our memories are polar opposites. We have the same mother, and although she and my brother have different biological fathers, we were raised together. My sister was seven, my brother was six, and I was one year old when my biological dad adopted my siblings.

I adored my mother, but my big sister was my role model. It wasn't until recently that I realized how much she has always loved me. I idolized my sister. She was known for her thin figure, beautiful face and hair, friends, talents, and intelligence. Most of the time, I wondered if she knew I existed. In my opinion, in her eyes, I was annoying, loud, and embarrassing. We laugh now, but she doesn't remember me riding the school bus with her.

If you had told me as a teenager that I would someday publish our story, I would have called you crazy. I heard my sister loud and clear this past year. She believes that telling stories changes and saves lives. I now agree. If we don't share our stories, our memories fade, and we lose the opportunity to hear different perspectives.

We grew up in a middle-class family in a small paper town in northern New Hampshire. We had pets, enjoyed camping, laughed at holiday parties, built forts, and picked berries in the summer. We were a "normal" family. I did not understand my sister's childhood experiences, mainly because of our age difference. I thought she had it all; it was easy for her. When I was a teen, she was "adulting" as a wife and mother.

When I was 13, a bus ride changed my life forever.

I knew something was wrong when I stepped off the bus. My mother always greeted me at the door on her day off from work. I sat down on the deacon bench my brother crafted and called my grandmother, with whom we all had a close relationship. I asked her where my mom was, to which she said, "She is at the lawyer's office. She is filing for divorce and leaving your dad." I felt like my world had fallen apart at that very moment. I felt immediate emptiness.

At this time, my sister was pregnant with her first baby, and she and her husband lived in Ft. Ord, California. My sister was experiencing our parents' divorce differently. Our mom decided she wouldn't be flying out to stay with her for the first few weeks of her son's birth.

The following eight months were a whirlwind. My mom and I moved in with my grandparents. A few months later, I was sent to my brother for the summer. He was in the Navy and stationed in Michigan. When my brief "vacation" ended, my mother and I moved in with a family friend. That fall, while visiting my bio dad, who ironically lived just down the street, my mom called and said I couldn't go home. She had just gotten married by the Justice of Peace on her front porch, and they wanted to be alone. I was shocked. I had no idea. Again, I felt alone and soon realized I was just an inconvenience to my parents.

I noticed that my mom and stepdad had started drinking every night after he got off work. When growing up, my mother only drank on holidays. Over time, one drink turned into two, and three and more until she was no longer the same loving, caring mother I grew up with. She was an angry, mean drunk. I felt like they didn't even want me around, and frankly, I didn't want to be there.

My new life became unrecognizable compared to my previous "normal" upbringing. During one of my mom's and stepfather's arguments, I told them I wanted to live with my bio dad. I followed her into her bedroom when she got up from the table. She grabbed a .38 pistol from her nightstand, put it to her head, and said, "Over my dead body." As I screamed at her to put the gun down, I remember pushing her onto the bed and shaking her arm until the gun fell out of her hand. Everything happened so fast.

During this time, my sister had moved back to our town to live with her in-laws with my four-month-old nephew while her husband waited for family housing for his Army tour in Germany. My sister's recollection of the gun event was one of anger. It took me thirty years to realize she raced to our house the next day, threatening to take me from my parents and adopt me herself.

My chance to escape came when my boyfriend asked me to marry him the night before he left for the Marine Corps. I didn't really want to get married, but I knew I had to do something. The night before I flew to

Florida to get married, I begged my mother not to make me go. She said, "He already bought your ticket, so you are going."

I needed emancipation to get married.

A few months after being married and living in Florida, I flew to Germany to be with my sister and nephew. She was struggling through a divorce and needed my help to watch my nephew so she could work. I brought my nephew back with me so my mother could care for him until my sister transferred back to the U.S. a few months later. This choice wasn't easy for us. Here we were, bringing her toddler into a volatile situation. Soon after, my sister returned from Germany to get him.

Once my husband finished advanced infantry training, he got his orders for Edzell, Scotland. We lived there for two and a half years, where I gave birth to my son. I was nineteen, married, and residing in a foreign country.

While I began my family in Scotland, my sister transferred back to the U.S. from Germany. With the distance, it wasn't easy to stay in touch. When my husband was discharged from the Marines, we decided to reside in Grand Junction, Colorado, where my sister and her family lived. My mom and stepdad also moved there, and I was anxious to live around family again.

Times were tough after our move. I became pregnant with our second child, and we argued a lot. I went into premature labor nine weeks early. My sister was there when my daughter was born. Soon after, I divorced my husband, and my life spiraled out of control.

The next portion of this story is recounted in my first story, "*Do You Want to Try IT*, in the book, *The Four-Fold Formula,* which my sister co-authored.

After my divorce, I met a man, and I became tangled up with drugs. My relationship with my sister became estranged for the first time. We ultimately became different humans. Growing up, neither of us drank or did drugs. Therefore, my "new" lifestyle certainly didn't fit hers. Once again, I felt like she had her shit together, or so it appeared on the outside. I later learned she had struggled with an eating disorder for years and perfection and imposter syndrome. At this time, she had her second child, who was recovering from a life-threatening illness, Group B Spinal Meningitis. Talk about two people living separate lives! She tried to rescue me, but I had no desire to be judged or rescued.

For nearly seven years, I battled loneliness, rejection, and physical and mental abuse. Although the drugs were in control, one thing never wavered. I knew I loved my children and family very much. I wanted to be in my children's lives. I wanted them in mine. But due to my unhealthy lifestyle choices and the people in my new circle, my sister stepped in to protect my children. I was sick and tired of her trying to "parent" me.

I felt everyone was against me and wanted to keep my children from me—especially my sister. A few days after his arrest, he was released and showed up at my apartment. He beat and brutally raped me. I was so scared that I never told anyone until years later. At my daughter's court hearing, my sister and children testified against him. It wasn't until the last few years that my sister told me the whole story. She was the one my daughter confessed to about my ex hurting her. They were making cupcakes for Valentine's. My daughter told her about being touched. It was extremely graphic and evident to her that a three-year-old could not make up such a story. Again, my sister stepped in to take over.

Unfortunately, there was a hung jury, and he was not convicted in my daughter's case. They got him about three years later, but horrifically, it was because he molested other children.

After the conversation with my daughter, my sister didn't speak to my parents and me for four years. Deep down, I knew why she was trying to help, but my addiction was in charge. She has many more reasons this estrangement happened, which she can tell you in her story below.

Years later, I remarried and had my third child. After ten years, we divorced. However, I am proud to say I have been sober for over twenty years. After raising my daughter by myself for years, I met an amazing man. I am in a healthy relationship for the first time in my life, and I am the happiest I have ever been. After two decades, I now have a relationship with my oldest child and hope my daughter will someday want me.

When our mother became ill in 2018 with MS, you can probably guess what my sister did. She grabbed her cape and swarmed in to handle the crisis as usual, but I was right there by her side this time. We learned how to communicate and lean on each other, which helped us get through a difficult time. Even though our mother was still an alcoholic, I loved her very much. Due to her failing health, I tried to keep our conversations light. I never communicated my feelings and how her alcohol affected me.

My sister might seem cold as ice, but she is The Mama Bear and The Fixer. You definitely want her on your side. She guided us through the end stage of life. During this time, we also became close with our stepfather. And he is now the healthiest he has ever been.

Even though my life choices affected those around me significantly, I have learned many things. The first is letting go of the anger and hurt. I am grateful for my special relationship with my big sister. We have learned to listen to and respect each other's perspectives about our experiences. At times we simply agree to disagree and move on. She is my hero.

The Big Sister (Peggy)

Angi shared that our memories and experiences differ even when raised in the same home. When I received my sister's story above as a submission for this book, I asked her if we could blend our stories in hopes that anyone—family, friends, or co-workers would understand "different perspectives." Here it is. We have come a long way, baby girl.

Digging up the past is always challenging. The good, bad, and ugly rear their heads. During this rollercoaster ride, we focused on respecting and loving each other. Our life has been like two people reading the same book or watching the same movie and having a completely different experience.

I raced home from school on September 3, 1972, to greet my newborn sister. Her entry into this world was a highlight of my life. Though

I was only seven, I dressed, fed, and protected her. Over time, siblings butt heads, especially as I entered my teens. I shifted from being a second momma to this strawberry-haired bundle of joy to feeling like she was a pain in the ass. And as sad as it is, I don't remember vivid details of us together until she approached her teens and I moved out. I take responsibility for that.

I lived in a tunnel. My quest for perfection drove me externally and internally; I knew I had to be perfect and fly under the radar simultaneously. My stepfather adopted me when I was seven, so perhaps part of it was to please him. The only connection we had was my schoolwork. Or maybe another reason was to show my mom I wasn't something to be ashamed of—my mom left school as a sophomore because she was pregnant with me.

An insane agenda dictated my every move. Fail at nothing, leave town, and be the first in our family tree to attend college. Become "something or someone." I didn't sleep. I didn't relax. And most of the time, I didn't eat. I had severe migraines and a poor immune system. DUH. Anything less than an A- meant there was work to do. "Extra time" in my schedule meant you were not busy enough. As the agenda filled up, my relationship with my sister faded. To note, through all my busyness, I never loved my sister less. I worried about her and wanted to "save" her.

**I hadn't reviewed my past until
my mother's death in August 2021.**

No matter the obstacle, I always pivoted, shape-shifted, cared for others, and continued to march forward. A big part of facing my past was reading my mother's journals which documented the first fifteen years of my life. I also found documents two days after she passed away while holding my hand. After reading all of this information about my life, I realized she "held" me back for decades. Most of this discovery was new to me, and I will share more of this story at a later date. The main takeaways, for now, are that I was "steered" to drop college, get married, and move away. In the past few years, I have become aware of "generational curses" and have dabbled in epigenetics. There are generations of fear, anxiety, and a sense of lack—oh, and patterning. One being my mom, sister, and myself – teenage brides and mothers.

When I left home after graduation, our paths separated. I thought I was leaving her in capable hands, a mother and father who would positively guide her through high school, and my little sister would go on to fulfill her wildest dreams. But, instead, within a few years, her life crumbled.

My sister and I both married soldiers, got out of dodge, and began traveling the world. At 19, I headed to California. The subsequent events changed our lives forever. My mother called me when I was 21, and Angi was barely 15. She told me she was divorcing our dad and dating a family friend and could not be with me for my first son's birth. I was devastated. It didn't take long for my sister to become a pawn between my divorced parents, and I became aware of my mother threatening to kill herself if my sister left.

Not long after the pistol incident, my then-husband and I discussed adopting my sister and getting my baby sister to hell out of there. I visited my mom's. She sat at the dining room table, consuming what might have been her third drink. After our "adoption" conversation, my mother called our father and begged him to sign papers allowing their daughter to get married; parents needed to sign off if the child was under 16. Everyone would wipe their hands from the responsibility of raising their last child.

The following years are a blur. I moved to Germany, and Angi married and moved to Florida. Unfortunately, after four years of marriage, I suffered an ugly divorce while living in a foreign country, raising a toddler, and working full-time. Leaving my son in daycare with a stranger made me sick. Angi came to the rescue. She stayed with me until her husband received orders to move to Scotland. I was stuck. To this day, the following decision is one of my regrets. She took my son back to the U.S. to stay with my mother and stepfather until I could figure out daycare. Ultimately, I returned to the States to get him and moved back to Germany.

After four years overseas, I eventually settled in Colorado with my new husband and son. My whole family followed; mother, stepfather, brother, and finally, my sister and her family. My drive to succeed remained high. I dove into a corporate wellness and fitness career, holding two jobs and raising a family.

I was in the delivery room when my sister delivered her second child. We joke that I must have gotten pregnant that night, as my second son was born nine months later. After that, our kids played together, I started training her, and our family felt normal. But it only lasted a year.

I always felt like the mother hen when it came to my sister or anyone, I guess. Over the years, my parents' drinking became more problematic. We only gathered for birthdays or holidays, and the excuses to dip out of every activity became apparent. Drinking came first. And when my mom offered my young son a sip of her drink, I made sure we never attended "happy hour" again.

About a year after my niece's birth, my sister divorced. I tried to help her with groceries, rent, or driving her and the kids to appointments. It was a year before I knew about her drug use or how volatile her relationships were. I started getting calls from her drug dealer boyfriend threatening to follow my son to school, so I cut off ties with my little sister.

When my niece was three years old, she told me my sister's boyfriend had taken advantage of her. I moved into stealth mode. I wrote a letter to the state to get the kids out of her care and to live with her ex-husband, their dad. Not long after, we were in a molestation trial fighting to put her boyfriend behind bars for what he did to my niece. Holding this four-year-old little girl in my arms was horrific as we looked through the chamber doors, waiting to testify against him. Seeing my sister, mother, and stepdad sit on his side of the courtroom was maddening. The molester. How did I become the bad guy in all of this?

**Here I was, trying to save my sister's kids
as I had tried to save her years ago.**

I didn't speak to my sister and parents for four years. Between the trial, my sister's path, and my parents' drinking, I was done. Once again, I kept my head down, pushed myself, and tried to do the right things.

My sister remarried a few years later, moved to a different town, got clean, and gave birth to her third child. This was when the family dynamics shifted in a positive direction. She became and still is one hell of a mother. We visited as often as possible.

Here is a stand-out moment when we began understanding each other's perspectives. We were all sitting around my mom's kitchen table. As usual, they were drinking.

In tears, I told my mother, "All I ever wanted to hear was that you were proud of me. I never receive attention from my family. I didn't get in trouble, kept my nose down, have been successful, and still, you have never told me you are proud." Finally, my sister piped in, telling me how easy it was for me. "Everyone likes you. You are smart, and you're so pretty." I then screamed back in tears, "You think it's been easy having to be "perfect" and be so busy there wasn't even time to eat? At least you have a father. My real father has never even wanted to meet me." We carried on for a bit and eventually hugged it out. I think this was the first time we realized how different our perspectives were, and when you don't have all the information, you cannot possibly understand.

For the next several years, we all did the best we could. Then, seven years ago, I moved to Florida after a 25-year stint in Colorado. I focused on putting myself first, living where I wanted, and starting a business. This time, no one followed me.

The next "different perspectives" aha came when my sister joined one of my women's online wellness series. After our first session, our relationship shifted again. I vividly remember one of her comments. "Sis, OMG, I had no idea what you really did. I knew you knew a lot about healthy stuff and did many things over the years, but I didn't know you were this smart. You know what I mean. I don't even know what a carb is." I then realized how many of my actions and thoughts I had kept to myself.

In 2018 when our mother became ill, we banded together on a deeper level. To this second, we have not argued. Letting her in and showing my emotions was not easy, but having someone "help me" care for someone else was a relief. I started to let her see the real me. Our stepfather, now sober, took care of my mom every day.

Last year, when we began writing and sharing our stories, we understood each other more deeply. In the first book I wrote with my co-author, Markus Wettstein, called *The Four-Fold Formula for All Things Wellness*, she revealed her drug addiction story for the first time. It is called *Do You Want to Try IT?* In that book, I also shared a personal story, *I am Addicted to Mania*. I learned how she became addicted to drugs and was beaten and raped. And she learned about my battle with perfection and food.

Our love and respect for one another grew as we continued to share our past. We realized that missing pieces of information make it challenging to understand or support each other. For example, she didn't know my role in her losing custody of her children and how my four-year-old niece told me about being violated. I was shocked by my sister's lifestyle. And I never realized she supported her boyfriend in court because he beat her. I also didn't know she looked up to me. I felt she despised me and thought I was privileged and treated special.

I have always felt an obligation and desire to care for my sister. If we do not tell people what they mean to us, how will they know? They say actions speak louder than words, but many actions are misinterpreted, and unless you can talk it out, you cannot hug it out.

As our paths have shifted over the years, we have walked side by side, holding hands, and also been disconnected, veering off in opposite directions. But our undying love for each other has never altered.

We are now best friends.

Walking alone feels horrible. Trying to live up to others' expectations is overwhelming. Opening up and shutting down. Running towards people and then running away. Helping others but not helping myself. So many of my assets are also liabilities, and I am not for everybody. But I am FOR ME.

We don't know what we don't know unless we share our stories. Unfortunately, we also tend to make everything about ourselves, rarely putting on another's shoes. I believe, at times, we need to look back to move forward. When flipping through the photo albums of our life (literally), we can learn and relearn. The positive growth of the family tree depends on it.

My sister's two oldest children were raised by their father and stepmother. But I am very proud to say she has rekindled her relationship with her son and has become a grandmother for the first time.

Sis, I adore you and am so proud of you for getting your stories out there. You have already affected many lives, and I am grateful for our relationship. I love you to pieces.

Angi ~ *I am thankful for my sister's tough love and that we have been able to get through challenging conversations and accept and respect each other.*

One of Angi's Personal Quotes

Life is too short to be unhappy.
Live, Laugh, and Love like it's your last day.

Peggy ~ *Thank you to my sister, who sits at the table and wins every hand, no matter the cards she is dealt. I adore you.*

One of Peggy's Favorite Quotes

A sister is a gift to the heart, a friend to the spirit, and
a golden thread to the meaning of life.

Isadora James

Catalyst

By Gina Lobito

It's interesting what goes through the mind during a crisis.

Gina Lobito (author, coach)

*A*n acquaintance recently asked me how I became who I am today. I interpreted this question as, "What happened in my life that was a catalyst to the PATH OF LIGHT I now lead?"

I believe everything a human needs to know already exists within the human circuitry of the nervous system, DNA, and cells. I will refer to this vast topic as human codes. Discussing the depths of the topic is not necessarily the purpose of this story as much as the event that unlocked something within my being. Knowledge and wisdom of human codes are unlocked based on experienced events and free will to choose, bringing each human being to their current place in life.

For a few days, the question was on repeat in my head. Naturally, many events have determined my path thus far.

One of the more prominent is the passing of a close friend and co-worker, Doug. We went hiking, went out to dinner, viewed plays, and took motorcycle rides to San Francisco. One of my favorite spontaneous out-ings was when we ordered the "Taste of the Menu" at Aziza, a Moroc-can restaurant in San Francisco. Full of flavor and the aroma of spices, I tried food I had never had. We savored every bite, including dessert and a cocktail.

When I had back surgery, Doug stayed with me for a week. He changed my bandages. I gave him a key so he could come and go according to his schedule. While I slept during the day, he watched movies quietly from the brown leather recliner. Periodically, I could hear him gingerly walking down the hall to check on me.

Caring for people was so natural and familiar to him. I wondered if caring for me brought up memories for him. Five years prior, he had become a widower. His wife died of brain cancer. That's when he transformed his life and health. He lost about 150 lbs. by simply changing his diet and exercising.

Sometimes, I would playfully remind him to "enjoy life" and have dessert.

"Well, you can always work it off with Karen tomorrow."

We looked at each other and just laughed. It did not take much convincing for him to say yes to the occasional dessert or cocktail. Karen was another co-worker, fitness trainer, and yoga instructor. She assisted Doug with healthier eating and exercise routines.

Often, I was mistaken for his wife. He was a very caring and attentive man. He treated everyone with the same admiration as he did me. It was his Buddha-like nature. We just cared for each other and enjoyed each other's company. We had a wonderful friendship.

One night, I happened to be working a graveyard shift for overtime in the Police Records Division. I had been logged on to my terminal for 10 or 15 minutes when the phone rang. One of the jailers, who happened to be working that evening, answered the phone. All I heard was, "I will do you one better. She happens to be working tonight." Next, I heard my name, "Hey Gi! The phone is for you. Line 1."

"Thanks," I said and asked who was calling. It was Karen.

Like a flash of light, I just knew something was not right. I felt a coldness run down my spine, and a sense of urgency and focus overcame me. I felt it deep in my bones. I just knew Doug was dead. Time slowed down, and the office became still and quiet. I could hear a pin drop which was rare in an office filled with radio traffic, conversations from across the room, and phones ringing.

I took a breath, exhaled, and picked up the phone.

"Hi, Karen, what's up?"

"Have you heard from Doug today?" she proceeded to ask. I have been trying to call him, and he is not responding. It's not like him."

"You know, I haven't," I said. "We are supposed to hike tomorrow morning, and he usually confirms with me the day before."

I told her I would give him a call and get in touch with Maria. Maria is Doug's niece.

I attempted to call and text Doug but got no response. Each moment confirmed what I already knew. I reminded myself to breathe as I could feel my chest pounding. I called Maria, and she answered.

"Hi, have you heard from Doug today?" I said.

"No. I am getting ready to go over there. I can't seem to find his house keys."

I told her, "Wait for me! I will pick you up. You are not going to his house alone!"

Fortunately, Maria only lived five minutes from the Police Department where I worked.

I quickly logged out of my computer and told my supervisor, Melinda, I had to go. "Something is wrong with Doug," I said. "Nobody has heard from him all day. I am unsure what's happening, but I will let you know."

I felt Melinda's nerves and sense of worry and panic kick in. You know that kind of worry a mother gets when she knows something is wrong with her children? She said, "Okay, let me know if you will be back."

I do not remember the drive to Maria's house, only that it was dark, and stillness was in the air. I remember walking into her home, and she was still searching for the keys to Doug's house. She always left them in her secretary, and they were nowhere to be found. I watched her shuffling through papers, looking in the nooks and crannies. With a concerned look, she said, "I can't find them. I always leave them right here."

I told her, "Let's go. We will break in if we have to. I will drive!"

We hopped into my black Honda Pilot and headed toward Doug's place. On the way there, I handed Maria a pen and pad of paper that

I kept in the center console. How Virgo of me, often prepared for the unexpected.

All I can say is that being prepared and having things in order comes in handy; this was one of those moments. I told her, "Now, we do not know what we will walk into. Write down any names and phone numbers of people you would like contacted, just in case." Maria took a big breath and began writing down phone numbers, telling me to call her neighbor first.

I vaguely remember the drive to Doug's house. My most vivid memory is that it was a dark and cloudless night.

Maria was focused and gave me directions which, for some reason, included side streets avoiding the main roads. About twenty minutes later, we pulled up to Doug's house. The house was dark; no lights were on. We could hear his cattle dog, Bella, barking in the distance.

Maria headed to the front door while I immediately headed for the side gate. My body stretched out, and my forearm scaped over the edges of the wooden fence. My fingers stretched as far as I could stretch them. I kept telling myself, "Come on, just get the latch!"

I was determined. After a couple of attempts, the latch opened. I quickly made my way to the back door. I remember thinking, "thank GOD the back door was open." I ran back to the front, got Maria, and told her I had got in.

As we entered the back door, Bella's bark turned to a growl. We paused. Once Bella discerned it was us, she stopped barking, looked at us, and motioned with her head where to go.

Maria and I followed into the darkness of the den. It was light behind us, but I do not recall either of us turning it on. I noticed our shadows cascade in front of us, blocking what little vision we had. Then, we discovered him.

I don't remember breathing, but I could feel my eyes get big and dilated. It felt like I was not blinking. I saw Doug's lifeless body in his favorite black leather chair. His body appeared jolted back with his hand raised to his chest and the permanent look of shock on his face.

It's interesting what goes through the mind during a crisis, or perhaps it was some of my police training kicking in. I noticed all the little details.

He must have passed away in the morning since he was still wearing his robe, and his body did not appear to be there for very long. His death seemed quick since there was no sign of struggle.

Maria and I went into first responder mode. We lifted his body from the chair to the floor. He was weightless. It was like he floated. Maybe adrenaline kicked in. It just felt like we had some help. My hands were hardly gripping his body.

Maria and I remained calm and focused. She began CPR while I called 9-1-1 and put the phone on speaker as I gave information to the dispatcher.

"Male, white, in his late 50's found non-responsive, possible heart attack."

I ran outside to get his address while Maria still gave chest compressions and breaths. To this day, I only remember the street's name, Southside Dr.

After a few minutes, Maria and I switched. I continued CPR and remained on the phone with the 9-1-1 dispatcher. Dispatchers follow a specific protocol when assisting with medical calls so the CPR and chest compressions continue.

As I continued to compress Doug's chest, I could hear the sirens in the distance. I told the dispatcher that though CPR is protocol, I knew he had been gone for a while and was not coming back. Therefore, I am stopping the compressions. I asked her to relay to the Fire Department to switch to a silent approach (no emergency sirens, just lights).

A moment later, the firemen arrived and assessed Doug's body. Maria answered the questions. I excused myself for a moment and called my supervisor Melinda.

I told her without any preparation, "Doug's dead! Can I speak with the on-duty Sergeant?"

I had to get off the phone, so I gave Melinda my number and Doug's address. She contacted the Sergeant for me and relayed the information.

The Sergeant and one patrol officer arrived at Doug's house for support as we waited for the proper authorities to arrive. While we waited for the coroner, I called people from the phone list based on Maria's priority. I also called Karen to let her know the unfortunate news. She immediately came to Doug's house along with another co-worker and friend, Taylor. Thank goodness they came.

While speaking to the firemen, they informed us about the neighborhood. Given that Doug lived alone and the neighborhood was in a higher crime area, people often watched for incidences like this and would break into homes they knew were now vacant.

Between me, Maria, Taylor, Karen, Sgt. Malae, and Officer Stephens, we packed anything of value into our cars. Documents, files, identification papers, taxes, heirlooms, and his 1957 Ford Mustang. We safely transported everything to Maria's home. It is strange to go through someone's home and personal effects while their dead body is in the middle of the room.

Doug's passing, which I can only describe as shocking, was a catalyst for a series of events that changed the course of my life and placed me at the internal emotional and mental edges of myself.

Shocked by the lack of compassion surrounding me when I returned to work a week later, my manager's statement still rang in my mind. She leaned over the desk toward me, looking me straight in the eye, and said, "We have accommodated you enough!"

She had refused to give me the day off to attend Doug's funeral. I can still feel my refrained expression and clinched jaw as I told her I would attend his funeral and would call in sick if necessary.

I did not know at the time, but that moment, in her office behind closed doors with two other supervisors surrounding me, hearing those words pass over her lips ignited a fire in me that I can only describe as being pushed up against a wall.

I could either roll over, take it, and shove down my feelings, or fight and do what I felt was right. In that moment, I felt my emotions and mental body stretch to their edges and chose not to conform and compromise myself.

More importantly, it's when I realized no one had any actual authority over me, and something deeper in me was calling the shots. That experience woke me up, unlocked an inner code, and I chose to start experiencing life from an inner authority that never existed before.

Not long after Doug's passing, I began the foundation of my spiritual studies, mysticism, metaphysics, and healing. I attended monthly Full Moon Drum Circles, working with crystals and sacred geometry, and began studying at the Diamond Light School of Massage and Healing Arts. I became a Bodyworker.

Reflecting on Doug's death and the events that followed, I realize that experience became the catalyst to my natural evolution of living life on a PATH OF LIGHT.

Gina Lobito ~ *I thank Robert Francisco Lobito (my dad). Who represents those who had the courage to create a better life for themself. Also, thank my siblings and all souls that have been in my life up to this point.*

One of Gina's Favorite Quotes

It is in your moments of decision that your destiny is shaped.

Tony Robbins

Besties or Betrayers

By Jacki Long

I believe in everyone's highest potential,
but I now put mine first.

Jacki Long (author, coach)

She needed me to reschedule her piano lessons again. I complied but with resentment. Why did I do this?

When Tory moved into my neighborhood, I was drawn to her. We became best friends and were inseparable throughout high school. We saw each other through joy and heartbreak. We smoked cigarettes and drank alcohol for the first time together. It was my parents who busted us. They considered her one of their own, even disciplining us without involving her parents when we stepped out of line. We shared holidays and were sisters from other misters. Our families merged.

We attended different colleges causing us to disconnect a bit. After graduation, she moved out of state. At some point, I realized she wasn't contacting me each time she visited home. In hindsight, it might have been my first clue that I wasn't as much of a priority for her as she was for me. I pushed away my sadness and focused on the good times we shared when we were together. Our humor, sense of adventure, and memories were more intense than many relationships. We saw each other through boy after boy, man after man, fiancés, and husbands. She was maid of honor at my first two weddings and would have been in my third wedding to Blake had we included anyone outside our direct families.

Tory supported me during the loss of my second baby. In turn, pregnant and scared with my third child, I got on a plane to support her when her husband kicked her and their newborn out of their home. We baptized our baby girls together. She was there when my first husband died of cancer. She saw me through my second marriage, one with many addictions and abusive behaviors. I saw her through an abusive husband and abusive fiancés. We were each other's rock through those pains. If I could, I picked up the phone every time she called. She typically didn't return the courtesy.

Early in my relationship with my third husband, Blake, I realized Tory and Blake would be an excellent professional fit. I nearly forced their connection as I knew their collaboration could make a difference in the world. I continued to share all the ups and downs of Tory's and my relationship with her new business partner, who was my boyfriend, then fiancé and ultimately husband. She continued as my confidante as my relationship with Blake regressed to my ex-husband, boyfriend, and, ultimately, my friend. Or so I thought.

Our communication became more distant. I texted her when I broke up with Blake the final time and told her I needed her. There was no response. If she had reached out to me, I would have returned her call as soon as possible. Yet another sign of inequality in our relationship over the years. I didn't listen to that inner voice. I loved her. She was my sister. I was willing to go to my grave, accepting these deficiencies and defending her.

Two months after my last unanswered message, I saw her for the final time. She told me that she and her boyfriend had broken up a few months prior. What? Why hadn't she told me? She was particularly odd during this visit in many ways. There were a handful of others around, and it was clear she didn't want to be alone with me. It felt way, way off. Tory told me that she would be spending a lot of time in our home city working with Blake. I told her she was welcome to stay with me anytime, and she said she would stay in an Airbnb. She said it more than once. Both her actions and my gut told me something was terribly wrong.

As this escalated, I turned to Blake. Though we had divorced, we remained friends. I confided in him and thought I could trust him. For six years, I shared my soul with each of them about the other, never doubting their loyalties and keeping those confidences sacred.

There were so many red flags. My gut was speaking to me, but I continued to ignore it. I had a sliver of hope that they were not "doing anything" together. They wouldn't do that to me! Or to our children, extended family, or friends. No. Way.

I was wrong. "It" happened.

When Blake and I developed a "friendship" after our final breakup, we agreed to tell each other when we would start dating somebody new. A few months after my last trip visiting Tory, Blake asked to see me; he wanted to talk. Since he was also my doctor, I surmised that either he was dying, I was dying, or he was seeing someone new. I had prepared myself for the day he would begin dating someone new. I was not prepared for what happened next.

I got the blow. He told me he was seeing someone, and the "someone" was my best friend, Tory. I immediately went into a panic attack because, in that moment, I had lost two friends. Not only did I lose two friends I thought were loyal and who would never do something this egregious and cruel, but there was no way I could remain Blake's patient. All three relationships were based on vows to protect, love, and care for me for life. This was such a despicable betrayal. Two of the most meaningful people I've had in my life violated most of my deepest values: love, loyalty, honesty, trust, and integrity.

My emotions spun. They each discarded me as yesterday's news. Worse, Tory ghosted me. I clearly wasn't important to her anymore, and I will never know why.

What their betrayals cost.

As of this writing, I am still going through one of the biggest WARs of my life, the treachery by my best friend and my ex-husband (friend and trusted physician). I dropped ten pounds in six weeks without trying. Since Blake's confession, I've cried over their duplicity most days.

Ultimately, their lack of integrity made it impossible for me to continue these relationships.

Other relationships are seriously damaged if not lost completely. Because these two had been in my life for so long, our families and mutual friends have been affected.

Some of my true, long-time friends pointed out that I had been making excuses for her for years. I blew off the unanswered calls and texts when I desperately needed her support. "I just broke up with Blake; please call me." I now wonder how long she had been praying for that news.

I questioned my ability to see others' true colors. Had she ever been a loyal friend? How can I love and miss them after such a betrayal? I wondered if they reflected on the fun memories with me. Did my confiding in each of them assist in creating their new relationship? Whether their relationship lasts or not, we have all lost.

My communication with Blake continued as I transitioned to a new primary care physician. Every time we talked, the shit melted away for a while, and I again felt connected to him until I reminded myself that he was now "connected" to Tory.

What am I doing to heal?

I knew therapy was required to conquer this battle. I didn't want to live a life filled with resentment and victimhood. My therapist gave me validation immediately, and she described "betrayal trauma." All the symptoms I described were normal for such a deep betrayal. I still see her; she helps me with dream interpretation and encourages additional self-care as I trudge through this time.

I have accepted that neither of them is likely to acknowledge their moral corruption or the contribution to the pain it causes others.

I allocate more time to friends who genuinely love and care for me. Without question, I now rely on my intuition rather than setting it aside because I'm afraid of losing someone I love. I believe more in the actions of others versus their words. I'm purging material items that trigger me and storing items I may want to revisit in the future. I focus on quality sleep, prayer, meditation, and taking care of my body. I'm journaling, and certainly, writing this story has been cathartic. Intentionally seeking gratitude brings more to be grateful for.

On my best day, I can understand.

I took a step back and assessed my previous relationships. Especially those where I have tolerated abuse or continued though there were signs it was unhealthy. I no longer ignore my gut. I believe our intuition and gut feelings are our higher power working in our best interest. It's up to us to ignore or take the advice of our churning tummy if it is filled with anxiety or even when it gives a gentle nudge.

I have also tried to assess my relationships with Tory and Blake fairly. What signs did I see? What signs did I ignore? Am I seeking validation in my relationships? How can I react differently when my gut speaks?

I have even focused on a sense of understanding—how could they have possibly done this? Over the years, before their relationship together, both Tory and Blake have had their fair share of heartache, setbacks, overwhelming life circumstances, and traumas. I recognize they didn't do this to hurt anyone. Rather, I believe their attempts to find joy and happiness led them to poor judgment without regard for anyone's feelings but their own.

Ultimately, this is where I will find my peace in accepting this betrayal.

What I've learned about myself.

By allowing this experience to enrich my life, I see their betrayal as a blessing and an opportunity in disguise. It has fueled my desire to win a war and take responsibility for my roles in relationships.

Over the years, I acclimated to Tory's unanswered calls and texts, likely hundreds of them. As I piece this all together, I realize that, even though devastation and betrayal, I tend to find the good in others, justify negative behavior, and remain loyal for far too long. Until now.

I believe in everyone's highest potential, but I now put mine first. Part of our chemical and physical makeup includes the crummy stuff that has hurt us, including the stuff we tend to ignore and allow to stick around way too long. The most destructive parts of our lives can turn us into fierce warriors. Focusing on the positive aspects of life is an amazing trait, and, to face reality, we must actively practice and enhance the skill of discernment.

The worst thing in the world is being used and lied to by someone you trusted. Misery is in wishing things would be different. I expected them to operate under my friendship, communication, trust, and loyalty rules. I wanted them to be different than they actually were. These are revelations I must work through. There is power in knowing I am the solution, even when others' actions are hurtful.

I grieved the loss of a baby. I grieved the loss of my first husband, who was only 54 years old, making me a widow at age 42. I grieved the loss of two relationships with people I never thought would betray me. BUT I am a mother of two beautiful children, an entrepreneur, and survived breast cancer. Ultimately, I have decided I am a warrior and take responsibility for what I have learned and what I choose to do with it.

Those who know me may have conclusions about where I'm supposed to be in this process, moving too slowly or too quickly. I still grieve, exhibit signs of betrayal trauma, and certainly have moments of deep despair about my situation. But I am creating my new story. I play an essential role in helping many people, something that is far greater than myself and those who have betrayed me.

When deciding to tell this story, especially since it is so current, I realized millions of people go through some form of betrayal from someone they trusted immensely. I realized that if I didn't share my story, I would miss the opportunity to help others, which made sharing my trauma an easy decision.

In an instant, my Besties became my Betrayers. I didn't know how I would heal. He stuck a knife into my belly; she jammed it in my back and twisted it. Yet, their betrayal fueled my purpose to help others – and to help myself.

Jacki Long ~ *Thanks to Lynn Hynes, my mastermind group, coaches in the ESS community, and my dearest friends and family for seeing me through…always.*

One of Jacki's Favorite Quotes

When someone betrays you,
it is a reflection of their character, not yours.

Unknown

The Forgotten Mourner

By Phil Williams

My human experiment for the human experience.

Phillip Williams (author, speaker, scholar)

*P*ermit me to begin by establishing a foundation of comprehension before I share my human experiment for the human experience. When you lose a member of your family, a close acquaintance, or another person to whom you were very close, you will likely go through several stages of grief, some of which you may recognize and others not. The following is a list of the seven phases that I have experienced.

1. Surprise

2. Denial of reality

3. Frustration

4. Bargaining (feeling guilty or good about how you behaved with the deceased)

5. Melancholy (The jumble of emotions that usually accompanies the grieving process can typically lead to feelings of depression, isolation, anxiety, and a sense of dread)

6. Gratitude and optimism (connection and support)

7. The operation of grief (there is no right or wrong way)

A Close Friend

As I write this story, starting at the beginning seems like the most obvious thing to do. But first, I should tell you that I believe in Christ. As a believer, I look to the Bible through studying God's word for what it says about my purpose, and it guides me in three significant ways: It declares why I exist, God's knowledge of me in the formation in my mother's womb, and it captures why Jesus died for us.

I changed several nouns to pronouns to include you as the reader. To help clarify a role that I played in the life of a dear friend, I should share with you my broad definition of a prophecy in light of my being a believer. In simple terms, prophecy is "hearing" from God and speaking what you hear to edify, encourage, and comfort someone. To prophesy is to hear from God and speak that which you hear.

In the fall of 2006, I received a prophecy from a respected Bishop, a message from God concerning me. In that prophesy, I would become an adjutant to my Pastor. Just to keep you, the reader, informed, in the religious realm, an adjutant is one who helps, assists, and gives strength and support to pastoral leadership. It is one who is able to consistently and willingly be in place to be an aid to leadership. As a member of my Pastor's church, it allowed me to study him as a member, hear him as a teacher, and see him as a father. As I began using my skills in critical thinking and building relationships, my Pastor could start to see how the skills obtained in the secular world could benefit him and the church in the sacred world. As I first started using my business acumen skills to support my Pastor, our business relationship also allowed us to develop a friendship over the following years.

At a certain time in each experiment, our lives are subjected to significant change. Given the significance of learning from one's mistakes for the human experience, it is only fair that my friendship with my Pastor would evolve over time. The brother of my Pastor, who was also a good friend of mine, was the one who initially introduced me to the Pastor. Even though we became closer over the years, I will always view my friend with the most profound reverence as my Pastor first and foremost, as well as my boss and my friend.

In 2008, after two years of working on various church-related projects, seeing the congregation grow, and witnessing how my friendship had developed, my Pastor received a devasting diagnosis that he had pancreatic cancer. People have no symptoms during the early stages of this type of cancer. The later phases have symptoms; however, they may be generalized, like loss of appetite and weight loss. After getting over the first shock of the news, my Pastor started looking into surgical removal procedures through consultation with the oncologist and any additional therapies and praying for complete healing from God at the same time. I also began researching because I was desperate for my friend and the Pastor to be completely healed. I anticipated complete healing after reading the biblical passages about healing and believing in the power of healing. I understand now more clearly that healing scriptures offer the readers counsel and consolation to ease the burden and give us hope.

Following a decision to remove the cancerous growth surgically, chemotherapy would be the next course of action to destroy any remaining cancer cells. After two years of what seemed like progress, in the summer of 2010, my Pastor was hit with further tragic news: cancer had returned in other organs. Like in the past, It was a privilege to serve as a member of the caregiving team and to be a friend. In the summer of 2010, my Pastor, boss, and a close friend passed away.

The road to recovery after losing a loved one is not always straightforward. When you join a church or other faith-based organization, the people there become your spiritual family, with the Pastor serving as the head of the spiritual family. A pastor cares for his flock, visits the sick and bereaved, and frequently leads us through challenging times. When a church's Pastor passes away, it profoundly impacts the entire Christian community.

The Forgotten Friend

After the passing of my close friend and Pastor, I found myself as an overlooked mourner. As a friend, when a friend passes away, you immediately rally around their family to see if you can help in any way while simultaneously putting a hold on your own personal sadness. Unfortunately, no one pays attention to your suffering and grief, and you are left to fend for yourself while trying to make sense of everything. I fully anticipated that in order to give my full attention to assisting my Pastor's family, I would have to neglect the agony that I was experiencing in my own life. I pushed my own sentiments aside and denied myself the right to have feelings or emotions of loss in the interest of assisting his family and being helpful. I did this because I felt it was my responsibility to do so.

My Pastor's passing was literally the end of my verbal contract with him as his assistant. Given those circumstances, instead of fighting for a position to be recognized as a forgotten friend, I took a flight to avoid the stress. I moved from California to Florida to be closer to my family. And despite the fact that I was moving away from the intense grief, it nonetheless found its way onto the plane with me. When I was with my family, I experienced feelings of further isolation because my family was unaware of the entire scope of my professional and personal relationship with a prominent member of the religious community.

The Forgotten Mourner

Losing a sibling feels like a different kind of loss. What you did in the past or how you treated each other makes it hard when your sibling passes away. Grief is often late, and there were times when I thought it wasn't there at all. My older brother, Artis Leon Washington, Senior, was 15 years older than me. I remember, as a child, being glued to his every word and move. I was probably only four or five years old when my brother graduated from high school. I remember it like it was yesterday. I wore this little person dress shirt, and the sleeves were too long. What did my brother Artis do? He made the shirt look like a French cuff shirt designed for me.

As a toddler, I may have begun to be more independent, learn some self-control, and develop new ideas. I remember that playing with my train set for long periods of time made me very happy. I'm unsure if I was excited to try new things, but I remember being annoyed that Artis wasn't there just to see how I was acting. He always asked, "What's on your mind, sport?" Those words meant the world to me! It was crucial to this story's conclusion that I provided this backstory regarding my close and intentional relationship with Artis.

As I previously indicated, returning to Florida after my Pastor's death gave me hope that there would be some water or life in my desert of grief. As time passed, in the spring of 2011, I received a rare diagnosis known as Steven-Johnson Syndrome. (SJS). SJS is an acute illness that has the potential to be fatal and is characterized by a painful dermo-epidermal separation from the skin. I was burning from the inside out. I was receiving treatment for an infection from the doctor for an illness with penicillin—an allergic reaction to penicillin brought on SJS.

My older brother, my hero, became my caregiver during my illness—the individual who catered to my needs. For you to comprehend the gravity of this assignment for my brother, he was not the most affectionate individual. And while he was not cold, emotionless, or unfriendly, he did not express himself conventionally, despite being an emotional man who cared for and loved his family and friends. Relationships between siblings are crucial. While friendships come and go, siblings are everlasting. My relationship with my hero is one of the longest in my lifetime. With siblings, you can rarely get away with being fake or phony. You share the same environment and, in most cases, the same parents and similar memories and experiences. This shared history with my brother has shaped who I am and made our relationship unique and priceless.

It was time for me to live alone again after recovering from SJS. Even though I would only be 10 miles away, I believe that in some respects, the notion of my leaving once more may have been a painful moment for my brother because he had grown so accustomed to having his little brother back home. Being unhappy or even feeling abandoned is understandable, especially if you are close to your sibling. After I earned my master's degree in human resource development, I realized that I needed to relocate to a major metropolis that was better suited to the HR profession. I uprooted my life and went from Florida to Atlanta, Georgia, expecting to find the ideal professional opportunity.

My family has a history of diabetes, and my brothers and I are all diabetic. Knowing the effects of having diabetes, I was sure that my brother kept taking his insulin as prescribed. I was mistaken. Insulin use is a necessary component of type one diabetes treatment. The disease requires the appropriate quantity of insulin because our systems can no longer produce insulin to maintain healthy blood sugar levels.

Sadly, because my brother stopped taking his insulin, he had a stroke, his health deteriorated, and over time he experienced vascular dementia due to blocked blood arteries. Dementia symptoms are caused by sections of the brain's cells that stop functioning over time. Such symptoms controlled my brother's life. Dementia is not a disease in and of itself; instead, it is a phrase that refers to a general condition in which a person's ability to recall, think, or make judgments is affected to the point where it interferes with their ability to carry out normal day-to-day activities.

My brother was not improving, and he couldn't be left alone for fear that he might wander away from home. As a result, my brother's spouse and children ultimately had to make the difficult decision to place my brother in the care of an assisted living facility. My brother's health continued to deteriorate throughout the course of the years leading up to his death, which occurred in the summer of 2021. Because I am a giving individual, I strongly desired to find a way to comfort my brother's family while they were losing. Again, I neglected to take care of myself while going through the grief process. As a result of my neglect, I had the unfortunate experience of becoming the forgotten mourner once again. Even though it was a natural reaction to my brother's death, I realized that my sadness was overshadowed by the grief my brother's children and sister-in-law were experiencing.

I hope, in some way, my story about grief and losing a pastor and my brother will inspire you to think about self-care and sibling relationships. What an experience this has been through the experiment of life!

We do a tremendous disservice to those who survive the death of a family member, particularly young children's parents. Grief is the ultimate cost of loving someone, despite the fact that nobody has the skills, abilities, or power to make grief disappear. To improve our health and hearts, one of the most effective and recommended methods is to privately express our sorrow, anger, and disappointment. I only wished that someone had told me to do this for myself when my mother and both siblings passed away. And while I am not blaming any particular group, we simply don't do this for our fellow man. I gave the parents of my deceased great-nephew a journal and a pin to help them move forward. To document how they have moved forward after days, months, and years. It is healthy to look back and see growth in our lives and perhaps wonder, "What was I thinking, then?" I use these same tools to move forward in my life. Grief is permanent, and writing down our emotions and sentiments helps us to move forward.

Phillip Williams ~ *I am grateful to my family, best friends, friends, acquaintances, colleagues, and strangers for making my life an experiment. The above encounters have shaped my personality, behavior, and communication. What an adventure!*

Phillip's Personal Affirmation

Stay in touch with the joy that brings me to the table.

An Extraordinary Reminder

By Sophia Long

I would have moved mountains for her,
but she lacked ambition.

Sophia Long (author, student)

My maternal grandmother was a force to be reckoned with; an attorney, teacher, feminist, and serial traveler, she had so much that she still wanted to do. Wherever my grandmother went, my grandfather, the love of her life, went with her. Although not the healthiest dynamic, it worked for my grandparents. She was stubborn but witty in her approach, and he was kind, patient, and goofy. They were like cogs in a machine and incredibly grateful to one another for the love and support they shared. James, my grandpa, was loved and liked by all he knew. When we lost him, my grandma Janet's downfall became more apparent to me.

I'm all too familiar with grief, but I was unprepared at such a young age for the intensity of my grandma's despair. As I processed my own heartache, I felt urged to comfort her as well.

She lived in a large house with her cat and my grandpa's dog, and she kept the television on to keep her company; she was lonely. I had always been close to my mom's parents geographically and emotionally, and I was happy to spend more time with her. Eventually, my grandma wanted to take my mother and me on an excursion.

I knew this trip to Italy would be no ordinary vacation.

My grandma was all of 90 pounds, as she had lost significant weight over the previous three years since my grandfather passed away. Her grief was slowly eating her away. She used a cane or occasionally a wheelchair to get around, which posed challenges at almost every destination. We knew getting her around would be strenuous, but my mom and me, and most certainly my grandmother, were determined to see as many attractions and attend as many activities as possible. All things considered; we had an incredible start to our trip. Our tour guide and group were amazing – some of whom I still keep in touch with today. Our tour group fondly referred to my grandmother as "Grandma" as she was the oldest lady in our group. I was the youngest girl at fourteen years old. Before our trip, I insisted that my mom *never* use the phrase "*when in Rome.*" This lasted only a few hours before our tour guide insisted it was rude to refuse wine at the table, including children. I shrugged at my mom, "*when in Rome?!*" and took a swig of red wine with a smirk. It was my first glass of alcohol; since then, my mom has ensured that I don't forget my hypocrisy.

We started in Rome and made our way through historical icons, which I knew little about. Even so, I was awestruck by the Colosseum and the Sistine Chapel. Pompeii was incredible and heartbreaking all in one. The ground to Pompeii was too uneven and bumpy for my grandmother; therefore, she stayed with the tour guide, disappointed. We were unwilling to risk her potentially falling and hurting herself during our excursion. We took a day trip to the Island of Capri, where I took the liberty to get sick off the side of the boat as we passed by beautiful caves. During our brief visit to Positano, we shopped, ate pistachio gelato, and dipped our feet into the Mediterranean Sea. This was yet another area with a steep, rocky path, and our tour guide once again generously escorted my grandmother as my mom, and I moved forward. We eventually landed in Sorrento, Italy, where we stayed several days to adventure the surrounding area.

My tour group stood outside, socializing as we waited to leave. We were headed to a dairy, olive, and lemon farm where we could make our own pizzas and learn more about Italian cooking. As our group prepared to board the tour bus, my grandmother walked ahead of us while we were talking with some of the other tourists. She was only about eight feet ahead of me when I saw her trip over a small crack separating two pieces of cement, twist backward, and fall directly on her femur. I remember crying, "*Grandma!*" and rushing over, not expecting what I would see. One of our tour friends, a nurse, rushed over to her side, who determined that she knew her femur was likely fractured and that she needed to visit a hospital to confirm this. My stubborn grandmother tried to stand up but stopped when the pain flashed through her. She and my mother rode to the local hospital in Sorrento, Italy, in a small ambulance.

Meanwhile, the tour group assured my mom they would watch and care for me, which they did. Given that I was traumatized and unsure of what would happen next, I'm incredibly grateful to the friends I made who kept me company when I was alone. We had the opportunity to construct our own pizzas and drink limoncello as I tried to momentarily forget the absence of the two women I relied on the most in the world. The tour group and the hotel staff at the property where we stayed were wonderful to us.

When our tour group moved on to the next city, we had to stay behind to stay close to my grandmother, who was in the hospital; she had indeed broken her femur and needed surgery. I woke up the day my tour left and was disappointed that I had slept through the last breakfast I was supposed to have with my group. I was frustrated and upset with myself, but I found a note under my door in the morning from a couple of my friends saying goodbye. It was bittersweet. I would not get to continue with our group, yet I was grateful to have been there in the first place. The hotel staff was shockingly warm and kind, letting us stay as long as we needed, feeding us, and transporting us to the hospital. Johanna and her family's hotel have a special place in my heart.

After spending four days on a gurney without a call button or the ability to converse in Italian, my grandmother was finally given a room. I immediately visited her. My mom stayed with her making sure her needs were met. This left me alone at the hotel most days until we could figure out our next steps. During my first visit, I remember passing by an empty hospital room with the door open, where blood was splattered and half-cleaned up in the middle of the room. I tried to hide my disgust when I found that we had to bring our own toilet paper and hand soap for the bathroom in my grandmother's shared room.

Several days after my grandmother's fall, my mom was anxious to get me home. Because my mom was with my grandmother the majority of each day, and I was only 14, there was not much I could do, so I sat around the hotel. My mom fought diligently to coordinate my solo flight home. As a minor, there were hoops to jump through. Airport personnel, who spoke both Italian and English, were not helpful. Luckily our tour company was willing to step up and guide me.

My mom arranged for a female taxi driver to take me to the Rome airport, which was over three hours away, forcing us to leave at the butt-crack of dawn. I slept the entire ride on my lumpy backpack. Almost everyone I interacted with helped me remain calm and comfortable for the bulk of my trip from Italy. The Trafalgar woman assisted me in getting through security and to my gate. She wished me good luck before we parted ways. Soon after arriving at the terminal, I boarded the plane and had an entire row to myself. Being supplied with a blanket and pillow, I sprawled out and slept most of the flight home. I even missed out on the hot meal they provided.

It wasn't until I got to the United States that things went awry.

My flight was late, and I was about to miss my connecting flight. I had managed to reach my mom by that point, who had encouraged me to speak up and ask if I could go to the front of the customs line because I was going to miss my fight. At that point, I was convinced I would miss it either way, and I was not yet confident enough to carry out any of her suggestions. Instead, I waited in line, panicked, but eventually got through customs. Racing to the terminal, still panicking, I reached the desk just in time to see the tunnel recede from the plane I needed to be on. I shakily told the flight attendant, "My name is Sophia Long, I'm a minor, and I need to be on that plane." I don't remember what the nice lady looked like, but I vividly remember that airport section.

I sat and waited for the next flight to Indianapolis for six hours. Post-panic attack, I refused to leave the boarding area for my next flight, fearful of missing yet another connection. I had family living nearby, but at the time, I hardly knew them and was confident in my ability to get home. Looking back, however, I recognize the benefits that might have come out of allowing my family to be there for me.

When I finally landed in Indianapolis, I was greeted by a familiar face. Although it was a person whom I deeply distrusted and disliked, at least I was home. The following two weeks were gruesome. My mom and grandmother remained in Italy while my grandmother recovered from her surgery. Mom played travel agent once again as she worked fervently to get my grandma out of the hospital and home. With much local help and the assistance of a U.S. rescue nurse, they arrived home about two weeks later.

The following months are a blur. I was starting high school with its unique relational and life experience challenges. I was grateful to have had the incredible opportunity to travel abroad yet simultaneously disappointed by the short-circuited journey; my trip felt incomplete, and I knew I couldn't push a rewind button on the worldly excursion with my beloved grandma.

Italy was her last grand adventure.

After having surgery on her femur and trying physical therapy, she still lacked the desire to heal her body. My family tried effortlessly to encourage her. However, I believe she was suffering from a broken heart and was unconsciously ready to be reunited with the love of her life, my grandfather. Her mind, body, and heart were wearied. A few months later, she entered the hospital for the last time.

Many of my final moments with my grandma were devastating. I couldn't understand why she would not eat or listen to medical advice. I witnessed my grandma emotionally and physically wither away. Her passing was not my first significant loss but watching her give up the will to live was frustrating. It was difficult to comprehend, given that she knew how her demise would impact her family, who loved her so much. I would have moved mountains for her, but she lacked ambition. I could not breathe willingness into her soul, and thus we lost her a few days later on Christmas Eve.

I will forever be grateful for the last exceptional memories she gave me before she passed. It was such a blessing to experience a visit to Europe with my mom and grandmother.

If she could see me now, I know she would be thrilled at the independent woman I have become. She and my grandpa can rest peacefully together, knowing I carry the torch from all the wisdom they taught me and the love they showed me.

Sophia Long ~ *For my Grandma, who I still see in autumn leaves and amber skies.*

One of Sophia's Favorite Quotes

You may not control all the events that happen to you,
but you can decide not to be reduced by them.

Maya Angelou

Take That Trip

By Anita VandenBerg

What are you waiting for?

Anita VandenBerg (author, dental assistant)

*G*rowing up, I was the youngest of six children and raised in a very loving, nurturing, and hard-working family. My mom was a stay-at-home mom, and she was the best mom in the whole world—even my husband says that if you look up the definition of mother in the diction-ary (or Google search for all your youngins), you will find a picture of my selfless, beautiful mom. My dad was a hard-working man and loved God, his family, and his friends. He never had an unkind word to say about anyone in the world.

My parents were also very trusting. They never locked their doors, and the doors were "always open." Though there were eight people at our dinner table, they always had room for more, and they were wel-comed with open arms.

Throughout my life, my parents enjoyed many weeks and weekends off "up north." If you are from Michigan, you will understand that any-where "north" of where you live is "up north." They usually headed to a resort town, a cabin or cottage in the woods, or spent time on a lake or river with their family and friends.

One particular trip sticks out in my mind when I think of what brought my mom joy. On a very early morning, my parents, two brothers, and I headed up north with the car loaded with all the fun stuff we could possibly need for the week. My dad and brothers fished from sunup to sundown, and I was in the water swimming as if I were a fish. Being able to travel was so exciting. In retrospect, this type of vacation was probably not as "exciting" for my mom, who still prepared three meals a day, not to mention all of the cleanup. But Mom loved nothing more than seeing everyone happy.

Over the years, my parents supported and emboldened each and every one of us to live OUR life. With six children, they got six different personalities and a million moods and emotions over the years. But they supported our dreams and never pushed their narrative on how we should be living our lives. I was the first in my family to go away and attend college. Others were successful in the blue-collar world and were amazing stay-at-home moms. We were all encouraged to do whatever we wanted, as long as we kept God at the forefront of our lives.

My dad worked in the automotive industry for a die-casting company. He showed up every day...literally...every day. I don't recall my dad ever calling in sick. In 1978, Michigan experienced one of the most severe blizzards on record that virtually paralyzed and shut down the state. My dad couldn't get his car out of the driveway, so he walked two miles to and from work that day. That was my dad. He was dependable, worked hard, and played harder. He and my mom were looking forward to retirement so they would have the freedom to do what they wanted and go on any trip they wanted on any given day. His plan was to retire at 62.

And he did!

By this time, my parents were empty nesters, and one morning my mom could not wake my dad up. After only nine months from retirement, he suffered a severe, life-altering stroke. He spent several weeks in the hospital and over a month in a rehabilitation facility. The strong man that took care of everything and was a beacon for our family had to learn to swallow, walk, and talk again. He came home, but his and my mom's lives were forever changed.

He never drove again. He had lingering paralysis on his right side and suffered from aphasia. Dad struggled to find the words he wanted to say. On occasion, he would blurt out very inappropriate responses that we would have to "sensor." My mom assumed the role of decision-maker and head of the household, two roles she never wanted to fill. My siblings and I fully supported her, and we leaned on each other for strength and guidance. Four of my siblings lived close by, and I was only 90 minutes away. A phone call away.

Their freedom to go and do whatever they wanted was no longer an option.

My mom remained steadfast through this long, tiring journey with a positive outlook on life. Even through the stressors of being a caregiver, she continually stressed to all of us that many others were not as fortunate as we were and that you can find countless blessings each day. However, just like many other caregivers, my mom simply wore out.

As with most caregivers, my mom put others first, putting her own health on the back burner. And in our case, it was for years. While caring for my dad, my mom's chronic health issues caught up to her. Unable to conquer her battles, she left this earthly world, creating a huge void in all of our lives. Our matriarch and loving mom joined her Heavenly Father. We all miss every single thing about her.

My dad then transitioned into an assisted living facility, where he lived another four years before joining the love of his life in Heaven.

I learned so many things from my parents, but one message always screamed louder than the others. My mom stressed to all six of us kids, "Do not put off those things you want to do. Do not wait to live your life the way you want to. Do not wait for retirement. TAKE THE TRIP!"

My husband and I have lived by this mantra ever since. We jump at every opportunity to "take the trip," whether it is an overnight getaway, a long weekend, or three weeks in sunny, beautiful Florida in February!

As we pack our suitcases, we always say, "Mom, we're taking the trip for you and Dad."

Over the years, the highlight of so many of our trips has been the amazing people we have met who have become dear friends. You never know when the boutique hotel owner, major league baseball rules official or famous author may become someone you look forward to seeing every year. Some of them we keep in touch with weekly. It's a great big world out there with fascinating, wonderful people that we would have never met had we not packed our bags. I cherish my mother's wise advice to "take the trip," and I encourage you to do the same!

Anita VandenBerg ~ *I have to acknowledge my parents for the gift of a faith filled loving family. Forever grateful for meeting Peggy by the pool.*

One of Anita's Favorite Quotes

*Let no one ever come to you without
leaving better and happier.*

Mother Teresa

HEART Commentary

By Coach Peggy & Dr. Markus

*M*arkus and I share our thoughts on these HEART Chapter stories, which touch on the six spokes of the Heart quadrant of the *ATW Wheel*^*TM*: coping skills, stress, emotions, relationships, self-care and self-love, and integrity and values.

Ziggy teaches us that gaming is more than the penned-up adrenaline and survival mode behavior patterns we saw in our children when they were growing up. Gaming can be a tool for people who struggle to communicate or connect conventionally. Gaming has created its own community. Ziggy has plenty of testimonies where gaming has saved lives. This is something we need to understand more. We definitely never looked at it as a self-care tactic, not to mention meditative. Thank you, Ziggy.

Christine exposes the agony of tough love. To recognize that others need help is one thing, but to use tough love to get them help is another. It is not easy to overcome internal battles and conquer doubts when you are applying tough love. A war between our integrity and values gets pushed up against the thumping of a parental heart. "Hurting" our babies is not easy—even when you try to save them. Peggy knows this first hand with her son, Tanner, who authored a story in this book. Congratulations, Christine, on creating victory for both you and your daughter. We look forward to sharing her story firsthand in the years to come.

Alysia, we were taken by your story. Your journey of self-love, acceptance, and overcoming self-deprecation has become too familiar for many of us. Becoming a good parent is a process, and the lessons come hard and fast. Your actions in the past do not put you in a box (bad mom). What you do now counts. Happiness is such a healthy reinforcement.

You are conquering the battles of parenting. It is like stepping through minefields every day when raising those tikes.

Angi and Peggy, many family feuds are based on a lack of communication and understanding. Anger makes us blind. And look at what happens when you really understand others. The way you shared your story is unique, and you two have a great thing going. Congrats, girls, Markus.

Gina, you showed us how life events can change our personalities. Some events remain seared into our memory. The details recalled by Gina are evidence of that. Gina realized she needed a change and was brave to dive into self-discovery and is now helping others.

Jacki, betrayal is one of the most destructive forms of dishonesty. Trust is the basis of any relationship. Once lies creep in, it's over. Hanging in there with distrust tainting the relationship is futile. Jacki, your story is raw and brings light to the importance of intuition and the emotional rollercoaster of emotions. We are proud of you for not suppressing them.

Phillip, we do a tremendous disservice by not supporting those who lose a loved one, particularly young children who lose their parents. Grief is the ultimate cost of loving someone, despite the fact that nobody has the skills, abilities, or power to make grief disappear. To improve our health and hearts, one of the most effective and recommended methods is to, at minimum, privately express our sorrow, anger, and disappointment. Markus: *I only wish someone had told me to do this myself when my mother and both siblings passed away. And while I am not blaming any particular group, we simply don't do this for our fellow man. I gave the parents of my deceased great-nephew a journal and a pen to help them move forward by documenting how they feel in the days, months, and years since their loss. It is healthy to look back and see how we have moved forward.* Phillip, thank you for showing us that the mourner, the one left behind, needs support long after a loved one passes.

Sophia, spending time with loved ones is something we do not appreciate until they are no longer with us. The trip with your grandmother, though short-lived, is something you will never regret. Also, thank you for sharing the special relationship your grandparents had with each other. It was touching.

Anita, too many of us are chasing goals or so wrapped up in a "busy" life, we don't take time away to appreciate how special life is. We have been programmed that taking breaks and enjoying life isn't acceptable. We must not forget to live. A vacation reminds allows us to reassess our goals and connect back to those things that make us happy. We find the ultimate goal to be the pursuit of "heart happiness." Joy!

SPIRIT CHAPTER STORIES

---

*Faith is unseen but felt, faith is strength
when we feel we have none,
faith is hope when all seems lost.*

Catherine Pulsifer

Consciousness

by Dr. Markus Wettstein

Cosmic consciousness, or spirit,
is the driving force of our consciousness.

Markus Wettstein (author, physician)

*W*hen I grew up, all things spiritual were claimed by the church. The Catholic Church had a considerable influence. But dissent over decades grew into the protestant movement and later religious affiliation.

My mother was Protestant, and my father was Catholic. These two religions were the choices for spiritual explorations in Germany. With both, you were expected to wear Sunday's finest and behave accordingly; sit still in church, and your clothes must remain spotless before and after church.

Once my parents realized the church directly taxed their paychecks, the thought of ex-communication meant more money in the bank. Because they decided to leave the church, I grew up with no religious background. In Germany, religious education was a compulsory High School class. So, when deciding which religion to choose, I drew a blank. Fortunately, a class in comparative religion was offered, and I chose that. It exposed me to different approaches to spirituality.

Despite this early exposure, my explorations turned to the sciences. All things spiritual were neglected. Then I married into a traditional Catholic family. As a result, my children had to experience the upbringing outlined above. But our children were loved, not disciplined with pain as a teaching tool which was my programming of "religious" upbringing.

Love as a central guiding force worked well for me. So I went through RICA, the Rite of Initiation of Christian Adults. Only after intense study of the religion did I notice a missing component. There was a strong separation between science and spirituality.

This discovery is a memory of my high school studies. I began meditating to develop my spiritual side. At the same time, science developed quantum mechanics. To hold true under scientific scrutiny, this theory invokes consciousness.

There is a bridge between science and religion through "cosmic consciousness."

Some call it the field, others the causal realm. It has many names that cannot give it justice. Nevertheless, this energy provides the blueprint of our existence. This blueprint makes up our fractal universe.

The fractal universe is a problematic concept. Essentially, it means a copy of the whole exists in any part of it. This is similar to the holographic principle. Here, a piece of an image contains the whole image in miniature form. In other words, as above, so below.

But there is also free will which is part of our individual consciousness. This is why we do not lead a pre-determined life. Our choices make for an easy life if we follow the blueprint. "Dis"ease will reveal and establish itself if we veer off our path.

Cosmic consciousness, or spirit, is the driving force of our consciousness. In other words, we are fish in the ocean of cosmic consciousness. And how do you explain to a fish what water is?

Some call "matter" a state of frozen energy. But our consciousness can exist on different planes or energy frequencies. Studies were performed on monks. They can attain different states of brain wave activity previously thought impossible. Any brain activity establishes an electromagnetic field that can be measured.

Also, this is one way we "sense" others' presence, mood, or hidden thoughts. Experts use this realm for clairvoyance or astral projection, to name a few. All this has been scientifically proven to exist, so there is no hiding the facts anymore.

Over time, it has become clear to me that whatever I do unto others, I do unto myself. In addition, I strive not to judge others. As a result, my anxiety has decreased, and the experience of oneness is blissful. Following this blueprint also alleviates my worries about death. I now find myself an extension of consciousness existing on a material plane.

Ultimately, I have concluded that we can influence our environment with our electromagnetic field. Have you ever felt the mood change when someone enters the room?

This insight is only the beginning of my spiritual journey. It gives me a clear sense that we are very powerful beings. Rather than becoming an obedient follower, I chose to exercise my spiritual freedom. But now, it is also my responsibility to act accordingly. I call this the W.A.R. (we are responsible) of the spirit.

I remind myself often that I am not alone. The blueprint is there; I just have to tap into it to ensure I am on track.

One of Dr. Markus's Favorite Quotes

Out beyond ideas of wrongdoing and rightdoing,
there is a field. I'll meet you there.

Rumi

Nursing a Soul Back to Life

By Lara Scriba

*My beliefs began to shift; recovery was not a linear experience,
and healing had no finish line.*

Lara Scriba (author, nurse)

I entered the nursing field in a desperate attempt to start over and begin life with a clean slate. My dream was to specialize in psychiatry and to work on an eating disorder unit. This would enable me to care for others with the same dignity, compassion, and kindness one of the nurses had shown me. Secretly, I wanted to pull back the veil and help myself finally heal while also fulfilling my purpose and passion for helping others.

Underneath the pristinely white, starched uniform I donned each day for class, I found I was simply a shell of a human. My mind, heart, and soul were marred by scars inflicted by both me and others. The deepest scars, though, were created by the demons of my own eating disorder and the wake of destruction within and around me.

I was determined that things would be different this time. It was a last attempt to phoenix out of the rubble. I had relapsed many times, and at that point, my eating disorder felt like a life sentence, one I was unsure I could bear.

Stepping into my new future, I felt hope yet conflict. Miraculously, the Western medical system saved my brother's life, healing his brain and broken bones after a life-threatening accident. I was deeply grateful for his recovery though I lacked confidence that Western medicine could heal me.

Hospitalization, therapy, and a multitude of pills weren't fixing me. I couldn't grasp the disorder's origins. Where had all this come from? With each relapse, I felt more broken and hopeless; another failure, another scar, and yet another example of how I couldn't outrun the burden. I was "attacked" during my weakest and most vulnerable moments.

Amid a relapse, there is a sense of feeling unseen and unreachable. Drowning just below the waterline where the screams of despair go unheard. Thrashing to reach air remains unrecognized. The tether of your disorder keeps you deep enough where only your fingertips break the surface, and perhaps a tiny ripple is visible from shore.

In the Tarot, the water element signifies emotions which seems appropriate as I felt completely and utterly engulfed by untamed emotions. As I tried to navigate my own path to recovery, I also felt the weight of the world and those around me. Articulating the language of my tormented heart and asking for help consumed me with fear.

A soothing voice entered my brain at times, promising relief and offering assurance that this time would end differently. Eventually, I would follow the voice as if in a trance, like those who follow the music of the pied piper.

Through my soul's insistence for survival, I entered this new career centered around healing the sick and fixing the broken.

Little did I know it would all unfold beautifully.

As a first-year nursing student, I had only been working with mannequins, so the idea of working with a live person was terrifying. As I stepped into the patient's room, my nursing instructor slowly turned and said, "Just you, leave your stethoscope and chart on the table." With my back against the wall, feeling anxious and sweating, I hoped I'd have the answers she was looking for.

As we entered the dimly lit room, she asked, "What do you see?" I took a deep breath and started anxiously moving through a general assessment in my head—ABC...airway, breathing, circulation. With a quiver in my voice, I rattled off my observations. "No labored breathing, unobstructed trach, skin pink and dry, resting peacefully, no distress noted."

She placed her hand on my shoulder, a subtle suggestion to slow down. "Try again. I don't want you to look with your eyes. What do you feel when you stand here beside her? What sensations are you experiencing in your body? If you listen with your heart, what do you hear her saying to you?"

I closed my eyes until my heartbeat settled, and then it all flooded in. "She feels alone, isolated, and empty. Her furrowed brow shows me she feels regret and is riddled with many unsaids. There is a sadness, wishing she could pull her family close and tell them how much she loved them, to feel the warmth of their touch, to feel loved."

I slowly opened my eyes to find that her eyes were now beaming. "Yes, THAT is the assessment I want you to perform—through the lens of your heart, not a sterile, clinical, or compartmentalized lens. See and feel the person you treat, not only the symptoms."

During that semester, I was introduced to the work of Louise Hay and dove into the possibility that the experiences within our minds and the emotions we feel can create a physical manifestation within our bodies. This gave me hope. It sparked memories of untraditional healing I had witnessed or experienced. There were moments of profound peace and stillness gifted to me by a nurse who led a guided meditation while I was in treatment for my eating disorder. My brother's nurse provided gentle acts of compassion when he was combative and disoriented as his brain healed from his accident. And the ease in my mother's eyes and the smile on her face after moving and breathing in unison with others during her yoga class.

A seed of hope was planted. I realized there were different ways to cultivate peace and healing while beautifully co-existing with Western medicine. Healing may not always equate to curing, but it is still possible to co-create your experience. Building awareness, integrating holistic strategies, and accepting all of our parts— even our shadows, is possible.

I cautiously wondered, was it possible to live my life through this lens? Had I found a way to navigate my heart and ultimately navigate life without destroying myself in the process? Could I find a way to release the deep shame and immense self-doubt I carried for so long and learn to finally accept, trust, and love myself?

During my second year, we were asked to "give back" to the unit or to one of our patients. My mind shifted immediately to a patient I had become close with. She was trying to recover from surgery yet struggled to manage her anxiety. It brought me back to that first experience I had with meditation during treatment. The stark contrast between the relentlessly rigid, unforgiving, anxious mindset that I entered with and how slowly, as each gentle word landed, my mind and body softened, becoming more malleable, a place of possibility. These new practices taught me to live in the present and to sense ease within my body and mind. It felt like pure magic.

I nervously clutched the meditation in my hand and hoped I could deliver a similar experience to her. As the words found their flow, I found that my cadence also slowed along with her breath. Once I finished, it was evident that the gift was received and valued through the lens of my compassion. When she opened her eyes, she, too, had a softness about her. and a gentle smile.

Through this lens, I realized that the tenderness and compassion I held for others was how I wanted to care for myself.

I deeply disagree with the saying that you cannot love anyone else until you love yourself. I found the exact opposite to be true. Through loving and caring for others, I slowly began learning how to extend the same love and compassion toward myself.

I found myself immersed in the miracles of Western medicine yet bombarded by the intensity of human suffering.

These experiences and realizations were like a buoy for my soul, keeping me afloat as I began to navigate not only the beginnings of my recovery but also the harsh reality of what I experienced working as a nurse in the Emergency Room. I found myself immersed in the miracles of Western medicine yet bombarded by the intensity of human suffering. It was an environment that demanded that I learn to navigate the depths and complexity of the human experience, or else it would swallow me whole. I had to learn to process, debrief, and collaborate with co-workers as we would experience the unthinkable together. I would learn to reassure, hold hands, sit silently, or hold space for those whose worlds had just collapsed.

Though I utilized my newly found tender lens, my heart fought against building a protective wall to shield it from feeling every ounce of the suffering I witnessed during the dizzying pace of the ER environment.

As I continued to study holistic healing, I was teased for being too soft, and co-workers laughed at the books I read. So it stayed hidden, tucked into the background, which reminded me of my mother teaching me to read tarot cards as a child, but then quickly throwing a towel to cover them as soon as my father arrived home.

It felt like a secret to be kept, something that was considered absurd, frivolous, or nonsense. A purposeful discarding of the feminine lens—a softness, depth, and fullness that had no place in this practical, masculine world. How can such a beautiful and powerful connection be hidden when it is the key to healing? I felt the rebel rise within. How could I find a place for this type of work in my life?

The devil you know is better than the devil you don't.

I felt I had found a system that spoke to the dis-ease I was experiencing in my soul. Had I found the key to my recovery? Slowly but surely, I continued to nurse my soul back to life, nourishing it with words of kindness, acts of compassion, and moments of stillness.

I began voraciously reading any book I could find, flooding my mind with positivity and possibility, crowding out and challenging the negative thoughts that seemed to constantly dominate my mind. I attended yoga classes with my Mom, creating a safe place to connect with others and my own body. I began exploring meditation, becoming more and more aware of the patterns of my mind, and though I couldn't quite shift them yet, the simple act of co-existing with them allowed a sense of curiosity to arise. If I listened to my developing purpose and what was underneath the surface of my symptoms, I would find the clues to set me free.

I began finding words to articulate the sensations I was experiencing and the emotions attached to them. Learning Reiki was a huge step in understanding the subtleties rising in my being. It often brought tears to my eyes and a smile to my soul. The grip of my disorder loosened as I not only worked on myself but also learned how to establish healthy boundaries. There was a system to process not only my energetic experiences but learning not to absorb the pain or suffering of others. I established rituals to care for myself and routinely release what was not mine.

I was looking forward to my future with hope instead of constantly looking back with despair, shame, and fear. Others had found a way through, so I knew there had to be a way for me, too.

My journey to true healing had just begun...

I began exploring the world as an empath, discovering the beauty and complexity of holistic healing, and recognizing there is so much more to us and our healing that extends far beyond the body. My nursing career became entwined with healing my own heart as I helped others heal. Transitioning later into Community Health, allowed me to provide Reiki as a service to my patients during my work day, which was such a beautiful experience. As I continued learning to interpret the world through energy and sensation, I found that the constant presence of peace and ease of energy continued to improve my own self-care. Each session resulted in soft eyes, blurred edges, and ease within the souls.

Understanding myself as an empath, I no longer felt that experiencing the world was a liability. My heart opened, and I shed my protective shield. I was more aware when I became dysregulated, anxious, or overwhelmed. Leaning into what was revealed rather than instinctively avoiding or numbing myself.

My beliefs began to shift; recovery was not a linear experience, and healing had no finish line. Rather healing is simply an ongoing process of evolutions and iterations as we experience the complexities of being human. A lifetime of devotion, awareness, and intention is required to gently nourish seeds of peace and acceptance while recognizing and pulling out the weeds impeding growth. Lovingly nourishing every cell of your being is possible by grounding the roots of your soul firmly into the earth, providing protection during harsh weather, and welcoming and celebrating the gifts of both the rain and the sun.

Not knowing my personal journey would become my life's passion, a new chapter had begun, a new sense of promise and possibility. There will be many more chapters of healing to experience and share as I continue to nourish my soul.

Lara Scriba ~ *I am deeply grateful for the unwavering support, trust, and love I've always received from my family, husband, and children during my many phases of discovery.*

One of Lara's Favorite Quotes

Nothing is so strong as gentleness,
nothing so gentle as real strength.

Saint Francis de Sales

From Bananas to Buddhism

By Mark W. Reid

Unlike the 13-year-old who was so pleased to have an identity,
I am more content these days to simply be.

Mark Reid
(professor, attorney, and Japanese paper maker)

I knew *about* God, of course, even from my earliest memories. My parents were self-proclaimed Baptists, but they didn't attend church themselves. We were the type to say a prayer at Easter, Thanksgiving, and Christmas, and that was the extent of our religious practice.

Things changed for me, and one might say my internal struggle commenced around the beginning of junior high school. Growing up in a suburb of Birmingham, Alabama, assured me that the vast majority of my peers were Christians, primarily Southern Baptists. As a result, many -invited me to their church's youth group activities on Wednesday evenings. These gatherings were a blast. We ate a nice meal around 6 PM, then moved on to a large meeting room by seven o'clock, where the entertainment would begin with an ice breaker—a group game or a humorous skit that some of the kids would perform. After that, we sat through a 30-minute, age-appropriate Bible study. We followed up by playing basketball, shooting pool or just hanging out. It was the adolescent equivalent of nightlife, like when my parents went to bars after work.

I was a fun and funny kid, so my friends invited me back often. I looked forward to Wednesday nights. My curiosity about Christianity grew in the process. I suppose that was one ulterior motive of the church, in addition to genuinely building a sense of community amongst the congregation. Unlike a lot of the other kids, I actually listened during the Bible studies. I began attending services on Sunday mornings as well. As encouraged, I read my Bible daily. I was, however, different from my peers in one regard. They grew up in the church. *The* message was spoon-fed to them for as long as they could remember. Since their time in the womb, essentially.

On the other hand, I was just beginning my study of Bible stories and Christian ethics as a 13-year-old. They didn't have much of a choice in becoming a Baptist. I still did.

One day, a youth pastor from the church paid me a visit at home. We talked about accepting Christ into my heart and saying it aloud. I knew of this required proclamation, but I still needed to understand what it meant. The pastor explained that it was a personal commitment to follow Jesus and live a faith-filled life. I thought hard about it for a few moments. What would I be giving up? Lustful thoughts about girls (as if I could)? Rock and roll music with pernicious lyrics? Saying "cuss" words out loud? These were heavy prices to pay for a 13-year-old boy. Nevertheless, the idea of pleasing God, and doing right in life, persuaded my young mind. I decided to pray "*the* prayer" and get my ticket to salvation.

In that moment, I felt something shift inside. A weight lifted off my shoulders. I felt a sense of peace that I had not experienced before. I had an identity. I became a Christian and was genuinely excited to start living that way. It was my first mystical experience.

The Next Evolutionary Steps

As I grew older and entered high school, my faith blossomed. While other classmates were goofing off or sleeping at their desks during study hall, I read my Bible. I even became my class chaplain (back when you could still have such a thing) at my public high school. At graduation, I led the assembly in our class prayer, which I had personally written.

Despite my involvement in the Baptist church, I still had questions of faith. I dated a girl who was a Pentecostal. On occasion, I went to her church instead of my own. I found it scary and weird when they spoke aloud in tongues and danced in the aisles, hands raised toward the sky, during the exuberant music portion of the worship service. No one ever behaved in such a way in my much more stoic Baptist church. How come? And if one is correct, the other must be wrong, I thought. My Baptist friends warned me against going to the other church, saying the Pentecostals misinterpreted the Bible.

On the other hand, my Pentecostal friends told me that the Baptists were only halfway living the teachings of the gospels and only halfway worshiping. We should be excited about God and out in the aisles, jumping for joy when praising "Him," not merely standing there in the pews, as the Baptists did, conservatively swaying and monotonously singing century-old hymns. I found myself standing in between my first religious culture clash.

To find answers, I prayed hard about the conflict and put my faith in the verses that read, "Seek, and ye shall find; knock and the door will be opened." I felt empowered by those verses to explore Christianity further. Surely, God would shield me from misinformation so long as I was seeking with an earnest heart.

The College Years and The Academic Study of Religion

At 18, I entered a large university, majoring in political science and minoring in Japanese. Those classes and the required core curriculum of science and math made up the bulk of my schedule, but I took a religious studies class as an elective each semester. I thought it would be an easy "*A*" since I had practically read the entire Bible at this point, starting with "Survey of the New Testament." I quickly discovered that the academic study of the Bible and religion is vastly different from the point of view one gets at church. I learned a lot more about the historical data, about the councils that chose which books to include in the Bible and which to leave out. Church just presumed God had orchestrated and ordained all that stuff. I came to realize that the decisions made by the religious bodies in charge at the time and throughout history were just made up by a bunch of men. Fallible, sinful men like me.

My worldview expanded exponentially. I no longer saw the world solely through the narrow filter of my Baptist beginnings but through a broader, more inclusive lens that embraced many beliefs and traditions. I took courses on Native American traditions and Eastern religions. I studied Judaism, Islam, Hinduism, Taoism, and Buddhism. I was drawn to the philosophical views, particularly of Buddhism, which taught precepts such as "attachments lead to suffering."

The most significant catalyst in my journey was a professor named Dr. Patrick Green. He was not simply a teacher; he was a mentor, a guide, and a friend. He encouraged his students to think critically and question everything, including their beliefs. His intention wasn't to dispel anyone's faith, but rather, if your truth is "Truth with a capital 'T,'" it should stand up to any level of questioning you could throw at it, right? He challenged me to step out of my comfort zone and explore different cultures, religions, and worldviews. He introduced me to the "social construction of reality." For instance, a banana is a banana because it was decided long ago that it would be called such, and a specific definition makes it so. We all learn about bananas at some point after birth and really have no choice in the matter. Bananas are just bananas, and that's it. Likewise, the concepts of who and what God is and means were also determined without my consultation.

By this juncture, I had no choice but to consider, "Did Baptists actually believe that their faith was the only *true* faith?" That's what many Mormons might say. The Church of Christ denomination holds a similar view. Add the Jehovah's Witness folks to that list too. If you aren't a part of those specific bodies of believers, you are potentially, even likely, on a highway to hell. That view, to me, didn't seem to comport with the idea that God is benevolent and forgiving, an infinite, omnipresent God to boot. Wouldn't omnipresence denote that God is with the Hindus in Bombay, India, just as much as the Protestants in Bloomington, Indiana? Would I really be sentenced to eternal damnation if I inadvertently screwed up how I'm supposed to think about and *believe* in God?

Japan and Graduate School

My first job after graduation was teaching English in Japan, rotating between six junior high schools in the countryside. There, I was finally exposed to a vastly different culture, an experience I had longed for most of my life.

I dipped my toes in the waters of Buddhism. In Japan, Shintoism is also prevalent, an animistic religion that considers objects, places, and especially nature, like trees, to possess a spiritual essence. These things are, in one manner of speaking, "alive." All of it intrigued me. Buddhist temples and Shinto shrines often exist next to each other. The Japanese accept and accommodate both as a matter of faith and don't see a conflict between Buddhism and Shintoism. That was a novel idea to me. You don't typically see a lot of churches and mosques existing side-by-side like that. I was now a far cry from the Baptist theology where my journey began so many years before.

After Japan, I pursued a master's degree in religion, philosophy, and ethics. I wanted to continue exploring the various traditions and beliefs that make up our world and deepen my understanding of the social and cultural factors that shape them. Most of all, I felt eager to study philosophy in more depth. I was inspired to write papers and read books by Aristotle, Nietzsche, Kierkegaard, Kant, and Hegel. During this time, I had a monumental epiphany: God was not some external end goal to comprehend or attain. He/She/It wasn't over there in a book or found high in the sky, away and separate from me. Rather, it was the pursuit itself. The process and effort of exploring my curiosities. The evolution of mind. My lifelong desire to know God, to "do the right thing," these answers existed *within* me the whole time.

A Continuation of Spirit,
A Journey With No Destination

It has been over three decades since the commencement of my journey. From Baptist to…well, where I am now. The past twenty years were filled with a lot of nomadic activity. I bounced around the world, New

York City, Los Angeles, Vermont, Florida, Seoul, Tokyo, London, and a tiny Greek isle called Ios.

I eventually went to law school and became an attorney for ten years before walking away. That, too, was a part of my journey of self-reflection, as I discovered big money and a fancy Brooks Brothers suit don't buy you happiness when you are doing work you feel is morally wrong and depletes the energy and joy from life.

So, when my midlife crisis hit in my early 40s, rather than buy the cliché sports car, I just walked away from law practice and returned to a land I love—Japan.

I returned to the path that spoke clearest to me after all of my "seeking that I might find" and "knocking that the door might be opened." Those verses were right, by the way. I did find it, and the door was opened. For me (and it might very well be something different, just as fulfilling for someone else), Zen philosophy is the best answer that fits me today. Does that make me a Buddhist? I guess. But I don't pray to the Buddha as a guy in the sky, and I don't concern myself with labels any more. Those labels are just as socially constructed as the concept of a banana is. Do bananas and Buddhism exist? Sure. But it doesn't matter what I call them or label myself. Things just are. Unlike the 13-year-old who was so pleased to have an identity, I am more content these days to simply be. To exist. To observe this life without judgment when possible. Will I still feel this way with the passing of two or three more decades if I am fortunate enough to remain here? That doesn't concern me one bit. All I have now and ever will have is the present moment. And, today, I suppose, I am a Zen Buddhist. Ask me again tomorrow, and you might get a different answer.

Mark Reid ~ *Much gratitude to Dr. Patrick Green. Great educators are essential in life to grow well. And to my greatest inspiration of all, my wife, Haruka.*

One of Mark's Favorite Quotes

*You are under no obligation to be
the same person you were five minutes ago.*

Alan Watts

Becoming Calibrated

By Peggy Willms

I am imperfectly perfect and perfectly imperfect.

Peggy Willms
(author, host, coach, motivational speaker)

I am intuitive! Let's start with that. That self-proclaimed declaration does not imply I always catch the signs and listen to my intuition quickly, but when I do…what a ride! By the time you finish this, you may have other descriptors for me: empathy, clairvoyant, visionary, psychic, crazy… Regardless, I welcome the feedback.

Intuition or messages come at me in many ways.
Here we go.

The Bolts: Bolting upright from deep sleep are my directive message. They feel urgent - do something about this! They are loud, almost like someone else might hear them as well.

Here are two recent examples. In January 2021, I woke, blurting James Redfield out of my mouth like I was being exorcized. I immediately look at the clock, and it is 3:33 a.m. There is the good ole Father-Son-Holy-Spirit sign. I had interviewed James on my radio show a few weeks prior; perhaps he was floating around in my unconscious mind. The message was to reach out to him, asking him to write the Forward of my first published book, which was coming out this year. I emailed him a few hours later. I told him about my dream, risking he might think I was a loony bin. He replied yes within hours, and the book is now published, called, *The Four-Fold Formula for All Things Wellness*.

One night this past August, I flew out of bed like the house was on fire, and as I was hobbling to the bathroom, up over my right shoulder, I saw my headshot, which was the size of a Volkswagen. And I was screaming, "It is your cholesterol meds. Get off them!"

About a year ago, my physician put me on statins against my will, but I agreed to prove a point.

My family has "hereditary" high cholesterol. I have hovered between 200 and 220 for a decade. Now I had hit the high 200s, driven by my LDL, the "bad" cholesterol you want to be low. It can be frustrating watching the number increase when I have lived a life of "doing things correctly." I don't drink, smoke, or eat meat, consume minimal dairy except for my whey protein or Greek yogurt, egg whites (no yolks), and I exercise. My vice is sugar. But if I cannot have a piece of carrot cake or a truffle occasionally, then shoot me.

I agreed to try the statins as a test. As a data analyst junkie, I pulled an, "If it drops significantly in a short period, we will know it is hereditary and NOT my lifestyle. I will come off that shit and wait until my numbers hit 400." Please don't come for me. I have heard it all from statins suck to you need statins, your lifestyle, your stress, Hashimoto's, or whatever. This one is great, "You get to 400, and it will kill you." TRUST ME, I know all the angles. I am talking about my vision here.

Over seven months, I went from minor skeletal pain to severe. Ultimately, I used a cane many times a day as I could barely walk without every joint area of my body hurting, including my toes and elbows. I was scared to death that I was on a fast track of multiple sclerosis as images of my mother, who had just passed from MS, popped in and out of my head. Every time I hurt, I would emphatically think or say NO! I am not going to end up like that. The vision I had during my night stroll to the bathroom - "It is your statins" caused me to stop the pills cold turkey the next day, visit my physician two days later, and become completely 100% pain-free within a week. Thank you, screaming message from my Higher Self.

Flashes: These are one of my other specialties (PS: again, I will say you are special, too).

They can be images, words, or internal conversations. Here are a few examples of this. Two days ago, we were headed north to check on our home, which is being renovated after Hurricane Ian's destruction. I felt overwhelming, heavy-chested anxiety that there would be a multi-care pile up in front of us. The message got louder and louder. I mentioned it each time to Dana, who was driving. As the voice and images in my head got louder, I told Dana about them more emphatically each time. When he pulled into the gas station, I told him. We jumped on Highway 41, I told him. We connected to I-75, and I repeated it. From the second we had left the hotel, every car around us was tailgating. Finally, on the interstate, I told him to make sure he didn't follow cars too closely because I still had strong visions. And about five minutes down the road, we screeched to a halt, almost nailing the car in front of us. From left to right, there were multiple cars, and 18-wheelers stopped on the road. The type of accident when you know you just missed it by a few minutes.

Random, unprovoked internal conversations are next.

These back-and-forth conversations are fun "party of one" chats, I call them. After my internal convo, my thoughts manifest in the material form, usually within 24 hours, sometimes within five minutes. People will say what I just said in my head, a commercial will pop up about the topic, a phone rings, and more. This has happened for decades. I think about receiving something special in the mail it shows up, a Tik-Tok video about the subject, or the person might become ill or worse. I am not talking about Big Brother listening when you talk out loud and ads appear on Facebook. I am talking about "in-my-head" conversations I do not share, and boom, they come to fruition.

Call and check-in messages. These are the ones where I see visions of a phone with someone's number on it or I get a flash of their name. I call, and about 90% of the time, something is up, or they are thinking of me. I called my friend to see if her son had gotten into "big trouble." She said no. That night he did. This even happened a few times with one of my authors, bloggers, and friend, Cyndi Wilkins.

Look into future messages. These are fun.

This is when I can see the "what and where" of people down the road. I envision what they might say, the profession they lean into, actions they will take, or even an illness. I have learned to take notes when I choose not to say anything until it comes to fruition and then share my proof. And at times, when I tell them where they are headed or what they may do, and they emphatically reject the thoughts, I have a bit of a "told you so" moment when they come back with their "you won't believe it" story.

Numbers. I have written about this in a blog on my website called Angel Number 11:11. This has happened for decades. I have too much data to ignore that these messages are simply coincidences. Elevens are when I feel connected to my purpose and dial into whatever I am doing in the moment. Eleven is my "listen more intently" number. This happens every other day or so, sometimes five or six times a day.

The number 444 is related to my profession. It always tells me to be patient, you are on track, and don't give up. I will be thinking about work and brainstorming, and a church bell will ring four times when it is 3 o'clock, not four. I see this number a few times a month.

The number 616 has been connected to my oldest son, Shane, and me since he was a teenager. He will be 37 in March…so it's been a damn long time. We both see this number and know that something is up with the other. We are talking shopping receipts, license plates or VINs, lottery numbers, billboards, addresses, and more. It stops us in our tracks, and we check-in. Just this week, 616 came up several times over two days, and

I called him. He has been struggling with the next steps for his future. He shared many details, including thinking about selling everything he owned and riding off into the sunset with his dog, which was precisely what I had been feeling for days. I have been spewing, "Peggy, go to Costa Rica, eat mangos and write for the rest of your life." We both are in a bit of "Run, Forrest, run."

Reoccurring dreams.

These are strong and, in the past, confusing, and scary. Dozens of times, for years, and I mean years, I had the following two dreams. They both stopped a few years ago. I am trying to remember if they stopped simultaneously. The first is a vision of myself during slavery times. I was always standing on the back porch of a mansion surrounded by large pillars wearing a long, bright yellow colonial dress. I am looking off into the field where enslaved people are picking cotton, and I feel anxious. They trustingly look up at me and trust me. I quickly look over my shoulder for my husband, their owner, and tell them to run. I am screaming, "RUN."

The next one was terrifying. It was black, gray, and white. I am walking down a country road. I see myself lying on my stomach in a small ditch on the left side of a country road. There was water in the ditch, and it had been raining. I am muddy and only wearing a T-back-type tank and panties. I am about 25 years old and have long, wavy hair ratted about my head and shoulders. Nauseated, I knew I had been raped and left like trash on the side of the road. That one stuck with me for a bit.

Meditation Imagery

I experience strong imagery when I meditate, which is nearly always a person...Cleopatra, Elvis, Gaucho Marx, Lincoln, Robin Williams, the Statue of Liberty, arch angels, and more. There is always a gold hue around them, except for Cleopatra, who sits on a mound of gold and jewelry. She has items and rays of vibrant red near her. My profile images are always solid black, with side profiles with shining gold light.

Finally, the I Don't Know visions or occurrences which often take some dissection. Today, for instance, we are staying at a hotel, and I am headed out to the pool with my laptop. I stop to use the restroom. While washing my hands, black and brown liquid (we can all figure out what it is) starts to bubble up from the floor drain, flowing upward and all over the floor. I barely got out of there and reported it to the front desk. As soon as I get out to the pool, I notice the hot tub jets are on high, simulating a fountain in Central Park. I mean, water is bubbling two feet up. No one is around. I start working around 5:30 AM, so no one is ever around. I interpret these two incidences as perhaps I am bubbling and am beginning to flow from within and release. Hmm. Wonder where those messages will go.

Bringing all of this together is based on a "directive message." I woke up with the urgency to share the above and literally saw this title on a page. The message was to connect with others that we all need to calibrate our intuitive abilities. Dial in! For years, I felt there was a right and wrong in how I should connect with a Higher Source. Once I let go of my left-brain, Western medicine approach to energy, I was entirely on board. I no longer give a crap about what people think. I sort of look at it all as a fun playground even though some of the messages and happenings are dark, I accept them as part of who I am.

I am working diligently to align my physical, mental, and spiritual calibration. We do not need permission or approval to do so.

Tuning in to my visions and messages will become more of a focus. But frankly, I sometimes don't hear or see them until they are screaming. Perhaps, today, my Higher Self is screaming again. And I HEAR YOU.

One of Peggy's Favorite Quotes

Throughout the infinite, the forces are in a perfect balance,
and hence the energy of a single thought
may determine the motion of a universe.

Nikola Tesla

A Soul's Journey

By Victor Acquista

*There is clarity in having a sense of purpose
that resonates with the core of your being.*

Victor Acquista (author, speaker, physician)

*D*o you have questions about past lives? Curiosity about this had been with me for many years. I believe we are spiritual beings having a physical existence. I believe an infinite essence of divinity that is our soul incarnates into a body-mind, and we get to experience a lifetime on planet Earth with all the challenges, lessons, and opportunities that present over the course of our lives. What about previous lives? What about different incarnations of other worlds? Do I have a galactic lineage? These questions had been percolating in my mind.

Then, an opportunity for answers unfolded.

She had a table at a consciousness and light exposition I was attending, but she was speaking, and the sign said "back at 5:00" or something to that effect. Her services listed: holistic practitioner, homeopath, channel, shaman, and soul-regression hypnotherapist, among other offerings. I waited. Good decision!

After a brief conversation, she suggested a between-lives soul regression which would give me the opportunity to ask my council questions. She lived two time zones away, and I felt reluctant to have her guide me by phone, but she assured me that she had done this kind of soul regression work remotely on many occasions.

In the few weeks prior to the session I scheduled, she asked me to list five questions. My major questions had to do with aligning to my higher self. How can I be the best person I am capable of being? How can I embody the spiritual essence that I carry? I had other questions about how to best help and support my wife, son, family, and loved ones. And I was curious about my galactic lineage. Mostly, I wanted to be more loving as I wrote in this "reminder to self" years earlier:

> *Be filled with love...let it overflow.*
>
> *You are a fountainhead of love...do nothing to restrain this, to hold it back. Do not try and parcel out your love.*
>
> *Can you contain the air or the oceans? Why would you want to try?*
>
> *So let it be with your love---at all times, under all circumstances, love with the fullness of your being because that's who you are in the essence of your being, a creature of love. You are happiest when you are the most loving because, at those moments, you give expression to your being...Express yourself more fully!*

My session lasted over two hours and encompassed four distinct experiences. In order to travel between lives, a death had to occur. I remember reading about that but not thinking it through very well. This was not a peaceful transition surrounded by loved ones prior to entering the afterlife. I relived hiding in a dimly lit apothecary shop. An angry mob hunted me as a woman accused of witchcraft, and I was very much afraid. I guessed I was in my late twenties or early thirties. My past life experience then shifted to being tied to a stake looking out at an angry and fearful mob of townspeople.

Mercifully, I did not relive being killed.

I think I was burned. I'm sure the dying part was painful. Yet, as my soul left my body, I could see the crowd staring at me. My guide asked if there was anything I wanted to say to them. My answer was one of forgiveness. They didn't understand me; they feared me. I told them that I forgave and loved them. Even writing these words now and sharing this part of my journey fills me with a sense of affirmation. This is my higher self. My soul is filled with love, compassion, and forgiveness. This is how I want to be in this lifetime. My guide later explained to me that I chose this past-death experience to convey that message of love and forgiveness.

I entered a place of extraordinary peace and beauty. It reminded me of the scene in *The Wizard of Oz* when Dorothy first enters Oz—vivid colors and light that I can describe as psychedelic and very real. I traveled briefly until encountering egg-shaped shimmering light beings who welcomed me back. This was home; I'd been here before. These light-filled beings were my soul family, and they acknowledged it had been a difficult life that I had chosen, and that I had done well. I felt their loving presence, and part of me just wanted to hang out in this realm of peace, beauty, and love. But I had prepared questions for my council, and my journey needed to continue.

My earthly guide asked me to call my spirit guide. He looked Native American but wore a white tunic. His brown eyes conveyed joy and peace, and he had a sense of humor. I asked his name and telepathically heard Aeo, or something like that. I traveled to a large open room where light-consciousness beings lovingly waited for my questions. I think there were nine, but it could have been seven. I sensed male and female energies. Communication with them was telepathic. The primary individual I conversed with occasionally flashed into a form resembling a Greco-Roman man in a tunic or toga. He had curly, salt-pepper black hair and a beard. Mostly, he appeared as a light body in my awareness.

In answer to my questions about integrating my higher self into my current life, he and the council assured me that I should just keep doing what I am doing. I recited parts of the 'reminder to self' and kept getting affirmed that this was indeed all I needed to keep doing. Regarding my galactic lineage question, I specifically resonated with a Lyran origin.

They did the equivalent of laughing and told me I had many previous incarnations in different star systems. In retrospect, the question seems a little quaint to me. Does it matter? What experiences and lifetimes my soul has chosen are less important to me than embodying soul-filled presence in this current life I am now living. I am here for a reason and purpose. Again, in this third portion of my between lives soul regression, I am reminded of that purpose—to be loving.

My Q and A with the council included reassurances that I could travel to meet back with them and suggested during dreams and meditation.

Aeo then took me to the library. I'm unsure if this "place" was the Hall of Records, the Akashic Records, or elsewhere. The librarian appeared as a man with a bushy white beard and hair, wearing a white robe. I called him Samuel, one of his many names, and asked about my soul contract for this lifetime and whether I was fulfilling it. He laughed while communicating that I already knew the answer to the question. I began reciting from the memo to myself. Just keep doing what you are doing. Samuel gave me the opportunity to ask about other past or future lives, but I declined. The message, once again—be filled with love and express it. That's what I'm here to do. Reminding myself over and over gives this intention more power. Be more loving, Victor!

Aeo and my earthly guide brought me back. I had no difficulty rejoining my celestial soul to this physical form. I felt filled with peace and love, in addition to having a renewed desire to keep doing what I am doing, to keep trying to embody the divine essence within through meaningful presence.

There is clarity in having a sense of purpose that resonates with the core of your being. We are spiritual beings, and we are on a journey to discover that spirit within. When you are aligned with this true self, the day-to-day experiences of life—the content—occur in the context of something much bigger, much grander, and much more authentic. When you more fully integrate this true self into the body-mind, you achieve higher states of health and wellbeing. The word health shares roots with the words whole and holy. Our soul journey is one of rediscovering that wholeness, that holiness, and living it. Perhaps my between-lives foray into higher realms wasn't needed. My soul regression reminded me of things I already knew. Yet, these eternal truths are easy to forget, lose sight of, or be distracted from. I am grateful to remember this. We are light beings meant to love. Let your light shine.

Victor Acquista ~ A special thanks to Laurie Wheeler, who guided me on this journey.

One of Victor's Affirmations

Be all that you are...

A Scarab, a Phoenix, and a Serpent Walk into a Bar

By Allison Kenny

——— ⭐ ———

I wanted my sense of self restored as the vivacious, loving, kind, and beautiful woman I always was.

Allison Kenny (author, dancer)

By age 27, I had spent eight incredible years wandering Ireland, Wales, and London, guided by a tribe of beings from the spirit world. Together, we explored the mysteries of the natural world: the elements, ancient landscapes, and the depths of our souls.

During that time of growth and transformation, I was often pushed out of my comfort zone and challenged to see the world in new ways. My spirit tribe taught me to see beyond the surface of things and tap into my wisdom and intuition. But even as I reveled in the freedom and adventure of my nomadic existence, I felt a stirring in my soul.

But soon, I would wind up in the fate of Eros, losing my grasp of will and falling madly in love. I had experienced crushes on boys before and mind-altering infatuations. Still, I hadn't fallen in love like that before, where marriage was the only possibility because the covenant was already in our hearts.

I traveled blissfully to California as a giddy newlywed, ready to take on my new life on the West Coast. As a couple, we had already achieved the careers we'd worked so hard for, which also served our deepest convictions. We made good money, gave back through our work, and enjoyed spending time with friends and family. I often told my husband I had to pinch myself to ensure it wasn't all a dream.

It all seemed so perfect for a time, and then it unraveled into hell.

During the night, I found myself besieged by a dark and ominous sensation that my very essence was longing for something more, buried under the heavy burden of suppression. I was reluctant to confront it, dreading that doing so might shake the very foundations of my seemingly perfect life. Despite my attempts to ignore it, the yearning only intensified until it became too great to ignore. I was resolute in not wanting anything to disrupt my marital bliss, but destiny had other plans.

One night, I finally mustered the courage to look at the persistent image that kept beckoning me from my spiritual depths. Without a shadow of a doubt, I understood its meaning, and I could see a hole in my heart where my passion for becoming a dancer and performer had never been filled.

In the grips of despair, I lay in bed and whispered with brutal honesty, "I refuse to die like this." The desire to pursue my passion lay dormant for too long, hidden away for fear of judgment and possible rejection. Despite trepidation, I allowed myself to feel its true course through my body. The thought of lying on my deathbed, haunted by regret, was unbearable. Standing at the ethereal crossroads, I had to make a decision. With a sigh of release and apprehension, I thanked my Being for visiting me and vowed to fill the hole in my heart, no matter what it took.

And just like that, my marriage started to give way to cracks that may have always existed, but I hadn't noticed. The endless emotional battles caused physical damage to my brain and nervous system. I could feel and even hear electrical surges inside my brain as if the emotional volatility was causing lightning strikes inside me. I would hold the side of my head with so much fear and desperation as though a severing was happening between my brain's right and left hemispheres.

I was too afraid to tell anyone what happened for fear of sounding crazy. So, night after night, I'd call from the depths of my being to God for help. Eventually, I had a profound spiritual experience that arrived from my very bones and ultimately ushered me out of that situation and into the next chapter of my life.

Like a soul disembarking a metaphorical ferry crossing the Styx River, I stepped out onto the shores of San Francisco to begin again. Despite the novelty of my surroundings, I felt fragmented, wounded by the relentless criticism of my nature and femininity. Memories of injustice and oppression stirred in me a visceral response of anger and sorrow.

I was determined to find a way to reconnect with my sense of self. This was not only for me but for all women and our collective ancestors who had endured misogyny and devaluation. To be restored as the vivacious, loving, kind, and beautiful woman I always was.

My heart ached to be dancing, and I found solace there.

As I immersed myself in dance classes, my joy slowly returned.

Then one day, I summoned the courage to take a class I had always been too intimidated to try. The instructor was stunning, with a fiery and witchy aura that resonated with me. Her energy felt like a safe haven against misogyny I had encountered elsewhere, and I felt empowered in her presence.

Guided by her mastery of tribal-style belly dance, I learned to move my body in ways that awakened my primal feminine essence. Each rhythmic undulation of my spine tapped into my sensuality's dark, raw, and untamed nature. This created an enchantment as if I was my own snake charmer, luring myself into the shadowy depths of my soul.

Like stirring an inner cauldron, I aroused the powerful kundalini energy that lay coiled at the base of my spine. With each sinuous sway of my hips, flutter of my belly, and rise and fall of my chest, I invoked a serpentine magick. This allowed me to shed my old skin and emerge more vibrant and enlightened. The dance was my alchemy, my medicine, my ritual of rebirth.

And then, one night, I was drawn to a venue where the music was already in full swing, and the energy pulsed through the air. Despite being told they didn't need any more dancers, I couldn't resist the call of the beat. So, I adorned my sparkling Egyptian belly dance costume, hidden by a long heavy coat, and approached the manager, offering to belly dance for the audience and complete the show.

With the manager's approval, I felt my heart race as I shed my coat and stepped onto the stage. The live band began to play, and the crowd erupted with excitement as I began to dance. Lost in the movement, the energy, and the mystery of it all, I felt my spirit soar like the phoenix rising from the ashes. At that moment, I knew without a doubt that I had found my calling as a professional dancer, fulfilling my destiny and living my dream. The manager hired me on the spot with a signed contract!

As I continued to follow my path toward authenticity and fulfilling my dreams, I began teaching belly dance, too. It was then that I stumbled upon an old piece of paper with my life goals scribbled in pencil from my school days. And there it was, written in my own hand: "dance teacher." At that moment, I realized that I had fulfilled another long-held desire of my heart. Teaching belly dance brought me joy and allowed me to share its transformative power with others. It was a way to help them connect with their bodies and like the phoenix, rise up to find their own empowerment.

With this sense of completion, I took a walk among the Redwoods towering above me like ancient sentinels and suddenly became aware of a profound feeling of wholeness within me. It was as if all the fragmented parts of myself had been reunited. To my surprise, I realized that the sensation of the once-separated right and left hemispheres of my brain had been fused back together, restored in a state of balance.

I remembered reading that the ancient Egyptian mystery schools used the sacred symbol of the scarab to represent the delicate balance between the divine feminine and sacred masculine energies within oneself. The beetle's back, with its distinctive markings, resembled the brain's hemispheres. It correlated to those energies, and thus served as a guidepost on one's journey towards wholeness and inner harmony.

Gazing up at the Redwoods, I raised my chest towards the warm embrace of the Sun. Her gentle energy infused every cell of my being with radiant light and enveloped me in soothing warmth. With a deep breath, I invited fluidity and grace, extending my arms to begin the sacred movement code of snake arms. As I moved in perfect synchrony with the rhythm of nature, my heart chakra glowed with an emerald green aura, filling me with a sense of oneness and love. With that inner strength, I knew it was time to leave the city and embark on a new chapter of my life. The gift of belly dance would be with me on this journey, allowing me to create inner harmony and balance wherever I went.

Allison Kenny ~ *Thank you to him who shall not be named for ferrying me across to fulfill my soul's desire and to Jill Parker, my trail-blazing belly dance teacher, for believing in me.*

One of Allison's Personal Mantras

A body prayer is done with simple gestures
of your hands and arms:
Honoring Mother Earth, Honoring One Another,
Honoring the Divine, and Honoring Yourself.

The Warrior Spirit
Bold, Empowered, Authentic

By Eileen Bild

———— ★ ————

I was not too concerned about tomorrow because there were times when I was not sure tomorrow would come.

Eileen Bild (author, coach, host, Roku developer)

"You can do this!"

One, two, three, lunge. Again, one, two, three, lunge. My personal trainer pushed me to my limits, yet it was exactly what I needed. I was on a mission to be just like her. Well, maybe somewhat like her. She was built like a tank! Not sure I needed to build my muscles that big, but she sure was an inspiration for me.

I was on the road to finally being in tip-top shape, as I had always wanted to be. My husband and I worked out together five days a week, and I busted my butt with my personal trainer once a week. Six months into training, the results were very evident. Solid biceps, the beginnings of a four-pack stomach (which I have NEVER had before!), nice curves, smooth legs, you get the picture. To top it off, I was in my early 50s, so this was an extraordinary accomplishment.

Then my world as I knew it came to a halt!

I woke up one morning with searing hot pain in my left wrist, itching, and irritation to the bone—no idea what could be causing this. Finally, after a few doctor's visits and blood tests, we determined that a brown recluse spider had bitten me. The venom almost killed me, and I live to tell the tale.

This story is not about the arduous journey I have been on to get my health back; instead, I will take you on a trip of the warrior spirit within who has stepped forward for my emotional healing and personal strength.

Prior to the spider bite, I had already awakened to a new way of looking at life from a previous health challenge. I had a moment of "Not again!" thoughts, then quickly changed my focus to set the stage for coming through my current situation with confidence, courage, and clarity.

It is not easy by any means to overcome life's incredibly unfair events that can leave us bewildered, confused, and angry. Yes, I was angrier more than anything. Forget the symptoms. They were minor compared to the fact that this tiny, itsy, bitsy spider just ruined my life!

What happened next is nothing short of a miracle!

As I clung to my will to live and took each day as it came, I was not too concerned about tomorrow because there were times when I was not sure tomorrow would come; I knew somewhere deep within, I would survive. As a practicing meditator, this became my saving grace. Turning inward, deep breathing, seeking spiritual understanding, and breaking down the walls still present, something incredible began to happen.

I can look back now and see that the warrior within me was empowered. It was not so much about my healing but about becoming fully and totally myself authentically. Healing was just a byproduct.

I feel I was thrust into unknown territory as a test by the universe and maybe even from my higher self. Perhaps I needed to pay more attention to what I was being guided to do, and this experience was a wake-up call.

Regardless of why it happened, here I am. I had a choice, and it certainly was not to die. The deep dive into the recesses of the places within changed me from the inside out. Nothing happened overnight. It took days, months, and even years to unravel, re-learn, and integrate the warrior within the human.

Determination is my friend, and my husband supports me unconditionally with love, compassion, and an unwavering desire to be the best version of myself. Together we dance to the tune of the whisper within the winds of time. He knows my strength now more than ever, and just as my trainer before, he pushes me to and beyond my limits.

Was I tired? Hell yeah!
Did I want to give up? Yes indeed!

But that warrior spirit of mine would not give in or give up. Each day that passed, I was still alive, and it gave me hope. I still worked, did household duties, and put on a smile. As a result, I gained immense confidence, courage, undeniable clarity, and a better understanding of what I value in life.

Moving from wounded warrior to divine goddess was a life course shift. I stood at a crossroads, and I felt intense energy as I walked through the path beckoning me. I could not ignore it. So, I stepped courageously on the track, not looking back. There have been many lessons along the way, yet each one is just as important as the next. Every one of them is a testament to my warrior spirit infused within for the benefit of growth and transformation.

Each turning point has its own theme revealing itself in the minor backsteps, triggers that surface, and ahas showed me the success achieved so far.

My awareness has become acute, causing me to observe life and the people around me. There is no judgment, just listening. There is no fear, just understanding. There is no pain, just forward movement.

My dreams are excellent indicators of unresolved dialog within myself and/or external circumstances requiring resolution. In addition, my continued meditations give insight into what I may not be seeing, what I have yet to see, and what I may be misunderstanding.

A bond exists between me, my warrior spirit, and the universe. Together, as a trilogy, we ebb and flow to the heartbeat of humanity, the mental part of the universe, and the invisible spirit in everything.

Miracles occur daily, and I feel blessed to experience the magnificence of these nuggets gifted to me.

In 2020, when the world shut down, it catapulted me even further into solidifying my warrior spirit. I had to make another choice about what steps to take to rise above the distractions of the world outside. A pivot was made, and a new vision was formed with a mission to be a strong leader for those with a dream.

My confidence and courage were now integral to whom I had become, and I am still evolving. The clarity of my life's work, and my passion was undeniable. Developing relationships became the building block for the new direction. This, in turn, expanded my ability to grow both personally and professionally.

Although some have found it difficult to accept the changes in me, they have learned to appreciate them over time. The respect gained is liberating for both me and the others. Conversations are now a harmonious give and take, with everyone leaving the exchange on a high. There is a spark that carries on into the future. It can't get much better than this!

Entwined within the tapestry of a life lived to the fullest is the heart that beats to the rhythm cry of the warrior. The descent into the darkness is the very thing that catalyzes a return to the light, our truths, and our strengths. There is an ascent and rebirth into personal empowerment. Through the pain of loss rises the joy of living. New perspectives, forged through the inner compass guided by the warrior spirit, are etched into the sands of time. As I slowed down to pay attention to what my body and spirit needed and the unfolding of the impermanence of each moment, I discovered there was more to who I was.

**I began to see my reflection,
the mirror version of the self.**

There is graceful strength that invites others to experience the world as I do. To focus on the good, all things positive, and allow for that which wants to offer me a helping hand to guide me through this process.

I sit in nature, nurturing my soul with the fresh smell of the morning air. Sometimes, an owl calls out, the sun is not quite peaking over the horizon, and I can feel a stillness that brings peace and serenity. Each new day reminds me of how far I have come, the road ahead not traveled; therefore, I am the creator of my continued journey.

My connection to others has become more sacred and meaningful. The quest to heal has turned into my warrior spirit, nourishing those aspects of me that are meant to be expressed. In conversations, I am calm, and decisions are made easily and clearly. I embrace living fearlessly and feel rejuvenated once again.

I am not done. There is much more to learn and more to accomplish. New people coming into my life offer insights into the magnetism of what I think and believe, bringing the same back to me. There is an incredible wealth of knowledge available to digest, sort out and apply to life experiences.

With my husband by my side, family, and friends supporting me, I know I can achieve the impossible. The goal is to balance mind, body, and spirit with healing and become better than before. When this is accomplished, my world will be extraordinarily bright.

There is a unique combination of wisdom and a warrior's strength; the alchemy of a higher truth revealed, ancient knowledge remembered, and the courage to act, protect, and stand up for the authentic self in the face of adversity.

The emerging warrior spirit brings integration and balance to disharmony, commanding respect because she has descended into the darkness and surrendered to a higher light. A wholeness develops, bringing about a fresh, untouched renewal. She is determined, focused, ambitious, assertive, goal-oriented, and self-sufficient, causing an aura of assuredness.

I cannot know what
Tomorrow may bring,
Today is all I have.

Encounters with surprise.
Outcomes, can leave me.
Facing new directions.

Gratitude opens the gates
Into the garden of red roses,
The symbol of a loving heart.

Things may not be as they seem,
I am but a spec in the greater
Cosmic overture.

Eternal soul, everlasting.
Transcend duality living fully.
The inner voice my guide.

Music to my ears
Are the sounds of cheers
And celebrations of today.

Standing at the water's edge
A beckoning to close my eyes,
Head tilt back and full surrender.

The warrior spirit has been released,
Fly high
The wind under my wings
Carrying me into the
Ever expansiveness of what
Is yet to come.

Eileen Bild ~ *I am so grateful for the support I have had in my life's journey. I want to thank my husband, Trevor Bild, incredible friends, and loving family! Namaste.*

One of Eileen's Personal Quotes

*Fear is only a mask in front of something
greater to step into.*

From a Ball of Clay to a Work of Art

*An Illustration of Transformation
Through the Potter's Hands*

By Teresa Velardi

———— ★ ————

*Some of us are in the kiln, screaming,
"Let me out of here; it's too hot!"*

Teresa Velardi (publisher, host)

*H*ave you ever wondered how a beautiful piece of pottery came to be on the shelf in the gallery? It's a process, sometimes painful, especially when considering it an illustration of life.

Those who know me know that one of my passions and gifts is making pottery. It's a gift God graced me with, and I have experienced great joy during the many hours I have spent at the potter's wheel.

I have learned, though, that God is the Potter, and we are the clay. He is the creator of all things, including me, and the process of pottery making is a wonderful illustration.

There are many steps to be taken in the process of transforming a ball of clay into a beautiful work of art. You may be saying, "Yeah, so what does this have to do with me?"

Prepare the Clay

This process is called wedging and is like kneading stiff dough. Wedging removes any air bubbles in the clay as it gets pounded, pushed, twisted, and manipulated into a ball that will go onto the potter's wheel and to the next phase.

The clay must be made ready for its transformational journey. Any time I plan to change, such as eating more healthily, I have to prepare. Throughout the years, I've heard many people say, "Plan your work and work your plan." And "If you fail to plan, you plan to fail." Sometimes just thinking about the cold hard truth of those two statements makes me cringe.

In my head, I hear things like, "What do you mean I have to throw out the cookies, candy, and ice cream? Can't I just eat it all and start tomorrow?" Or how about the things my grandmother used to say that make me feel guilty about throwing food away? "Do you have any idea how many children are starving in India who can use that food you're just throwing away?" "Do you know how much money you're throwing away?" "Do you know how much that food cost?" "Just eat it… you'll feel better!" Ughhhh…

Center

The clay gets forcefully dropped onto the wheel so it will stick. Then, while the wheel is spinning very fast, the potter pushes the clay toward the center of the wheel. It is centered when there is no "wobble" in the clay. To make that happen, the potter's hands must be still until the clay feels smooth and almost looks like it's standing still when perfectly centered.

Forcefully? Really? Yes, really… every time I step on the scale, I'm forced to wrap my head around the number staring back at me. My head spins just thinking about what I have done to my once slender body. That slim body was alive and well a long time ago in what seems like a galaxy far, far away! Getting the wobble out of this "clay" will take more than some force.

The process of centering takes focus. It's getting still in the process of deciding what you want, so you will know the next steps to take in taking care of yourself. I tend to take care of everyone else before I take care of myself, especially when someone I know and love is in a crisis. What's even more "remarkable" is this: whenever I've needed a helping hand or when I'm in crisis, those whom I've helped seem to be nowhere to be found. Interesting.

Getting quiet through prayer and meditation helps me to focus and get centered.

Open

After centering, with the wheel still spinning very fast, the potter opens a hole in the center of the clay. Using both hands, the potter moves the clay outwardly to define the inside and outside, preparing for the next step.

Opening the clay brings definition. Okay, so how do you define what is inside and outside? When I look at a bowl, a vase, or even a box, I see the difference. But when it comes to defining who we are, inside and out, that's a much more challenging task.

Most of us tend to get confused by all the chatter in our heads, in the news, on the front page, or on social media. The voices of so many others tell us who we are, what we are, where we belong, or how to be in any given situation that we forget who we are.

Be open to learning who you were created to be. I've often heard that once you know who you are on the inside, the outside will take care of itself.

Mold and Shape

With one hand inside and the other outside, the potter "pulls" the clay upward, pushing with fingers both inside and outside, causing the clay to grow taller or wider, molding and shaping the clay into the desired vessel shape.

Once shaped to the potter's satisfaction, the piece is set aside to dry slightly.

Each step needs the one before it to ensure the pot is strong. The potter is ever so careful in the molding and shaping while relying on the decisions made in the opening.

With an ever-so-gentle touch, the potter moves the clay while carefully examining the effects of each motion and the pressure applied while determining the final shape of the work. Once satisfied with the form, the pot is set aside to dry a little.

Interestingly, I tend to beat myself up in ways that hinder my well-being. When it comes to molding and shaping my life, gentle seems to be taken out of my vocabulary. Whether we are talking about food choices, getting some movement into my day, or simply taking time for myself to do something I enjoy, like making pottery, I find ways to exclude myself from the long list of "priorities" in my life.

I'll take a lesson in "being" from the vessel on the shelf, just waiting for the next step in the process, and be gentle with myself.

Trim

Once the piece is leather-hard, it is turned upside down and re-centered on the wheel, and the potter will trim away any excess clay from the bottom. While the wheel turns, the potter uses sharp tools to trim away whatever is seen as excess.

The bottom of the pot is trimmed to create a foot it will stand on. Any excess clay left at the bottom while the potter molded and shaped will be removed.

With the trimming completed and any design elements gently carved into the leather like clay, the potter marks the piece with an identifying symbol or signature, claiming it as His creation, and sets it aside to dry thoroughly.

This part of the process begs the question: Who and What can I trim from my life? What is literally weighing me down? The "who" is getting easier as I learn to weed out the naysayers and unsupportive people in my life. You know the ones I'm talking about. We all have at least one person in our lives who needs to get the proverbial boot! And in the same light, I have to ask myself, who am I allowing into my world? Whether I'm talking about friends or those I do business with, I have to take inventory of the energy vampires and time-sucking people in my world. Every one of them is a testament to the process of letting go.

The "what" is another story. There are lots of things and tasks I can trim down. Another inventory is appropriate. Releasing things I don't need has recently made it to the very top of my list. Seriously, how many books do I really need in my library? How many do I actually read? Oh yes, the intention was there when I bought each one of many, but honestly, there are only so many hours in a day.

Learning to say "NO" (and yes, it is a full sentence) is just as important as learning to let go.

Into the fire (purification of the clay)

Once completely dry, pieces are placed into the kiln to be "fired." During firing, impurities are burned out of the clay, and the pottery is made strong while being exposed to extreme heat.

Oh, the extreme heat I have experienced in my life! You too? Why am I not surprised? I've faced many "fires" and come through them stronger than before I entered the fire. Being IN the fire is a different story. I can't tell you the kicking and screaming I've done! And the begging for whatever I was going through to stop or begging for something to change, including the number on the scale or the bloodwork results, and all the while asking myself what I could have done differently and playing the blame game in silent suffering.

Feeling out of control and being at the mercy of the "fire" is definitely not where I want to be, but I've learned that there is strength in the fire. Better choices and a sense of accomplishment come from the fire.

Once the kiln cools, the pieces are moved to the next step.

Glazing

After the firing, the pot is dusted off, and the potter now has a "blank canvas" to add color and design.

A glaze is a scientifically formulated mixture of elements and pigments from the earth that bring color to the work once it goes through the second firing. (Yes, another one!)

Glaze can be applied by dipping, brushing, spattering, and many other ways, depending on the look the potter wishes to achieve.

Each piece is unique and carefully thought out, just like you! We were all created with a unique look, on purpose, and for a purpose. Likewise, each piece of pottery has a purpose, and the potter gets to choose the colors and how they will be applied to the pottery.

No matter what, each piece is unique, beautiful, and deeply loved by the Creator.

Into the fire (beautification)

Yes, again!

Once the glaze has dried, it's time to go back into the kiln. This time it's even hotter than the first. The glaze fuses with the pot, and the heat creates a chemical reaction causing the color to come alive during the firing, creating the finished look.

I call this the "beautification" fire.

Trust me; there's a lot of noise in this firing too. Mostly complaining, but in the end, it's worth it. If you looked in the mirror when you were just a ball of clay and then looked at yourself after the beautification fire, you wouldn't believe the difference.

You are strong, confident, beautifully dressed in your favorite colors, and ready to face the world! So go ahead… show off a little!

It's showtime!

Many times, potters will show their work in galleries. It's a special event when people gather to look at all kinds of beautiful art.

Each piece is different and carries a beauty like no other. We are all different and all inspired by the creator to not just look good but to do good for ourselves and for others with purpose.

So there you have it, the ball of clay, with the touch of the potter's hands, has become a beautiful work of art.

This process is also a metaphor for our lives.

Some of us are in the kiln, screaming, "Let me out of here; it's too hot!"

Others are spinning around, not knowing where they are, what to do, or how to stop what's happening.

While we wonder how to stop the spinning or get out of the fire, God is there. He's the potter. He watches over us through every step of our lives, even when we think He's absent.

We've got to trust Him. Every decision we make affects our lives. Trying times, provided that we face and endure them rather than running away, build character and make us stronger, better people.

God has a reason for creating you and a plan for your life.

"For I know the plans I have for you," declares the Lord,
"plans to prosper you and not to harm you,
plans to give you hope and a future."

Jeremiah 29:11

He's also there with us when we are in the fire, protecting us from harm and helping us through it. Ask me how I know this. There's something about the fire!

He was in the fire with Shadrach, Meshach, and Abednego in the book of Daniel. (Daniel 3:16-28)

He wants us to seek Him and trust Him.

Draw close to God, for He is the potter, and we are the clay.

Teresa Velardi ~ *For all those who are looking for a purpose and a path. It's already in the clay searching for you, and ready for the Potter's hands. Find Him and your adventure comes alive!*

One of Teresa's Favorite Quotes:

"For I know the plans I have for you," declares the Lord,
"plans to prosper you and not to harm you, plans to give you
hope and a future."

Jeremiah 29:11

Starved My Mind To Save My Soul

By Andy Vargo

*I've spent the last seventeen months searching for something
I could not find for the previous forty years.*

Andy Vargo (author, speaker, comedian)

*T*ent, sleeping bag, pillow. That's all I need. Oh, and maybe some food. I should definitely take some food. I don't know where I am going, but I have to get away.

I've been on a journey to find myself, yet the harder I look, the more lost I feel. Last year, I jumped. I leapt off the cliff of comfort and changed everything. That was the night I told my wife of twenty years that I was gay.

I know what you're thinking. *Ouch!* But we were not in a happy marriage. Things had been trailing off for years for reasons beyond just my gayness. Though it definitely kept me from bringing my best self into the marriage. Even more, it held me back from demanding the respect I deserved in a relationship.

I did not see it so clearly at the time, but our marriage was toxic. I would like to believe we were two good people who, individually, had great traits, but together brought out the worst in each other. Like bleach and ammonia, which have great qualities apart, but when combined, we were lethal.

I had to separate. I had to save myself.

But the next year and a half would be hell. Sure, it sounds great to finally be yourself, and not question what people will think of you. To just go out into the world without hiding under the trench coat of pretense. To experience life like never before, free.

Free from the expectations of those around me. Whether spoken or created in my own mind. Free from the fear of being outed, from my darkest secret crushing the world I had created. Free from the pressure to not let everyone down. Free from the need to pretend, fit in, and be like everyone else, if such a thing exists.

But it's not that easy. You still question yourself. No one talks about how bad you feel for the lives you've changed. Everything that defined me seems ripped out of my hands. No longer a husband. Not feeling adequate as a father. Not knowing who my friends are anymore. Everything is left in question.

Even my career is shot, having been fired three weeks after coming out. They said I was not keeping up, then hired three people to replace the territory I was covering alone. So maybe, looking back, my not keeping up was understandable. But I don't care. I am glad to be free.

But what does it mean to be free?

I've spent the last seventeen months searching for something I could not find for the previous forty years. I thought I would find it the night I broke my silence. Since that night, I've had seventy-eight weeks of heartache, wrestling with hope, leaving me exhausted, wondering which one will win in the end. Heartache or hope? I still don't know.

Which brings me back to where we started, a sleeping bag, a tent, a pillow, some food, and most of all, an open road. An open road and the chance to find myself somewhere along the way.

It's time to reset. To tune out the things that influence my thoughts. My rules are simple, no outside influence. No alcohol. No movies. No listening to music with lyrics. No social media. In fact, no getting online in any form. Just me and my mind.

I have to starve my mind.

I have to stop letting it fill with the crap that I have been feeding it. The things I think will make me happy are only distractions hiding future let-downs. I have to starve my mind to nourish my soul.

I decide to leave and find a place to settle for a few days off the grid. I don't know what I want other than peace, quiet, and the chance to get alone with my thoughts.

My drive begins in loud silence, competing with the thoughts racing through my mind. Nobody prepares you for your grief during a major life change, even one you thought you wanted. Your fondest memories turn against you, stabbing your heart as a reminder of what you no longer have.

Two hours into the drive, I see the perfect campground. It's got hills, forests, and beaches. And best of all, I have never been here. No painful memories to wrestle with. Now that I've found a place, I can try to find myself.

Tent, sleeping bag, pillow. I am all set up. I have never camped this simply in my life. But that's the point. I am not here to be distracted by card games and snacks. I am here for the ultimate search and rescue.

The first night goes by so slowly. I walk down the trail from my site in the upper campground down the cliffside to check out the beach below. It's the end of a sunny day. The blue skies and white clouds trade places with bright pinks, purples, and oranges as the sun sets over the water.

The families who littered the sand earlier have made their way back in for the night, leaving the beach wide open for me, my thoughts, and the few couples who have found logs to snuggle on as the sun fades into the sea.

Me and my thoughts. I wish I had better company.

I wish they would just shut up sometimes. Immediately the same questions flood my mind. I have been haunted by the same questions for the thirteen thousand hours over the last seventeen months. The worst of all is the big one: What was the point?

What was the point? I have asked myself this every day since I came out. If I did it to be happy, then I failed. My kids hate me; at least, this is the story I tell myself. My finances are ruined. The moments of happiness from my adventures fade as soon as I walk through the door at home and am left alone with my thoughts. The one man I've dated long enough to call a boyfriend doesn't bring the comfort I expected to have when I finally found the one. Maybe he's not the one. Or maybe he is, but I can't expect him to be the solution. Maybe I'm just not ready yet.

What was the point? Life is definitely not any better than before I threw myself off the cliff. It's definitely not any easier, that's for sure. But I can't go back. Honestly, I don't think I really want to go back anyway. But can I go forward? What is there to go forward to?

What's the point? I am left with this question lingering as I am surrounded by darkness as the sounds of the waves splashing on the shore slap in rhythm with the recurring question. The same sound, over and over again, yet so relaxing and peaceful. Not annoying like a heavy-breather sitting next to you while you are trying to read. Soft, slow, repetitive, relaxing. Soothing my mind as I grapple with the question.

The next morning I awoke to the gentle light of sunshine cracking through the trees and tickling the top of my tent. I don't remember the walk back up the hill from the beach or falling asleep the night before. But I feel somewhat at peace after a long sleep in the fresh sea air. I don't know where today will take me, but I am a bit more relaxed.

Fixing my coffee and having a couple of the boiled eggs I packed for breakfast, I am tempted by the urge to check in online. To see what is happening in the world. It doesn't matter. But it's the distraction I have taught myself to use instead of focusing on myself. I resist the urge to get my phone out of the car.

I need to get my thoughts on paper. Feeling it's the only way to sort them out. I grab my pen and notebook, and of course, a snack, then start working my way back to the beach. My log was available from last night. It's just far enough away from the parking and camping areas that the families aren't crowded around it. I can sit with the waves once more and let them dance with my thoughts.

Day one is long. I sit for hours waiting for the words to come, but they are trapped in my head, locked behind the doorway of fears I am too afraid to unlock. They stay safe behind the door. What's the point? If I don't answer the question, I will never have to be responsible for making it happen. I want to keep that door locked.

I'm tempted to open the door, but it's too scary.

Tears stream down my face as loss and loneliness take over. I sit with them, for I have no one else to sit with. Time seems frozen during their visit. I cannot say how long we sat on that log together, but it was long enough to reminisce and know we could part on decent terms.

At dusk, I treated myself to a burger and a cold lemonade from the food stand by the parking area. It's the most basic burger yet the most delicious I have ever had. Day one comes to a close as I sit alone on a rickety picnic table, eating my burger and watching the families laugh their way back to their sites to light fires and have s'mores. For some reason, it doesn't sting so much. I don't know why.

Back at camp, I lit a fire of my own while I sat with more welcoming company than my companions earlier in the day. The fire brings peace and contentment as it pulls my focus away from the darkness around me, enticing me with the waltzing flames of light before me.

I wonder how much time I have spent focusing on the darkness in my life, ignoring the light begging for my attention. I sit with the flames and feel the warmth landing on my body, soaking into my heart as the night continues.

Day two starts the same as day one, the gentle alarm clock of nature easing me into an even more peaceful morning. I feel more at peace as this day starts. I don't feel the urge to get my phone out of the car. The big question isn't the first thing that comes to mind. Knowing what the point is no longer seems quite as important.

I head down to the beach. I am in no hurry now. I am here to enjoy as much of this time away as possible before I have to return to the responsibilities waiting for me back home.

I find my log once more. Today grief and loss do not come to visit, but rather peace and contentment sit with me as I watch the families play, and the ships pass by. A thought comes to mind: I feel okay.

I can do whatever I want. I can walk in any direction I please. I can experience whatever I want. Maybe that is enough. For the first time ever, I feel free.

Finally, I have an answer to the question: What's the point?

To live. To choose. To experience.

As I sit on the beach with my answer and a new sense of freedom, I decide that I have the choice to define happiness however I want, and that is the point of it all.

Andy Vargo ~ *To those who knew me before I knew myself and to the rest whom I have found along the way, I dedicate this part of my journey to you.*

One of Andy's Favorite Quotes

Two roads diverged in a wood, and I—
I took the one less traveled by,
And that has made all the difference.

Robert Frost

SPIRIT Commentary

By Coach Peggy & Dr. Markus

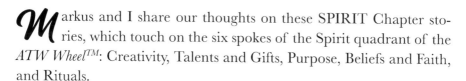

*M*arkus and I share our thoughts on these SPIRIT Chapter stories, which touch on the six spokes of the Spirit quadrant of the *ATW Wheel*^{TM}: Creativity, Talents and Gifts, Purpose, Beliefs and Faith, and Rituals.

Lara, you get it. Sharing your personal and professional career experiences teach us how vital it is to find harmony. Presto! Giving creates heartfelt happiness in us. However, certain types of giving may lack a return. Therefore, it is of utmost importance for us to extend this giving to ourselves occasionally. A massage appointment may hit the spot "to recharge the battery." Otherwise, we burn out. Lara's story taught us that you can keep moving on your path even with a low battery; just recharge a bit.

Mark shares an awe-inspiring story about self-development. By living in the now, his heart, mind, and spirit are synchronized; great place to be. His inquisitiveness and drive to find his own answers are inspiring and motivating. Your life experience is admirable, and your story was very captivating. You will affect many lives with this one!

Soul regression is a relatively new topic to us. There are similarities to guided, psychedelic-assisted therapy. Victor's experience showed us that with a willingness to trust the process and learn different aspects of being, there is a possibility of acceptance, stress resilience, and room for living a heart-centered life, oh, and without using drugs. Victor is one of the leaders in this field, and we are grateful for his contribution.

It is refreshing to read what happens if we align with our blueprint. Heartfelt desires, if followed, can lead to the deconstruction of our programmed life. But in return, we enjoy unfolding a life in happiness. If only we can muster the strength to unshackle ourselves from the programs. Thank you, Allison, for showing us the way.

Eileen, your story hits home. Just like your bite, medical emergencies can surprise us. They can stop us in our tracks and be overwhelming and discouraging. You show us that mindset not only makes a difference in coping, but likely makes a difference in the speed of recovery and overall outcome. Your focus and determination are to be commended. [Markus: *Thank you, Eileen, for this deep insight. As a scientist, male contributor, I find my warrior to aim at ground zero. The place between all things positive and negative is zero. Neutrality opens the portal to everything = cosmic consciousness. The heart is the portal. A war led from the heart is always won as it is connected to, thus fueled, and guided by, the causal realm, or God, or whichever you prefer to call … .*]

Teresa, you are a talented potter, and you have shown us that the steps to create a piece of beautiful pottery relate to the process of improving our health and wellness.

Andy, living a heart-centered life and following your own path is beyond admirable. It is never too late to be our natural selves. You teach us that beautifully. Your painting with words made us feel like we were sitting next to you on the log as you drained those tears onto paper. You also teach us that laughing at ourselves is good medicine as long as self-deprecation isn't the driver. We are very proud of you. Your story will genuinely change and SAVE lives!

MIND CHAPTER STORIES

———— ★ ————

Success is the ability to go from one failure
to another with no loss of enthusiasm.

Winston Churchill

Happiness Affects the Bottom Line

by Peggy Willms

— ★ —

Shoving behavior change down people's throats
doesn't work – especially AT work.

Peggy Willms
(author, host, coach, motivational speaker)

*D*o you love your job? Enjoying what you do and with whom you do it directly affects your physical and financial health. Unfortunately, companies have lost sight of their role in making you healthy and happy, especially at work! Hear me, employers, you have more power than you know when changing the course of disdain and sadness in this world. Now smarten up!

We are born to seek happiness and joy. Literally. If babies don't like how they feel or what they are being asked to do, they express their feelings by wailing or physically tossing about in temper tantrums. Obviously, these responses are not adequate coping mechanisms when we transition into adulthood. Therefore, emotions become bottled up, causing us to become unhealthy and joy depleted.

The pressure to select your career begins years before ordering your cap and gown for high school graduation. By age ten, many of us have already been asked this question dozens of times, "What do you want to do when you grow up?" Venturing out into the world feels like being thrown into a pack of wolves.

Social rank and financial independence press up against our simple childhood desires to seek professions that feel meaningful and create joy.

Many parents and mentors encourage jobs that "make money" – doctor, lawyer, or engineer or suggest we consider jobs with security such as a firefighter, cop, or teacher. But you might have heard, "Writing, painting, and playing guitar won't pay the rent!"

In my experience coaching and training people for over half my life, a tiny percentage of the population loves what they do professionally. Punching time clocks and "surviving" the workweek becomes dreadfully mundane and is far too familiar. I know for a fact that workplace joy, or lack of it, affects every single aspect of a person's life and affects all of us! Whether you work for someone or not, you are directly affected by whether someone is happy at work. That grumpy customer service rep, your son who drinks too much, or the road rager who just cut you off on Highway 75 is probably unhappy at work. Sounds crazy, right?

Like many of you, I have earned a paycheck since my mid-teens. I learned early on how to play by the rules. I never had to be told, "This is the job you applied for, do it, and you will get paid." This is not to say I didn't push the envelope. In most of my positions, I found myself in a supervisor's office suggesting efficiencies or asking to develop new projects. My desire to improve employee and customer satisfaction or to improve the company's bottom line fueled my passion. One hundred percent of the time, I was heard and, at minimum, permitted baby steps. The pace was often frustrating, but every step of the way, I have been blessed to love almost all of my jobs. Knowing my purpose early on gave me a jump in the game. My purpose led me to seek employment I aligned with, and the outcome has been job satisfaction.

In my early 20s, I became aware of the "job satisfaction" concept though the term wasn't mainstream. Then, the "wellness movement" began softly pushing prevention at work, not just at physician offices. Increased activity, healthy nutrition, and stress management appeared on meeting agendas. Wellness Committees were formed to promote fun challenges, self-awareness education, and self-assessment tools were developed. Playing a role in this movement gave me life.

Employees who reported and improved their personal health data, such as weight, blood pressure, and cholesterol markers, were rewarded.

New habits were created in the workplace, resulting in dramatically positive results. However, over time, the light-hearted approach of "let's get healthy and happy at work" evolved into using a heavier hand—financial dings. Whenever your personal health data or the aggregate health expenditure of your company were unfavorable, or when you did not report your attendance at the gym or daily step counts, your wallet suffered. Resulting in a rise in health insurance premiums.

Your personal health information was assessed based on the statistical norms of your coworkers, and if you fell outside the "healthy" zone, your premiums jumped. Yes, companies who paid for your insurance could request aggregate medical claims and diagnoses that drove big spending. Living through the pre-HIPPA era was quite a ride.

In 1996, HIPAA (Healthcare Insurance Portability and Accountability Act, HIPAA) was signed into law.[1] Between 2003-2005, Protected Health Information (PHI) hit the managed healthcare world hard. I spent half of my corporate career working for a managed healthcare company. I held a wellness coordinator role during this time and was a HIPPA and physician utilization analyst. Interesting combo. When PHI arrived, it sent a loud message—no one has legal access to your medical data, and corporations listened as the fines were astronomical if you didn't play by the rules. This affected corporate wellness. Companies were forced to care about their employees' health.

As employees gained power, they refused to share personal medical information with employers, allowing those in the wellness lane to be heard. And I jumped for joy. Finally, employers would understand that the most effective way to maintain healthcare costs would be to listen to their employees and help them find happiness. I thought they would listen to and respect those who kept their business's doors open. It seems so simple to me; figure out why someone wants to work for YOU and why they would want to stay. Frowns will be turned upside down, and creativity will catapult.

Shoving behavior change down people's throats doesn't work—especially at work. Sure, we feel better when our weight, blood pressure, and cholesterol numbers are within normal limits, but physical health doesn't always drive happiness. I chose this approach: "If you seek a robust bottom line, don't focus on the data you can no longer access Respect and listen to your staff because those stress-reduction lunch and learn classes and your push to make them walk 10,000 steps a day are not enough to stop your unhappy employees from whining or throwing temper tantrums. And if they don't like working for you, they will leave!"

By 2005, the dozens of employer groups I served revamped their recruitment and sustainability campaigns. Television commercials and print advertisements spoke loud and clear. "Our employees are healthier because they are happy." This approach, as you can guess, lit my fire. Gone was the day when individuals flocked to businesses because they had hearty benefits packages. They wanted the job because they would be treated with respect and dignity as if they were stockholders or as if they, too, were swinging around leather chairs in the boardroom. Back then, employers and employees were a team. If employers cared, employees cared. And when people care, they are happier. And when they are happier, they are healthier. DUH!

The term job satisfaction continued to spread like wildfire, which was a more mature way of addressing our childhood; how do we prevent employees from complaining and throwing tantrums? Ask. Listen. Act. "Do you like what you are doing and want to do more of it? If not, how can we change that?" As the middle management problem solver, I spent years trying to keep the peace. I would race upstairs to explain to execs why their employees were unhealthy and pissed off. Then, I would run back downstairs to share with employees why management made insensitive decisions that lacked common sense. I became hopeful that they would understand each other. Improved job satisfaction reduced my head spinning. After all, it was daunting and heartbreaking explaining to staff why twenty people were laid off before the holiday or why we could no longer have payday pizza parties.

Job satisfaction affects health. Period.

Job satisfaction is a direct correlation to a sense of purpose. I am sure you remember the conversation between a janitor and President John F.

Kennedy. During JFK's visit to NASA, he stopped a janitor in the hallway and asked him what he was doing. The janitor replied, "I am helping put the man on the moon." Believe it or not, all employees matter! But empathy and respect have to start from the top. Janitors, hotel maids, or someone who throws your weekly garbage in a stinky truck needs to feel valued and heard.

Liking, loving, or hating your job affects relationships and the world. Being happy at work affects the healthcare system and improves the dance we all play in government policy. When we are happier, we are healthier, and the world turns on its intended joyous axis. Why is this so difficult to understand?

During the good old days, my fingers got busy developing anonymous, aggregate survey tools that armed me with more than enough information on improving workplace happiness. Time and time again, the more management listened to its employees, creativity improved, attendance and retention numbers became unprecedented, and the bottom line stayed in the black. We were on our way. Or were we?

WHAT HAPPENED? Who is to blame?
Why have most people lost joy at work?

So many things…politics, employer policy changes, the environment, mental health, the pandemic, and so much more have shifted our joy at home and especially at work. I won't go into these things individually. I will keep it simple, which is probably why it continues to be ignored. It is too simple! Joy results from the masses identifying one goal…taking one path…agreeing on one mission. And that is, we must have the desire to play well together. There is no place for ulterior motives regarding happiness and joy. You either want to live happier and share it, or you don't. Perhaps asking, listening, and acting are too simple.

Strikes, mass exodus, and even mental health issues will continue if we do not address workplace happiness. Conversely, isolation, anger, and or depression can be improved if the world's employers gave a hoot.

Like most things, improving anything takes time and must remain consistent. Unfortunately, the day may not come when eight billion people wake up and say, "That is it. We are all a ball of joy from this day forth." We are human, and this isn't Whoville. However, we can either live in collective misery or prepare the troops for battle.

Employers, do you want happy employees?

For those who sign paychecks, I suspect you did not intend to create a hostile, despondent, and contemptuous work environment. But it is more common than not. You can make a massive and expedient shift towards happiness and improve the world's health! Swing that pendulum.

Based on 2021 labor data, about 167 million people worked in the U.S. Over 50% of our citizens and 81% worked full-time.[2] What a shift employers could make towards happiness, especially with nearly 3.5 billion working around the globe.[3]

I am not saying everyone is miserable at work or hates their job. Conversely, I am not saying every worldly problem would be solved with job satisfaction. I am simply sharing my experience of the rise and fall of our work environment. Today, we are lucky to find individuals who want to work at all. Desire and purpose have fizzled. Can we do something about it, or should we wither away in a corner and give up? We all know the answer. We must remain steadfast. Every person needs to take responsibility, especially if they have the power to make and sustain change. Starting at work would blow the joy factor to infinity and beyond.

I left the corporate world in 2016. Why? I was no longer satisfied and happy. I chose to ride off into the sunset and do my own thing. I was grateful my lengthy career had evolved over the years, allowing me to gather the education and experience I needed to go solo. My direction was clear. Moving to warmer weather and reaching more people by coaching virtually, conducting wellness retreats, radio, and more was a natural progression. My satisfaction with my last employer declined, and

I could no longer watch the mudslide. It was like watching an armored tank being thrown in reverse from the top of a large mountain. The leadership was aware, yet little was done about it. The company's vision became obscured because it ignored its "soldiers." Though they held the pot of gold, management barely noticed their troops fleeing base camp and no longer supporting their mission.

Resignations occurred at an alarming rate. I watched joy arrive and then sadness or even hatred walk out the door. I fell to my knees in defeat and anger. I had been a part of making people healthier and happier just to witness their white flags of surrender flail. It was too heartbreaking to continue as my magic wand, which once wielded enough power to make a change, was now empty. My cries to "abort the mission" fell upon deaf ears.

But this is not a story of retreat or forfeiture. It is about continuing the fight and taking personal responsibility. Becoming mindset masters and continually seeking joy in the work environment is crucial. There is a beam of light shining on all of us. It is called hope!

Ask. Listen. Act.

I still believe workplace wellness is critical and possible. Unfortunately, most people still work 50-60 hours a week for companies where they don't even want to clock in. As a result, many employees are not praised for their creativity. Instead, they are expected to show up with a smile, get more done than is humanly possible, and hit the repeat button the next day. Employers, you can do it. We can do it.

Employers take responsibility and spawn motivation. It would be remiss for me to acknowledge that there are kick-ass employers out there who get this message. I beg you to shine a light on how you value your workers! Help us out! Tell the world what works for you; share the love!

As they say, if you want tomorrow to look different than yesterday, you must change today. Start with positive shop talk. Turn negative language into laughter. Become the head cheerleader. Find a support system in your home away from home. Alternatively, it may just take a change of employment or career.

The bottom line, build happiness wherever you go, and ultimately it will follow you.

One of Peggy's Favorite Quotes

I guess we all like to be recognized
not for one piece of firework,
but for the ledger of our daily work.

Neil Armstrong

Exceed Expectations Every Day

By Marshall Townsend II

We need to go the extra mile, give more, carry more,
be more, and always exceed expectations.

Marshall Townsend II
(author, veteran, executive coach)

There was something in the tone of his voice when I heard the call for a Medivac on the radio. It had a sense of desperation, a sense of urgency. My only thought was, "This can't be good...."

It was 1985, and I was stationed at Fort Knox, Kentucky, as a tactics instructor at the U.S. Army Armor School. I was a young Captain assigned as a Team Lead for what was known as the "10-Day War." Newly commissioned 2nd Lieutenants, assigned as Armor Officers, reported to the schoolhouse for a 12-week Basic Course designed to train them before they reported to their first duty assignment. The final event, before graduation, was to go to the field for 10 days and live and train on the tanks as if they were a tank platoon leader. These training teams comprised of four M1 Abrams Tanks with four Lieutenants on each tank.

During this 10-Day War, six teams were in the training area known as 5-North. My team was in a remote section of the training area when I heard the frantic Medivac call. I knew it had to be a bad accident, so I immediately instructed my senior sergeant to take over the training and told my driver to fire up the Jeep. It would take about fifteen to twenty minutes to get to the location by road. However, my driver had a better idea, and he took a straight line path, cross country, arriving in about ten minutes to the site.

When we arrived on location, I found one of the most catastrophic sights I have ever witnessed.

The other team had been training their platoon in a hilly, wooded area. When they completed their morning exercise, they parked their M1 Tanks on a hill with the gun tubes over the back deck. They dismounted to conduct an After Action Review of their performance. At this moment, one tank's parking brake snapped, sending the 60 tons of steel rolling backward down the hill. One Lieutenant was still inside the turret, and one Lieutenant was on top of the tank.

Instead of jumping off the tank, the Lieutenants rode it out. The tank went down the hill, up over a dirt road, and rolled upside down into a large ravine trapping the one Lieutenant inside and crushing the other underneath the tank.

As my Jeep approached the scene, I could only see the other crews standing around and my counterpart, their Team Lead, standing next to his Jeep, talking to the Medivac helicopter. I immediately jumped out and asked him what was going on. He told me about the rollover and the location of the two officers, and he told me that one of his sergeants was under the tank talking to the Lieutenant, who was crushed by the rollover. He also informed me that the Medivac was five minutes out, and he had called for an M88 Heavy Recovery Vehicle, which we could see coming down the tank trail at its top speed of 25 miles per hour.

I then went to the ravine and was greeted with a view of the upside-down tank, about 10 feet below the edge of the ditch and boxed in with trees and brush. I slid down the embankment and crawled under the tank to be greeted by SSG Robinson and the trapped Lieutenant. Not at all what I had expected. He was conscious and in pain but could not feel anything below his chest. We could also talk to the officer trapped inside the tank. He was beaten up a bit but safe and sound. Just trapped.

SSG Robinson asked me to retreat with him out from under the vehicle, and we had a quick and candid conversation. SSG Robinson said that the LT was wedged between some camouflage nets stacked on the back of the turret and the Commander's Weapon Station. This gave him a very small space to be trapped in and was why he was not crushed outright during the rollover. He assessed that he might be crushed from the chest down, and if we tried to drag him out, it would kill him. We both agreed that we could not dig him out as the tank started sinking into the soft ground, and we didn't have much time. We concluded that we needed to lift the tank to get to him. However, we were concerned that taking the weight off him might also kill him.

We concluded that we had one option. Lift the tank.

While SSG Robinson went back under the tank to be with the Lieutenant, I inspected the M1 to find fuel, battery acid, and engine oil dripping out of the engine compartment and draining into the hole where the solder was trapped, which indicated that we needed to act now.

By then, the M88A1 recovery vehicle had arrived and was working its way down into the ravine to get close to the vehicle. The driver pushed it to the limits to try to get the vehicle in position as quickly as possible. Suddenly the earth gave way, and the vehicle slid down the hill stopping less than two feet from crushing me and slamming into the tank. Both events would have been disastrous. But it turned out to be the quickest way to get the recovery vehicle in the ditch and in the correct position.

The M88A1 is a unique tracked vehicle. Designed to recover, tow, and repair heavy armor vehicles, the M88A1 wights about 51 tons and can tow the 60-ton M1 tank on level ground. It also has a 40-ton wench that can pull tanks out of the mud. But the item we needed was its A-Frame boom which can be raised above the vehicle to lift up to 23 tons with a steel cable and pulley system. Its primary mission is to lift engines and transmissions out of tanks to conduct maintenance and repairs under field conditions—the perfect vehicle for lifting the tank.

I climbed up on the M88 and directed the crew to put up the boom and get ready to lift the front end of the upside-down vehicle. Once the boom was up, they lowered the cable down to me, and I prepared to hook it onto one of the forward lifting eyes on the tank. I asked the crew to give me the 40-ton D-Ring to connect the cable and pully system to the tank, and I was told they did not have one as they had loaned their D-Ring to another M88 that was not in the field.

I was stunned. You might say the D-Ring is the Lynchpin in the connection between the lifting cable and the vehicle you are going to lift. (The truth is, the D-Ring is the D-Ring to the operation. Lynchpins are just safety pins.) Unfortunately, this D-Ring connector between the cable and the tank is also the weakest link and, historically, the number one point of failure in all lifting accidents. So, I had to ask, "If you don't have a 40-ton D-Ring, what do you have?" The M88 crew handed me a 13-ton D-Ring that is used to lift lighter items on smaller vehicles.

I looked at the situation and realized that between the fuel leak and the tank settling into the ground, we did not have time to run back to the garrison and find the proper D-Ring. We had to act immediately if we wanted to save this soldier. I attached the 13-ton D-Ring to the vehicle.

Now, I need to ask a question.
Have you ever had a conversation out loud with God?

Not so much a prayer but an open dialog with the guy upstairs where you explain to him what you are doing and why. More like an in-progress update, as you are doing something sketchy. Well, that is what I did at this moment.

It went kind of like this. "OK, God, this is what I am thinking. We have a 60-ton tank upside down. We have a boom that can lift only 25 tons, but the weakest link is this 13-ton D-Ring. I think the fuel tanks, engine, and gun tube are the heaviest parts on this vehicle, and they are all at the back. That means that of the 60 tons, I estimate that 40 tons are at one end. We need to only lift the opposite end, the front of the tank, which might weigh about 20 tons. I think the D-Ring is rated for 13 tons, but it is made in America, out of cold hard American steel, and I bet it was designed to exceed expectations. So I am counting on it to hold 20 tons, just long enough for us to get that soldier out from under the tank. So, God…how am I doing on the math?"

I did not get an answer outright, but I had an overwhelming sense of calm as I completed attaching the cable. I climbed up on the M88 and told the boom operator he had one mission. We are going to lift this tank about three feet. His mission was to be steady—no jerking or bouncing- and maintain eye contact with the D-Ring. If it started to stretch or distort, start yelling so we can get out of the way.

We were then ready to go. The Medivac had landed, and the crew was down next to the tank with a backboard, and SSG Robinson was pulled back so the Medivac crew could go in once the vehicle was raised three feet. The word was given to start lifting, and the tank came up, and everything was proceeding as planned until suddenly, the Medivac crew aborted. They said there was no way they would climb under the tank, and they stepped back.

The hero of the day was SSG Robinson, who grabbed the backboard and slid under the tank to start moving the Lieutenant himself. Immediately two other Sergeants and I followed him, and the four of us were able to move him to the board and out from under the vehicle.

I was scared to death as I was the only one under the tank who knew it was hanging on a 13-ton D-Ring. I remember our backs touching the tank's steel as we crawled on all fours to get around the Lieutenant to carefully slide him onto the backboard. If that D-Ring snapped, there was no way out.

Once he was clear of the vehicle, the Medivac crew took over and started First Aid. We lowered the tank back to the ground. I checked the D-Ring, and it looked like it was holding. We then yelled to the Lieutenant trapped inside the vehicle that we were going to raise the tank four feet this time. This would give him enough room to slide out of the loader's hatch and escape. So, holding our breath, we raised the tank again, and the young man came out like a wild animal. He moved on all fours with a purpose. Everyone was alive, and through all of this, the 13-ton D-Ring exceeded specifications. You might say the D-Ring pulled its weight and then some.

When it was all done, the Medivac crew transported the soldier to the hospital. He had both legs and pelvis broken, and it took about six months for him to recover and continue his service in the Army. It took four M88 recovery vehicles and a couple of days to get the tank out of the ditch and back on its track.

As for the 13-ton D-Ring, I removed it from the tank that day and took it to my office. I was sure it was damaged and should not be used again. I decided that it has a far more important job. I had it on my desk for several years as a reminder to myself and my team of the events of that day.

While the D-Ring exceeded specifications and became the champion of the moment, the actions of all the soldiers exceeded expectations, and they never gave up on the lieutenant trapped under the tank. The D-Ring was our reminder that no matter the situation, the job, or the challenge, we need to go the extra mile, give more, carry more, be more, and always exceed expectations.

I challenge you to take a moment and look around and find the people in your life that exceed expectations daily. It may not be significant, and it may not be noticeable to anybody else, but they are there for you. They support you when you are down, they challenge you when you are up. They are the D-Rings that are there when you need them, the connector that binds you together, and the strength that keeps you safe.

Take a moment and exceed expectations by telling them thank you for being in your life and when the moment comes, be there to give them a lift when they most need it.

Marshall Townsend II ~ *I would like to thank the men and women of the U.S. Military that I served with and had the honor to lead. They continue to inspire me today.*

Marshall's Core Philosophy

Leadership is not an individual sport but a team sport.
I don't believe in leaders.
"Directing Actions" from the sidelines. Instead, leaders multiply their success when they
"Step Into Action" and place themselves on the field of battle with their team.
I used this approach to serve thousands of key leaders and organizations in the military,
and it is the foundation of my corporate training programs and teachings.

The Fruits of My Struggles

By JoAnna Baanana

Staring at the pink semi-dried cake batter in the stainless-steel bowl,
I knew my life was at a crossroads.

JoAnna Baanana (author, marketer)

I gave up. I started waving the little white flag. It wasn't that I ceased to fight. I simply couldn't do it alone anymore. All of the tips and tricks in my toolbox stopped working. Time and time again, I failed. And this time, it was life or death. To choose life, I needed to stop pretending and figure out what was next — time to surrender. But I had to surrender without giving up and losing hope. It was time to build my tribe and surround myself with people I could lean on. People that would hold me up when I couldn't stand on my own. Fighting alone wasn't going to be enough to win this battle.

It was a relatively cold day in early March. The police had left my home about a half hour ago. I had successfully gotten both my children down for naps. They were each snuggled in their respective rooms upstairs. I sat alone on a bamboo stool at my red-linoleum kitchen island, with an eerie silence surrounding me. I stared at a stainless-steel bowl filled with a semi-mixed strawberry cake batter. It had been sitting in the mixing bowl for so long that the edges had become dark and dry. How did my life get to this? What happened today? Why was I so fearful of my raging husband? How had it gotten to the point that locking myself and my two children behind a door wasn't enough? I couldn't believe it had escalated to the point that I had to call the police. I had never called the police before. I've called crisis lines trying to de-escalate his behaviors in the past, but today's fear was for my life and my children's lives. He lacked impulse control, possessed an entitled attitude, and had a propensity toward rage, not to mention several loaded guns in the home. Though I doubted he would intentionally plan to hurt us, our lethality risk was determined to be high.

Over the past month, I read a book titled *F*ck Feelings* by Michael and Sarah Bennett. It opened my eyes to much of my disordered thinking around feelings, love, marriage, and emotions. I also began seeing a therapist. My husband had convinced me that I was crazy. And so, I decided he must be correct, and I sought help. These were the first two steps in giving up and seeking help from others who knew more than I did.

Psychologically my life had unraveled, but it was also affecting me physically. My weight quickly dropped. Despite being 14 months postpartum, I was the thinnest ever. A normal body mass index (BMI) is between 18.5 and 24.9. Mine was 16.1. My medical symptoms piled up. At one point, my primary doctor sent me to the emergency room for an evaluation because of blood pressure issues. I also had periodontal disease, which required cleanings every three months. I worried something was seriously wrong. My primary care physician ran a multitude of tests. Fortunately, everything came back clear. Unfortunately, I had no idea what was causing my health problems.

And while I didn't know my life trajectory, I knew my life was at a crossroads. Sitting at that red-linoleum counter, staring at the pink semi-dried cake batter in the stainless-steel bowl, I knew that whatever I did from that moment on, I would be on an entirely different path. At my next therapy session, I explained to my therapist what had occurred since our last visit. I shared how my fears had led me to call the police and that they removed the guns from our home. I let her know I moved in with my aunt and uncle because I feared what my husband would do to us if we continued to live under the same roof. His text messages and phone calls were erratic and scary. He blamed me for everything that happened. I asked her how to change my behavior to reduce his rageful outbursts. How could I change myself so I wouldn't have to face his rage?

I wanted to help him but couldn't figure out how. My children were one and three, and they had seen enough. Being exposed to a chaotic and unsafe environment was harmful to their development. How could I prevent it from happening again? Finally, my therapist suggested I contact my local domestic violence shelter.

What? A battered womens' shelter?

She must not understand the dynamic. He's never touched me except for that one head-butting incident, but that was years ago. I didn't need this type of help. They had no idea what I was experiencing.

As you may have guessed, I'm a people-pleaser. I did what most people-pleasers would have done. I made an appointment at the shelter so I could tell my therapist I had completed my homework. At the first meeting, I was given a nice big information packet. I dutifully took it home along with the recommendation to read the book, *Why Does He Do That?* by Lundy Bancroft.

Can a book change your life? Perhaps. But I know for sure that a book can change your perspective. Lundy understood and described my situation in a way I hadn't been able to conceptualize. He opened my eyes to exactly what was happening. He made me realize it wasn't my fault. And even if I could change myself, it wouldn't resolve the conflict.

After discussing Lundy's book with my therapist, she suggested another. *The Body Keeps the Score* by Bessel van der Kolk. This book opened my eyes to identifying and understanding some traumatic events in my past. Bessel's book also pushed me back into yoga and begin a meditation practice. Though terrible things have happened, I learned they didn't define me. As Bessel says in his book, "As I often tell my students, the two most important phrases in therapy, as in yoga, are 'Notice that' and 'What happens next?' Once you start approaching your body with curiosity rather than with fear, everything shifts."

I quickly became an insatiable bibliophile. Next on my list was *The Deepest Well* by Dr. Nadine Burke, *Adult Children of Alcoholics by Dr. Janet G. Woititz, Finding Me by Viola Davis, inward by yung Pueblo, No Visible Bruises* by Rachel Louise Snyder, *Wintering* by Katherine May, and *The Four Agreements* by don Miguel Ruiz. The more I read, the more content my therapist and I had to dissect. And the more I began to understand myself and the world around me.

Having a solid support system was empowering. So many people were in my corner. My aunt and uncle offered me and my two children a safe living space. My cousin and a few close friends let me cry on their shoulders when needed. They offered me a place to be vulnerable. My therapist helped me become more emotionally stable by organizing my thoughts and becoming more grounded. My children gave me the strength and courage to endure tough times. A domestic violence shelter provided me with crisis counseling and a myriad of other invaluable resources. As I became physically and emotionally healthier, I hired an attorney to help with the divorce process, which in my case, also involved a Restraining Order.

Most importantly, I found myself.

I learned to trust and depend on myself. Homing in on my internal voice and following my truth became a skill. I was discovering who I wanted to be and taking the necessary steps to soldier forward. In giving up, I found that everyone around me would hold me up until I could gain my footing.

There have been many twists and turns, but I've begun to see the fruits of my struggle. I'm a university-educated female. I have a well-paying, reliable, and graciously flexible job. I bought my own home. I practice meditation and yoga daily. I practice gratitude. I graduated from my regular therapy sessions, although she's available if I ever need her. I've gained back the thirty pounds I'd lost from toxic stress — my body's reaction to living in constant fear. And the myriad of other health issues slowly began to melt away.

The peace I'm experiencing
on this side of life is priceless.

When I look back at how my life was four years ago, I'm proud of how far I've come. I'm also able to see the steps I took to get to where I am today. Many of the steps were taken subconsciously. But they were motivated by my work to strengthen my resolve and my insatiable need to learn. What root causes led to my current situation? Where do I go from here? I wanted to learn how to protect myself and my children during this tumultuous time. So, I approached the issues with curiosity, not rigidity.

**I am forging a path of my choosing
— a path of my making.**

The body, mind, and spirit work in tandem. Improving my mind allowed me to actively work through therapy, improve my cognitive abilities, and deepen my self-love. Yoga and meditation were eye-opening to me. My progress would be compromised if my body and spirit weren't aligned.

Practicing yoga helped build my physical strength and provided the initial connection between my mind and body. As I learned how to connect with my body's flow, I became skilled at noting certain areas of tightness. As a result of years of living in a toxic and stressful environment, my body held tightly onto my previous trauma. Yoga poses, and stretches teach you to recognize and release the tension.

Meditation taught me to connect to all three—mind, body, and spirit. Calming my mind and relaxing my body allows me to connect with my spirit. Guided meditations have changed my life. My internal talk has become more positive. Meditating has helped me understand the importance of gratitude, how to build a peaceful life, and the invaluable skill of manifestation.

When life hands you a battle, you don't need to fight it with weapons, rage, and aggression. You can handle it with grace, peace, and gratitude. Battles will come. Life will not always be peaceful and conflict-free. Life is a roller coaster filled with ups and downs. How I choose to handle my past battles will now dictate how I live my future.

Regardless of what I must face, I'm ready for it. Anne Rice wrote in the book *Interview with the Vampire*, "The only power that exists is inside ourselves." Power has always existed inside of me. And now, I can uncover and cultivate that internal power. I let it lie dormant for far too long. Continuing to develop this power requires diligence and commitment. And I know I'm up for the challenge.

I'm proud of my progress. And I can't wait to see where I will be in the future. By caring for my mind, body, and spirit, I will continue to build a life worth living.

JoAnna Baanana ~ *I would like to thank my cousin Jessica Smith for always supporting me and loving me. I'd like to thank Mark O'Brien for always believing in me and being patient with me during difficult times. And I'd like to thank my children for giving me the courage I needed to move forward.*

One of JoAnna's Favorite Quotes

True power is living the realization that you are your own healer, hero, and leader. it is when you share your truth with compassion and peace. your power grows when you make progress in your own freedom and wisdom. those who are truly powerful do not harm themselves or others; instead, they use their energy to enrich all they know with love.

yung pueblo

In Search of More with Less: Breaking it to Make it Better

By Dennis Pitocco

———— ★ ————

*Most everything works better if you unplug
it for a few minutes, including you.*

Dennis Pitocco
(author, business owner, reimaginator)

*M*y life today is not far from what I envisioned in my 20s in many respects, borne of an entrepreneurial spirit coupled with a willingness to be a risk-taker from day one.

Looking Back: Our Road Less Traveled

I grew up in Pittsburgh, PA —one of eight children —a happy childhood, but with no prospects to attend college due to family economics.

Following my military service, I moved into a banking career (via a USAF job placement service) and spent 30+ years rising through the ranks. I left banking to start a financial services business with a good friend and never looked back, as we ultimately found success across the USA, Canada, and the UK.

I met my wife, Ali, in the UK, and together we decided to sell all of our business interests and settle down in Tampa Bay to begin the next chapter in our life. Away from all the "noise," our morning walks helped us define this chapter.

We ultimately decided to devote our time, talent, and treasure to give back. This led to hands-on involvement with nonprofits (locally, nationally, and internationally) from the grassroots level to the Board Room level. And it ultimately led to the creation of 360° Nation, our global media enterprise, and GoodWorks 360°, our pro-bono, nonprofit consulting foundation –all created as "for good" versus "for profit" initiatives, allowing us to create something unique, something different, and something driven by what made sense versus cents.

As we launched 360° Nation, we faced several 'expectations,' battles borne of our nontraditional "constructively disruptive" approach to running a business. No business plan. No marketing. No advertising. No bottom line to achieve. No kidding.

We started with the notion of reinventing traditional media publishing routines, intentionally putting our writers and our audience first by removing all industry-standard boundaries (e.g., topics, timelines, word counts, etc.) Essentially, we removed all the barriers to creativity.

From that point forward, working with a blank canvas, we allowed our global audience to shape the direction of our business over time.

We've reacted, reinvented, refocused, and repositioned all we do along the way. Our goal was to best serve our global community while holding forth on our constructively disruptive approach with "Why Not?" decision-making, provided that all of our initiatives fit nicely under our "rediscovering humanity" mantra.

We've felt our job was to figure out what the world is trying to be and then help the world be that, be better, and be even more.

We believe that the world depends on everyone showing up and being present as best we can, individually and collectively, creating positive ripples of change with one person, one voice, and one step at a time.

As our business continues to expand, we continue to reflect upon and embrace the storied quote, "Sometimes, the only available transportation is a leap of faith."

It's been a remarkable ride, with the Pandemic forcing us to step back and reposition our approach to rediscovering humanity. It ultimately triggered the launch of 360° Nation Studios and several other virtual/production channels focused on elevating voices across the universe "for good." The silver lining beneath it all was a reinvigorating purpose and a greater opportunity to deliver our "for good" promise.

With a decade plus now behind us, our battles continue to take the form of doing whatever we can to change mindsets for the greater good of humanity.

Some folks have joined us, grabbing the wheel, and accelerating into a better world. Others have slammed on the brakes or veered off the road, not wishing to venture beyond the status quo.

We've learned it's not about cheering from the sidelines. As individuals and a global community, we must take responsibility, grab that wheel, and do what we can to navigate a better path. We must lift our eyes higher than our circumstances and the trials and tribulations around us, looking up versus down and looking forward with hope.

We also began to understand the increasing importance of self-care, particularly as we became more and more consumed by the depth and breadth of the uphill climb borne of our "rediscover humanity" battle cry.

My perspectives have been formed over substantial international travel, allowing me to watch the evening news through a more informed lens. It's all about rediscovering humanity at its very best, being a part of something bigger than ourselves, and embracing the magic of authentic community, thriving with people who share different interests, bound together with a common goal.

I have never imagined going back to an earlier stage of life – zero regrets, but rather I focus all my thoughts on (re)imagining and crafting my particular corner of the future.

Looking back, my most valuable lesson learned without exception is that I continually strive to do the right thing even when no one is watching. That includes "walking my talk" regarding the many values I and we espouse across our "for good" activities.

The unexpected and extraordinary strength, borne of community and "genuine" connection, has allowed me to spread my entrepreneurial wings far and wide, discovering infinite possibilities while engendering amazing, genuine relationships along the way.

These days, it seems almost like a foreign concept to be unplugged even for 24 hours. Texts, emails, and phone calls that aren't immediately returned are interpreted as being ignored. But what are the implications of that constant feeling of connectedness that binds many of us for as much as 16 to 18 hours per day? Perhaps it requires unplugging to truly assess how far-reaching this technology has become in dictating our lives. We increasingly miss out on the critical moments of our lives as we pass the hours with our noses buried in our devices.

As the depth and breadth of our enterprise consumed more and more of our time over the years, we approached the end of our first decade with a mix of excitement and wonder, underpinned by a desire to recognize this pivotal anniversary in a constructively disruptive way –that is a way that would not simply benefit us, but perhaps those who continued to follow our journey.

After considerable thought, we decided to do the unthinkable, particularly as it relates to what had by design become a 24/7 operation. We decided to unplug!

Unplug? Are you kidding? Far too many write about it, think about it, talk about it, and understand the need for and value of it. But few do it with conviction, even if for a few hours, let alone a day, a weekend, a week, or more. Face it—we're all addicted to our devices. Period.

The Oxford Dictionary defines unplug disconnecting (an electrical device) by removing its plug from a socket.; remove an obstacle or blockage from "a procedure to unplug blocked arteries;" relax by disengaging from normal activities such as "they've gone up to the cabin to unplug."

Disconnecting to Reconnect – Our Radical Sabbatical

Having spent countless hours over the prior decade focused on our "occupassion" —our 360° Nation, our global media digest, my wife and I decided it was time for us to "walk the talk." That is, to step back, exhale, and smell the roses. It's time to bring real meaning to the notion of self-care. It was time for our entire 360° Nation team to disconnect so we could reconnect with each other and what's really important. We were further inspired to "just do it" as we stumbled upon this brief story from a publication called *Our Daily Bread*.

In 1952, in an effort to prevent clumsy or careless people from breaking items in a shop, a Miami Beach store owner posted a sign that read: "You break it, you buy it." The catchy phrase served as a warning to shoppers. This type of sign can now be seen in many boutiques. A different sign was placed in a local potter's shop, saying, "If you break it, we'll make it into something better."

The notion of "breaking it and making it into something better" became the framework for what ultimately transpired over the course of our extended break, christened by us as our "Radical Sabbatical."

Most everything works better if you unplug it for a few minutes, including you. A few minutes? How about a few months? In our case, three glorious months —and boy, are we 'working better' because of it.

So many folks across the universe lifted us with their words of encouragement and support as we set off on our long-planned Radical Sabbatical.

We promised to keep an "unplugged" journal for sharing upon our return. And we did, in hopes that sharing the highlights of our experience would encourage others first; to recognize that "self-care is not selfish" and second; to take a break by totally unplugged from the internet, mobile phone, computer, iPad, and other online devices for a day, two days, a weekend, a week or even longer. Call it a digital detox; we are taking as much time as possible to rediscover that elusive "gift of presence."

Our Journey of Rediscovery

Looking back, our escape from it all fell into three natural phases that can best be described as re-discovery.

Month one was the "decompress and let go month," with us pumping the brakes each day to gradually slow-down from 24/7 hustle to 24/7 calm; a month of letting go, transitioning, exhaling, and ultimately surrendering to serenity.

Month two was about (repeatedly) permitting ourselves to breathe and relax, not seeking to fill every minute of this newfound time with "stuff."

There was a lot of reflection and recovery. It was less about ability and much more about our availability; more awareness and authenticity, a state of peaceful bliss as we cultivated our presence —with less "doing" and more "being." There was more spontaneity, more fun, and we rediscovered the magic of having meaningful discussions with our undivided time and attention versus whatever's left of both at the end of the day.

Waking up in the morning and just sitting back, becoming more of a participant versus an observer, brought an unexpected sense of relief, liberty, and a priceless moment to enjoy each moment —just as it is. Listening and talking to each other without distractions felt a bit like old times, like when we were children.

Noticeably, we became calm, free, careless, and lighthearted in our days without interruptions or anxiety. Days of peace and quiet and intentional, wonderful silence. A feeling of timelessness. Surprisingly, the feeling of restlessness or boredom never entered the picture, as we were so enamored by a feeling of liberation. We were hooked on the notion of enjoying more with less. Less noise. Less compulsion. Less discomfort. Less reliance. And we developed even more gratitude for the simple ingredients for a joyful life.

Somewhere between handling challenges, taking care of business, and juggling responsibilities, you may have lost pieces of yourself that you long to recover. Perhaps they were buried and forgotten long ago.

Rediscovering is more than just being reminded of these golden treasures.
It is being able to excavate your riches by pulling them out,
polishing them off, and allowing them to shine again.
Susan C. Young

Preserving the Magic

As month three, our final month, came around, we naturally began contemplating our return, but with an escalating determination to fully grasp and preserve the "magic" of our sabbatical experience, along with the priceless wisdom gained.

Back on the "business as usual" hamster wheel was not for us. We soon recognized that it wasn't really about chasing that elusive work/life balance but rather cultivating the notion of work/life harmony.

In other words, we needed to step back and "reimagine" our approach to all that we do to ensure that "self-care" remained at the forefront and that we didn't simply fall into the "Groundhog Day" trap —repeating history day after day.

As our final month took us into the new year, our thought process shifted away from the age-old concept of "resolutions" towards the fresher concept of "dissolutions" —taking things off the table that work against harmony while applying a bit of "if it ain't broke, break it" unconventional wisdom —perhaps making it into something better.

Having escaped all the noise for so long, we could move forward with a bit of reckless abandon coupled with fantastic clarity and oneness of purpose. Our forward motion was galvanized by an unwavering commitment to approach the "reimagination" process differently. Question everything. Ditch the unnecessary. Let go. Declutter. Set reasonable versus lofty expectations. Say yes more often without hesitating to say no more often. Nothing sacrosanct. No boundaries. No exceptions. No kidding.

Finding our Flow

We immersed ourselves into what's called a "flow state."

In positive psychology, a flow state (also known colloquially as being in the zone) is the mental state in which a person performing some activity is fully immersed in a feeling of energized focus, full involvement, and enjoyment in the process of the action. Flow is characterized by the complete absorption of what one does and a resulting transformation in one's sense of time.

And that's what we did. And boy, was it transformational across our personal and professional lives.

On the personal front, we immersed ourselves into a series of deep-dive discussions of anything found within our daily "life as usual" bucket.

People. Relationships. Travel. Fun. Not Fun. Auto-pilot stuff, etc. We were taking stock of our lives in every respect imaginable. Then, we emptied the bucket, sorted out the contents, and determined what was important and what was not. We refilled the bucket by intentionally shifting our time, attention, and focus to the former. A lighter bucket emerged, but one full of more time to discover and enjoy what matters—an opportunity to bask in the glow of fewer stressors.

We brought the same mindset to everything in our "business as unusual" bucket. Routines. Schedules. To-do lists. Post-it notes. Clutter. Expectations. Pressure points. Angst. Stressors.

It was time for business as usual to morph into "business as *unusual*." We reimagined everything under our 360° Nation umbrella. Every Page. Every Channel. Every Event. Everything was ditched or refreshed, including a renewed commitment to GoodWorks 360° —our "for good" foundation.

Looking Back as We Look Forward

Ultimately, our digital detox evolved into an unplanned, extraordinary journey of self-rediscovery from top to bottom.

We developed a keen appreciation for the fact that time is a finite resource; once spent, it's gone. We can't get time back, but we can be selective and purposeful with our time and how we spend it.

We can take control by "saying yes to less" and appreciating the white space in our diary. We can protect our precious time from the activities and people that give our lives the most meaning and joy. We rediscovered each other and reaffirmed our purpose, or our "why."

The "why" that fuels our passion encompasses our work, our relationships, and wrapping around everything we do. We emerged from "finding our flow," ready to live our lives more intentionally with a sharper focus on everything that matters.

Take it from us. We are liberated when we learn to use, enjoy, and experience the benefits of technology, but not be attached to it or dominated by it. With liberation comes keen awareness of the simple ingredients right in front of us for a joyful life.

Our relationships are our bedrock, our foundation. We need to nurture them with the love and attention they deserve. Though we may be caregivers or breadwinners for others, we must remember to care for ourselves along the way, because self-care truly isn't selfish.

As you ponder our story here, step back, look deep within, and consider disconnecting to reconnect –with yourself and everyone and everything that matters. Because you, too, can break it to make something better.

Dennis Pitocco ~ *My story is dedicated to my amazing wife and life partner Ali, without whom my extraordinary search for more with less would never have been completed.*

One of Dennis's Favorite Quotes

Too often, we underestimate the power of a touch,
a smile, a kind word, a listening ear, an honest compliment,
or the smallest act of caring,
all of which have the potential to turn a life around.

Leo Buscaglia

Don't Rock The Boat

By Faith Pearce

True love doesn't look like this.

Faith Pearce (author)

*T*his has been one of the hardest stories I have ever written. I started over a year ago, and it has been a battle as every part of me has fought the process. I have talked myself out of it so many times and so many times wanted to quit. But this is my story and mine to tell.

To explain, I need to go way, way back.

When I was about two, I came home from my Nan's house. And said to my mother, "Please don't kiss me down there." She confronted her mother about this, but my Nan said she thought it was perfectly normal. The subject wasn't challenged further or raised again, and we continued to visit them. So I complied. I kept quiet. "This is normal," I told myself, and I didn't rock the boat.

My dad was always the peacekeeper. Always laughing, joking, and laid back. He never reacted to conflict and saw the lighter side. One of my earliest memories was when I was three years old and sat on his shoulders, waiting for the father-daughter race to start. He was so busy talking to the guy next to him that he missed the sound of the bell. He thought it was hilarious, but I was devastated, and I remember my mum holding me, trying to console me.

I was four when my mum disappeared.

Where was my mum? I remember my dad and me driving to a large building with many corridors. After waiting for what felt like forever, we entered a large dark room. Beds were lined up on both sides of the room, and sunlight came through the frosted windows at the far end of the hall. I saw my mum sitting on a bed at the far end of the room and was so excited and happy to see her. As my dad approached her, he told me to wait. As soon as she saw me, she burst into tears. In my mind, I didn't understand what I had done wrong. Why was she upset with me? I stood silently, scared to do something wrong, and upset her again. I felt so small and helpless. Would she leave again? I didn't know she had a breakdown and was hospitalized. It was too complicated to understand as a little girl. After her breakdown, I felt the distance between us but was unsure if it was her or me, but something had changed.

My dad continued to be the peacekeeper. When faced with conflict, he would use humor, and laughter and detach or say don't upset your mother. He was a great teacher of how to avoid conflict and not rock the boat. I wanted to be good and not upset anyone or make them leave. But the voice inside constantly screamed, "Don't rock the boat."

I carried these behaviors with me, and from eleven to fourteen, I was sexually abused again. This time it happened at night when I was sleeping. I would awaken to find someone sitting, watching me, touching my arm, or stroking my hair. At first, I wasn't sure if it was a dream. Had I made it up in my mind? When I realized it was real, I felt confused, yet special and important as he always flattered me, but I hated what he made me do and wanted him to leave. Was this normal? His visits became more frequent, and his timing was unpredictable. Each time I was pushed to do more and more, and he wouldn't leave until he was satisfied. I felt so confused, ashamed, dirty, and scared. The confusion was immense. Was this my fault because I didn't say, "No?" I didn't tell him to stop. I must have caused this. Did I want this to happen?

The behavior didn't stop until he was kicked out of our family home due to his lies and deceit. I hated myself so much and felt empty inside. I needed to change. It was my fault for "allowing" it. I couldn't share what he had done or how I felt, and I continued to punish myself. I hated my body. I would starve myself for days or binge eat until I became sick. Anything to not feel the hurt inside. These patterns continued for many years. Shortly after, I watched my dad have a breakdown and was unable to work for over a year.

The following year when I was 15, my father was killed in a motorbike accident. In the hospital room, I promised him I would stay strong for Mum. I kept my word. But to do so, I had to detach even further from myself.

**I needed to be strong for everyone else.
My feelings were not important.**

The following year, the anger started to bubble as I wanted to confront my grandmother. I was angry at so many things, and I wanted to write her a letter asking her how she could do what she did to a small child. I wanted to tell her how disgusting she was. My anger was the culmination of being abused by two people whom I should have been able to trust and grief from losing my dad. Being silent and putting others first was exhausting and eating me alive. But I was told again, "NO! Don't upset her. It's not worth it." The message was clear: Don't rock the boat, or you will upset others.

I felt so alone with no outlet. Not wanting to upset anyone and not wanting to be a burden, I was filled with anger, shame, self-loathing, and fear that everyone would leave me or reject me. I was scared of being alone but had learned to disconnect and isolate from others and myself.

I used any means to disconnect from what I felt so I didn't have to feel or speak up. I had told myself for so long that I was the problem. I pushed myself into therapy for years, which helped me process some of the feelings inside, but still, I could not talk about the abuse. Depression followed for many years. The emptiness was immeasurable. My secrets remained locked up inside.

I threw myself into perfection—the perfect wife and mother, a successful career, charity work, and always helping others. Following my divorce in 2008, I tried even harder. Anything to prove to myself I was good enough. While constantly seeking external validation, I needed to be strong and never wanted my daughter to go through what I had.

In 2017, things came to a head. I didn't realize at the time that I suffered from PTSD (post-traumatic stress disorder). For nearly two years, I had extremely disturbing nightmares and flashbacks of the abuse. Sleep felt unsafe. I would do anything to stay awake because I was terrified of seeing the images. I could no longer silence the negative voice inside. Things had resurfaced following the sale of my childhood home, and everything was bubbling to the surface. I was a single mom, and my daughter was having issues with her mental health and feeling suicidal, and I was scared of losing her. I was buying a house, fundraising for various projects, managing a static caravan rental, and had a massive project at work.

Something snapped inside me, and everything crashed down. My worst fears came true. I was so burned out that I had a breakdown and could no longer function. Was history repeating itself? Had I failed everyone? Washing, eating, or getting out of bed were challenging. My emotions consumed me. Leaving the house gave me massive panic attacks. I hid my situation from everyone. Shame consumed me. Would everyone see what a failure I was and my weaknesses? The voice inside me screamed louder and louder, "You are not enough. You are weak, and everything is your fault. Don't rock the boat!" I didn't work for five months and was prescribed medication for 18 months.

Finally, I started to get more organized and felt ready to reconnect and address why I was so unhappy. So I stopped taking my medication.

I had no life. No boundaries. And never said NO!

I hated my job and my body. I drank daily, was overweight, and my finances were in a terrible state. It wasn't an easy process, and I continued to fight myself. My internal war lasted for years. Everything resurfaced when the medication stopped.

I hated being at home as well as being at work. I hardly saw my daughter and had terrible mood swings. I was raging with anger over little things or shutting down completely. I couldn't stand to be around myself.

Then the universe "gifted" me lockdown. I was forced to work from home and could no longer avoid my daughter. Everything blended into one, and I felt overwhelmed, trapped, isolated, and alone.

But things improved. My daughter and I started to open up and talk. It was time to do things differently. I signed up for a five-day challenge, connected with different people, and expanded my spirituality. Part of this challenge was reconnecting with my inner child and setting a stake in the ground where I wanted to go. I was clear that there were two intentions. First, I wanted to stop drinking, and second, I wanted to feel comfortable in my own body. The first was much easier than the second. I immediately stopped drinking and have never gone back to drinking daily.

Being comfortable in my own skin was more challenging…things needed to surface. I began working with someone who helped me return to when I was first abused. With much resistance, I could finally connect and step back into that time and say the things I was never able to say.

"NO! This isn't right. I want love, but not like this."

I held that small child and showed her she was safe, loved, and seen. I told her it wasn't her fault and that I was there for her and would never leave her again. For the first time, I built a relationship with the younger part of me that had felt so alone. Through my adult eyes, I accepted that my circumstances created the strong woman I am today. I could not use my voice back then, but now I am an adult and will no longer be silenced. I started to give myself the love I desperately needed.

Building trust and vulnerability with myself and others has taken time. Recognizing when I was being reactive or suppressing my feelings, I began listening to myself, offering reassurance or space.

By taking very small steps, my improved self-awareness has allowed me to continue opening up. Sometimes I regress and fight with myself, but I never want to feel trapped inside again. Learning to set healthy boundaries has been challenging. When I feel rejected by people, I have learned it is because we are not aligned. They are not rejecting me, we are just taking different paths, and I just need to stay true to myself.

An inner voice still surfaces, stating, "Don't rock the boat." I now recognize it was trying to keep me safe. However, there are better ways to cope, and I am steering now. I don't need to make myself smaller at the expense of ignoring and hurting myself.

I continue to learn and relearn every day because baby steps matter, and we take them one day at a time. I check in with myself regularly to make sure that I am not overworking, over or undereating, or retreating to avoid what I am feeling. When I am overwhelmed, I connect with my body to identify my feelings and why. By writing and sharing my thoughts, I have given myself permission to be heard. I continue to become more vocal in my daily activities and share what I want and don't want.

No matter what I have been through or will face, I will continue to grow and improve because I believe in myself.

This is my ship, and I am the captain.

Faith Pearce ~ *Thank you to everyone who has been part of my journey, especially to Peggy who believed in me when I didn't believe in myself.*

One of Faith's Favorite Quotes

*The hardest thing to remember is that what we each really want
is the truth of our lives, good or bad. Not rocking the boat
is an illusion that can only be maintained by the unspoken agreement
not to feel, and in the long run it never really works. Let go
of saving the boat and save the passengers instead.*

Kenny Loggins

Hey, Kid—It's Just You, Me, and the Cats

By Christopher Rausch

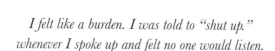

I felt like a burden. I was told to "shut up."
whenever I spoke up and felt no one would listen.

Christopher Rausch
(author, coach, podcast host)

Where It All Began

*C*an you imagine how different your life could be if you got out of your own way and stopped all your excuses? Lord knows! I could have a million excuses that would give me reasons for unhappiness and unsuccess— that's for sure. Please allow me to share some of my story with you and strategies that have worked for me and my clients. They will shift your life permanently! Are you ready? Let's go!

What I'm about to share with you is 100% true about my life. I grew up without a shred of confidence, belief, or trust that my life would ever amount to much of anything. My childhood years were excruciatingly lonely and painful. My mother struggled with Multiple Personality Disorder, and to compound matters, she also suffered from autism. She found solace in pain medication, alcohol, and cigarettes.

My biological father was nowhere to be found as he was already married and had his own family. Together, my mother and I survived on welfare and food stamps while living in a cockroach-infested house in the roughest part of Los Angeles. I felt like a burden. I was told to "shut up" whenever I spoke up, and I felt no one would listen.

Needless to say, I cried a lot, and my pain was unbearable.

My mother never wanted to be a "mother." So, she would mentally and physically abuse me regularly. As a result of her frustration, anger, and self-injury, she turned to substances. I was a shy little boy. I felt abandoned, alone, and scared that no one would ever love and care for me the way I saw others being cared for.

Life became unbearable when, at thirteen and in the middle of the 7th grade, I was forced to drop out of school. Sadly, my mother lost her job and spent all our savings — we would be homeless, but not "just us." My mother was also the "Crazy Cat Lady," bringing eighteen of her thirty cats and four dogs along for the journey. As a result, we began living in our family station wagon for the next *four* painful years! FOUR!

As a consequence of my environment, I followed in my mother's footsteps turning to drugs and alcohol. They became everyday staples during my teenage years. Then, at just seventeen, and miraculously after two failed suicide attempts, I knew my journey would end in one of three possible outcomes. Knowing this, I faced the most significant life decision I could ever imagine. Do you have any major decisions you've been ignoring making for *your* greater good?

The first painful realization and option confronting me was winding up in prison. Why? Oh, because I was doing "bad" things with bad people. The second outcome was ending up dead in a pine box. The final opportunity made me sweaty and nauseous to think about. Then, finally, it hit me that if I wanted to stay alive and out of jail, I would need to escape the tragic situation. This would entail leaving my mother behind and venturing into the world alone. Essentially, taking responsibility for *my* life instead of constantly hoping my own mother would step up and take proper care of me as she should have.

I'll tell you this. Choosing option three was the hardest, most challenging, soul-crushing decision I ever had to make in my life!!! Yes, it's true! I endured what most *adults* can never handle. Although it was gut-wrenching to move on, I know with absolute certainty that either option one or two would have played out, and you wouldn't be reading these words now.

Make the right choice.

Ultimately, I decided to surround myself with those who believed in me before I could believe in myself! Even though we've never met, I want you to know I believe in you from the bottom of my heart! Without question, you have greatness in you. You, too, can UNLEASH YOUR GREATNESS!

Prepare for change.

Once I made my gut-wrenching decision, I returned to school at eighteen, earning my G.E.D. diploma in three months. Then, without missing a beat, I invested the next twelve brutal years in accelerated college courses to finally graduate with a master's degree. The same year, I purchased my *first* house! A SAFE ROOF OVER MY HEAD.

While in school, I worked full-time. Furthermore, I began building my passion business as a highly sought-after Motivational Speaker, Life (Mindset) Coach, Top 10% Globally Rated Podcast Host (Raw & Unscripted w/Christopher Rausch), and published author. The best part is sharing this all with my wife of twenty-one years while raising our incredible six-year-old son. Life is amazing! You know what? Your life can be amazing, too. RAW & UNSCRIPTED are two words that perfectly describe my life.

Now it is your turn.

Without exception, the first critical step is finding your true WHY. Your WHY must be so exceptionally huge because it will drive you in every single moment when you are exhausted and want nothing more than to give up and go back to what's safe, comfortable, and certain. When you have a big enough WHY you'll undoubtedly find your big enough HOW! Leverage is key. My why was in my face after four years on the streets.

Let's be honest. Most people struggle to survive daily, much less build the life they dreamed of when they were kids, right? So I hope to catapult your confidence, clarity, and discipline to a whole new level! Are you game?

Start at the end.

We must get comfortable with being uncomfortable to gain clarity. Gaining crystal clear clarity requires us to do something super uncomfortable but life-changing. We must *begin* thinking with the *end* in mind. "The end of what, Chris?" The end of *your* life, my friend. Yes, your first assignment, should you choose to accept it, is writing your own eulogy!

Now, I know your butt probably just puckered, and that's okay. Not too many people are comfortable thinking about how their life will end. I get that. It's much like traveling to a new destination in your car. What do you do first? Of course, you pull out your handy dandy cell phone and type the *destination address*. The same applies in life!

Dream big.

I want you to dream big, too. and consider the incredible impacts and milestones your life's journey will ultimately create for you personally and professionally. Be specific. What special acknowledgments will you be remembered for? What family and friends will mourn your transition? Did you become famous? What adjectives do you want to be remembered for? Write all of this down on paper.

This exercise became inspirational while I was attending a funeral. Suddenly, I thought, "If I died tomorrow, who would show up, and what would they say about me?" The answers came rather quickly, and honestly, it wasn't pretty. But then, it hit me in the face! I needed to shift much of my focus to change this potentially lackluster outcome.

On the drive home, with this still stuck in my mind, I pondered, "Maybe I'll write my eulogy? Then, each day following, I can be specific and intentional about creating that incredible ending with everything I do and say with my life now."

A few hours later, I crafted a one-page hand-written eulogy of my life! I wrote it freely until the end and then read it aloud. I had no idea what to expect. But, soon enough, I had tears streaming down my face as I read about my significant and impactful life, affecting millions of people worldwide! There's something very cathartic in reading your eulogy out loud and ultimately believing in your story—the one you create.

Right then and there, I was committed to creating my new life! One of meaning, passion, and living in my true zone of genius. Essentially, in that short time, I went from *surviving to thriving*! This will happen to you too! I know it!

One of my first actions was realizing how much shit I tolerated from myself, others, and even inanimate objects. I was honestly shocked at how much I put up with from every aspect of my life because I was constantly in "Survivor Mode." However, I realized in those moments how much of a people pleaser I was and how little I worried about my true happiness and fulfillment. Perhaps you are now feeling a bit like this yourself?

Be the captain of your own ship.

Take another sheet of paper and create three headings. What do you tolerate from yourself, others, and objects that cause you angst or anxiety when you think about them? You *must be* 100% painfully honest with yourself. This exercise will be challenging, but I promise it will be worth it! Most likely, you'll find yourself with a whopper of a list. Don't be embarrassed. This wasn't easy for me, either. You are a beautiful work in progress, just like the rest of us.

After completing your list, consider one of two actions. First, what is the biggest toleration from each category? Then choose and eliminate those. Ensure those will free up either time, money, or sanity! Or, if this is too overwhelming, start with the low-hanging fruit. Pick two or three *small* tolerations to eliminate from each category that will again provide you with the same above benefits.

Right here, ladies and gents, are where your *excuses* pop up. And this process helped create who I am today—The No Excuses Coach. For example, your excuse might go something like this. "Well, I'd love for my kids and husband to help out around the house, but I know they won't, and I'll just end up doing it myself anyway." Trust me. You are certainly not alone.

To this, I counter you with, "Well, if you got permanently laid out tomorrow by the proverbial bus that hits everyone, I doubt your husband and kids won't figure out how to do their own laundry and pack their own lunches, right?" Yes, they will survive, but it's up to you to have those challenging conversations now. Role-playing through such conversations and uncovering the excuses and rebuttals is a great tool. If you need practice, give me a buzz! I'm good at it.

Find the positive *leverage*. This gives you the strength to do what you haven't done to get what you haven't gotten. Dr. Wayne Dyer said it perfectly, "When you change the way you look at things, the things you look at begin to change!" Without the leverage, you won't be doing your <u>best!</u>

We are all more powerful, resourceful, and resilient than we can comprehend! Listen, you've survived 100% of all the shitty situations that have happened in your life so far!

Here's a game-changing perspective.

What if everything that's *happened* and everything that's *happening* now is *preparing* you for what's next?

Listen, no one is coming to save you. There are no magic pills. And most of all, there isn't a "someday" on any calendar! This is *your* life, and there are no do-overs. So living with regret is *my* leverage. According to a hospice nurse, the top regret of dying was that people lived the life they *thought* they should live instead of living their own life!

Can you imagine the intense pain, anguish, and sheer heart-crushing self-talk you would experience if *you* reached the end of *your* life and realized so many regrets? Now that's <u>leverage</u>!

Someone believed in me before I did.

I'll leave you with this something said to that seventeen-year-old street kid. My mentor Bill White told that long-haired, cigarette-smoking hoodlum, "Christopher, you are only limited by the parameters of your own mind!"

And guess what? I believe in you! Even if you don't! But only you can do the work! When the teacher appears— the student must be ready! I'm here for you!

And if you had told me while walking the streets of Orange County. at 13 years old, I would eventually write a book—well, I won't tell you how I really would have responded. PS: my entire life will be published in the Fall of 2023!

Christopher Rausch ~ *Barbara, thank you for all your love and support, especially these last three years, and to my incredible son, Jackson - I love you so, so much!!!*

One of Christopher's Personal Quotes

You are only limited by the parameters of your own mind.

Saved by the Pastie

By Ashley Romero

Awe-stricken is putting it mildly—the hair stood up on my arms as I watched her prance.

Ashley Romero (author, host, dancer)

A drag queen gave me my stage name for a raffle contest at the first burlesque bar show. I had the opportunity to be a stage "kitten" (stage assistant) or the person responsible for picking up the "stripper droppings" (costume pieces) from the stage between routines. If you have no idea what half the words in that first sentence are, that's perfectly normal, but by the end of this, we'll have you talking like a burlesque expert, and you'll be more than prepared to sit in the audience of your first live show!

Shall I introduce myself? I am Lana Montreese, an international burlesque sensation, multi-city burlesque producer, drag king, and host of the *Banking on Burlesk* podcast and Transformation Talk Radio Network radio show. My first taste of the burlesque world was in August of 2014, and I've been performing since 2016.

Into the maelstrom.

Looking back and taking into account who I was and how much I was suffering mentally, emotionally, and spiritually, and teetering on a path of self-destruction. Five months can feel like a lifetime when you live in a world of drugs, alcohol, sex, and toxic friendships. Add to the mix a lifetime of untreated trauma and mental "illness." The result is one dangerous cocktail. I spiraled and hit rock bottom when my two best friends shared with me their desire to enter into a relationship with each other and requested my "blessing." I not only refused to give my "blessing," but I chose to be the cruelest, inconsiderate, and hateful human I've ever been to people I called my best friends. After I lit the match and watched that bridge burn, I decided that life was no longer worth living because the feelings that I was running from and that I didn't share was that I somehow managed to fall in love with my two best friends and was terrified of them running off into the sunset without me.

Through the maelstrom.

Planning to end your life is a surreal feeling. The rinse and repeat of daily life reminded me that those around me might be seeing me for the last time and not even know it. Ultimately, I released associations with negative people that I wasn't fond of and was able to recognize those I admired—those who wore their scars like a badge of honor. One of those people was a co-worker who filled my teller position when I was promoted to a banker. They were bright and bubbly, but they wore their trauma on their sleeve and didn't shy away from talking about their bipolar "disorder," anxiety, and depression, which was completely foreign to me. Being my authentic self was something I hadn't even fathomed at that point. I planned to end my life that next Sunday, but we all know that plans sometimes have a way of falling through in just the best way possible. My co-worker asked me what I was doing that weekend, and with a "whoa is me" attitude, I told them I had no plans because I had no friends, and without skipping a beat, they immediately retorted with, "Great! That means you can run the merch table for our burlesque festival! We need volunteers for both nights." I half-heartedly agreed, and little did I know I was in for the ride of my life.

Burlesque saved my life.

I've never witnessed so many beautiful, sparkly, and confident people occupying a single space before; it was exhilarating. Although, at the time,

I had no idea what burlesque was other than the movie with Cher and Christina Aguilera, every burlesque performer will point out that they are not the same. I had also assumed that the performers in the festival were local to Albuquerque, or at least the state of New Mexico, and boy was I mistaken. They hailed from all over the US.

While working at the merch table, I met a gal selling rhinestone hair flowers. We chatted a few times, and I watched her table while she snuck a peek at the show. After intermission, she put a sheet over her table. I thought I would take my own backstage peek. Guess who the performer was. The lovely person I had been chatting with who was selling her hair flowers on a table next to me. She did a classic burlesque number in a breathtakingly sparkly gown and a feather headpiece. She was adorned with rhinestones, and I wondered how she could balance that headpiece. To say I was awe-stricken is putting it mildly—the hair stood up on my arms as I watched her prance, pose, and peel each article of her costume off perfectly while captivating the audience with a teasing wink and smile. I was hooked! My heart was full, and my soul was on fire. I'd never felt so inspired in my life.

The beginning of my sparkly life.

From that moment forward, I not only fell head over heels in love with burlesque, but I also unconsciously made a choice and a commitment to step into my own light and power, and I've never looked back or questioned that decision.

When the festival ended and we were on the mend from the glitter crash (burlesque hangover), I asked my co-worker how I would get into burlesque. She had a simple answer: join their burlesque troupe and learn the ropes. Well, that sounded easy enough. I was ALL IN! Over the next two years, I grew from a "stage kitten" to learning the ins and outs of production operations. Finally, in March of 2016, which seems like yesterday, after several months of rehearsing, it was finally time. The feeling of butterflies consumed me like never before, the same butterflies I feel to this very day before stepping on stage, the same butterflies I can feel right now as I sit here and reflect on that first moment I stepped on stage as Lana Montreese. That energetic and momentous feeling is why I say I'm a whore for the stage, and even in my most cringe-worthy performance moments, I feel like a poetic being.

I don't do burlesque for the money, though the money doesn't hurt.

Two years into performing allowed me the opportunity to travel to multiple cities across New Mexico and Colorado paired with my production knowledge, opened the door for me to produce my first show in my hometown of Las Vegas, New Mexico (the original Las Vegas, which was on the map 70 years prior to the one in Nevada). The show sold out, and I remember being backstage dancing with Trader Joe's grocery bags full of money. It felt unbelievable knowing I could pay my cast significantly more than the $25 each, which was the guaranteed base pay. That's not a typo. The bar guaranteed a base of $200 for the performance in case no tickets were sold. We would have to split that between eight cast members. Unfortunately, in New Mexico in 2017, making $25 a show wasn't uncommon. In fact, at the time, it was the going rate. Being able to pay my staff and cut a profit for myself filled my heart. That night, I also realized that there is an untapped market for live entertainment in small towns like mine where there is little to do, nonetheless something like a burlesque or drag show for attendees to excitedly throw money at the naked humans entertaining them.

Shimmying to Seattle.

The moment I fell in love with Seattle is a moment I'll never forget. At a crossroads in my burlesque career and after a falling out with my local community, I wasn't sure if I should continue performing. But instead of quitting, I decided to attend Burlycon (a con for burlesque people), held in Seattle every November. It is like a three-day-long burlesque summer camp and sleepover combined. We get to network whilst parading around in our best workout and pajama attire, wearing no makeup, and trying to identify each other because most of us had only met on social media or, if in person, we looked completely different out of makeup and costume.

That weekend was phenomenal, and it opened my heart and allowed me to recognize that the burlesque community is vast and the drama going on back home was small potatoes comparatively. To top it off, Burlycon weekend is the Sunday Night Shuga Shaq, an all-POC (people of color) monthly review, only for the Burlycon weekend, it's Shuga Shaq on steroids. My mind was blown, my face melted, and my heart was once again enamored over burlesque. I wasn't quitting, I wasn't going anywhere, and if I had it my way, which I did, I would move to Seattle.

When I returned home, I immediately searched for open positions in my company and within two months, I secured a job, an apartment, and moved from New Mexico to Washington. I produced my own going away show in my hometown on New Year's Eve 2017, and I remember a friend telling me how proud he was of me because I followed my dreams. That comment took me aback because I hadn't remembered sharing my dreams with this person, especially the dreams about burlesque because it was such a new endeavor in my life. He shared that one night on my 23rd birthday, in a drunken stupor, I had shared with him and a group of friends that my dream since I was a little girl was to be on stage, and here I was doing just that. At that moment, I knew I had met my calling.

The last frontier and a global pandemic later.

While in Seattle, I began building a foundation and becoming comfortable with myself. Acknowledging and healing from childhood trauma and letting go of toxic patterns and relationships began to unfold. Amidst this, I decided to leave my banking career and pursue burlesque fulltime. To make ends meet, I walked dogs and drove for rideshare apps… then my car was totaled. My new Seattle life ended abruptly when a

16-year-old driver hit me. I called my grandma, not knowing what to do. She had a solution up her sleeve. The only catch was that the solution was in Alaska. I took the plunge, uprooted my life, packed my belongings in storage, and moved to Fairbanks with two suitcases and my little dog. Then it happened again. In the dead of winter in sub-zero temperatures, I fell in love with another city.

It's been three years, four cities, three states, and a whole-ass global pandemic since my three-month winter affair with Fairbanks, Alaska. But, just like burlesque, it has shaped me and my mindset, bringing me to a place of grace, allowing me to heal and be curious with the childlike wonder of the world I inhabit in my mind and in the universe.

You never know where life might lead you. Take a risk. Heck, it may just lead you to a burlesque show, or stage, the world is your oyster.

Ashley Romero ~ *Thank you to every performer who has ever and will ever grace the stage as a burlesque entertainer, may this art form bring as much magic and healing into your soul as it has mine.*

One of Ashley's Favorite Quotes

Dreams don't work unless you do.

John C. Maxwell

Paradigm

By Alexxa Goodenough

I realized that all the voices I had been listening
to and allowing to play repeatedly in my mind were lies.

Alexxa Goodenough
(author, entrepreneur, master's in social work)

I have spent much of my life trying to convince myself and others of who I am. It has always been vital to me to live with integrity and make sure I live by example. However, I have always felt sensitive about how other people perceive me. I spent much time concerned about what others thought of me and working hard to change how I thought they felt. Some of these perceptions were labels that came inadvertently as the people around me shared information or made statements that left me with an understanding of what they assumed about people like me; foster children, girls, poor kids, children of addicted parents, children from broken homes, and more.

To be clear, I was often not given labels directly. Mostly, I listened as people talked around me and to me. People say so much without ever realizing what they just told you. The most powerful messages were not spoken but inferred by what I saw all around me in life, at school, on television, and even in church. The affection, support, and love I saw others get spoke powerfully to me. It is common for people to make generalizations about certain groups or assumptions about individuals with little or only a small amount of experience or information. Interestingly, social workers, foster parents, and other professionals working in the system often make judgments based on a case file or a synopsis given to them; many of the people deciding who you are have not even met you. Oddly my attorney did not meet me until I was in the system for about nine years; this is one example and another story to tell some other time.

I lived in 22 homes throughout my 15+ years in the system; I was not raised in a typical home with family holidays, outings, and support. A childhood like mine, living in multiple foster homes, having social workers, and visitation (with my family, however sporadic), meant that a system primarily raised me and did not have attachments that are so critical in early childhood. The inconsistency I experienced, like so many others in the system, was detrimental in ways that are not obvious. During our first five years of life is where most of us learn we are safe, loved, and worthy.

I was very young when I knew I was not safe, loved, or worthy.

In foster care, people often discuss outcomes and the detrimental effects of what brought someone into the system. For me, that was physical and sexual abuse and severe neglect. There was another reason listed in my file that I do not recall. My parents struggled with mental health and substance abuse, and my mom ultimately lost custody of me. Throughout my years in foster care, I learned that abused children statistically become abusers, and mental health and addiction have similar outcomes. I knew I would likely become one or all of those statistics. So my focus became proving that was not me at all.

I spent most of my life struggling with who I am and loving myself because I did not have love and stability in the way most children do, and that led to me working hard on who I am as well as every part of my life and trying to excel at being certain no one could think anything less of me. Unfortunately, people's perceptions are what they are, and we can't always change them.

I started my advocacy work at age 15 and was very successful in many ways. However, as I matured, learned more, and understood the complicated truth of the matter, I realized that I was being tokenized.

Beginning with foster care system advocacy, I was used or tokenized because I was naive to the realities of the world. I did not understand my worth and value. I did not realize that my experience alone had value and that I also had valuable knowledge and skills. I was not motivated by money. I just wanted the system to be better for everyone. I freely shared my knowledge and story and worked in many capacities to improve the system. I worked on many projects and spent countless hours as an advocate, speaker, facilitator, curriculum developer, event planner, and more. My life was focused on this work from every angle. This work was more than a job or a project; It was my purpose. I created and worked hard on many projects. Other people I worked with were well-paid while I struggled. I did not know the pay standards for the work I was doing.

At a conference held yearly at the Asilomar conference center, I was asked to speak on stage. I was on a panel. During the panel, an audience member asked what we were doing to ensure that we had specific youth representing a particular race. My first response was to point out that a youth of said race was a group member. I continued to explain that cultural competence and sensitivity are not about checking boxes to ensure that we have someone representing each category but instead creating ways to support, accept and welcome anyone joining. Essentially, this work is not about having x number of this or that but making sure that whoever joins can participate like anyone else. Just like after my first speech, I received a standing ovation. This was a very proud moment for me.

Following the event, a well-respected woman whom I looked up to asked me what training I had received in order to speak as well as I had. I tried several times to explain that it came naturally to me. I have the ability to identify areas needing improvement and create a strategy. I shared that this wasn't the first time someone had noted my skills, and I had been contacted many times to speak and offer advice. She was puzzled and continued to push back in disbelief. We had previously worked together several times, and I now know that her opinion of my skills and the reality of who I am is different.

Unfortunately, because I started so young, I found that one of two things often happened: people were either highly impressed by my work or suspicious of my accomplishments or skills. Before I turned 18, I was featured in the newspaper, on the news, and in other media, telling my story and sharing my work. I worked in the California State Foster Care Ombudsman's office. This office acts as an objective third party to uphold the Foster Care Bill of Rights as well as other responsibilities. I have done policy work and keynote speaking. Even now, I feel compelled to describe my experience as I share this story. Although it is not necessary information, it is part of the program (in my mind) that I catch running on autopilot.

Eventually, I earned my associate's, then my bachelor's in management, and finally, my master's in social work, adding multiple trainings and certifications. It was imperative to get these. I believed I needed them to prove my knowledge. They were pieces of paper showing I was more than the labels and statistics.

Now, I had value, provable worth.

One of the first times I realized people saw my worth was when I needed recommendation letters to get into my master's program. One letter made me cry. The director of mental health in Los Angeles County wrote a letter of recommendation. I admired him, and we served on a board together. His letter was titled *Diamond in the Rough*. He talked about my competencies, abilities, and who I was as a professional and as a person. I realized that all the voices I had been listening to and allowing to play repeatedly in my mind were lies. However, it was hard to shut them down because there were still so many other people in the world who didn't see me that way or didn't value all of my skills and abilities.

And most importantly, one of those people has been me.

I have a passion for learning new skills; growing personally and professionally, whether in business, healing, or other areas I have specialized in. I have come to recognize that a big part of me is still wounded by people (along with other related situations and trauma) who couldn't see my value and use what I could give them to their benefit.

I once worked on a non-profit project. I was so passionate, dedicated, and excited for the non-profit to come to fruition and serve the foster youth community. The idea was to provide mentorship and support for former foster youth that had aged out of the system. This service did not exist. I helped create this non-profit from the very beginning. When I started working on the project, we only had the name. Unfortunately, the non-profit did not continue after I no longer worked on the project. The person I was working with took advantage of my services, skills, and knowledge. I helped create the bylaws, devised what the non-profit would do, researched, and connected with potential partners, and created fundraising ideas. Unfortunately, this person only saw me as a token, a former foster youth. She paid a lawyer a retainer in case she needed her to help create everything I had already created. Then she paid for a non-profit training certification. After spending thousands of dollars, she came to me and apologized because she realized everything I had told her and the work I had completed was done perfectly. She had paid so much to all these other people because my only value to her was a token, former foster youth. In reality, I had built a strong foundation for what would be a fantastic organization.

After that experience, I was deeply wounded and hurt, and it was hard for me to continue working this way on other projects. I have had to do a lot of healing on my own, even after getting my master's in social work. I'm currently in an Executive MBA program. After 20 years of working in several areas, such as non-profits and multiple businesses, I still struggle to sell myself. I am not always confident because I still hear the whispers and lies of the tokenism and trauma I have experienced. I have allowed the negative voices to be louder than they should be. Now, I am getting another degree because I need another paper to prove that I have the knowledge I already have. While this degree might help me, it's likely just another degree, another certification, and it will be never-ending. I love learning, and I will forever learn new things.

But more importantly, I'm on a journey to learn my worth and value. It is something that I have worked on for many years and am becoming better and better at. I'm skilled at helping others recognize and work through their issues because I know how difficult the journey is. I have learned so much about myself as I work to help others build their businesses and heal their wounds. It is still a challenge for me to separate my professional and personal life. I continue to heal and get over the traumas, to erase them from my life. But I do see how it is all connected. I know now that I need balance, not to erase but to create a new understanding and find ways to use what I have learned.

In the end, I have realized that I am one whole complicated person who is unique, and to progress in any area of my life, I need to heal, see, and accept myself entirely. Despite my trauma and learning from them, growth is not an easy process, but changing my point of view to create balance and use the lessons has only made me a better person and professional. Instead of trying to separate or erase my unique experience or skills, I now incorporate them into my work. I am an expert and highly skilled professional that is beyond competent. I now excel at working with others holistically, using my unique flexible, and integrated strategies to help others create balance and grow their careers or business. My personal growth is a tool to teach and guide people through their journey so they can excel in their life and become the author of their unique stories. They now dictate their labels as I now do my own. I am not the labels they gave me.

We see ourselves through the paradigm of our experiences, things that have happened, or things that have been said to us. Much of my paradigm evolved from trauma and the opinions of others. Over time, and with much inner work, my paradigm shifted. We need to see ourselves for who we are, not our trauma or other people's assumptions.

I am truly a diamond in the rough.

Alexxa Goodenough ~ *To my children, you are my heart. I am grateful and proud of you! To all current and former fosters- You matter and are my foster family. I hope my work leads to a better world for all of you.*

One of Alexxa's Personal Quotes

*The wounded are the best healers, and the healed
are the best survivors. Together we Thrive.*

Who Are You Kidding

By Sylvie Plante

*I now live the happiest moments of my life,
and my future looks simply amazing.*

Sylvie Plante
(author, coach, and mentor)

*I*f you've read my previous story in *The Four-Fold Formula*, you know I
struggled for about a decade to find my way and live every day feeling
blessed, peaceful, and happy doing what I love.

So, let me share some of the elements that made this possible. From
my perspective and experience, one of the key elements was taking
responsibility. Yes, taking FULL responsibility—100% of it. Not even 1%
less. Why do I say that? Let me put this into perspective.

Most people think they are only 50% responsible for what happens
TO them and that everything is shared. Why do we automatically think
so? Because there is always another party involved—be it a company, a
boss, or a spouse, to name but a few. Well, sorry to annihilate your belief
and break it to you this way but being 50% responsible doesn't exist. I
know we all think we share responsibility. That is a big NO!

We are 100% responsible for life and for the events that happen FOR
us, not TO us. Yes, I said it. Ask Tony Robbins! I hear you, "That's not
true. It takes two to tango. We are not the only ones responsible." It can
be challenging to accept this and wrap our heads around this. But, if we
really take the time to think it through and look at our lives, we'll see that
everything, good or bad, happens FOR us because of the actions and

choices we took or did not take. How we react makes the most significant difference. Is it easy? Hell no! It takes courage, humility, admitting and accepting without judgment, and living without regret. What is done is done. We can't change anything.

How did I take 100% responsibility for what has happened to me, and how did I learn to take responsibility?

I started struggling after I left the corporate world. I didn't know what I wanted to do. I had lost my self-confidence and found myself spinning in circles trying many endeavors that did not pan out, putting me in a precarious financial situation. Finally, after years of being either sick, on medical leave, or simply not performing at an acceptable level, I felt hopeless and prayed for a profound miracle to happen.

However, I believe that tiny, small, or big miracles happen daily if we just take the time to see them. This belief has brought me to where I am today and where I want and need to go.

Back to HOW. Back to 2017. Through one of the online businesses I was trying (yes, trying) to build, I was blessed to meet a gentleman who became a mentor of mine. He was a fascinating man, an exceptional orator, and a thoughtful leader who inspires people the same way Les Brown does. As a matter of fact, he is a close friend to Les. His name is Byron Nelson, and I am forever grateful for meeting and having him in my life. During one of our discussions, he reassured me that I had all the skills and competencies required to succeed in this business. Yet, despite his belief and support, I was not progressing. I told him I felt stuck, scared, and discouraged. He asked me what I was scared of. I couldn't figure it out. I had no clue.

He said, "Girl, have you heard about the Landmark Forum?" I told him no. He replied, "Let's see when the next Forum is and get you registered." I absolutely trusted Byron, so when he said register, I registered. Financially it wasn't a wise decision, but I was desperate to get out of my funk.

It was the beginning of a new me. I have completed development programs before, yet Landmark is in a class by itself. I began gaining insight into who I was in this world and what I needed to do. These programs taught me the true meaning of responsibility and keeping your word to yourself and others. Respect your commitments. Do what you say you are going to do and do it when you said you would. If you cannot keep the commitment, acknowledge it to yourself or, in the case of a commitment to someone else, communicate the status with the person. I began recognizing the role I was playing in my own movie. I had to accept the decisions and actions I had taken or, in some cases, those I had not. I couldn't undo anything I had done. I could only learn from it and move forward. It is what it is, as the saying goes!

I thought I had taken full responsibility for my experiences, and to a certain degree, I had. But I began looking at the whole picture. What role did I play in becoming sick and losing my job? Why couldn't I get a break? It hit me in the face. I was the only person who could escape my situation and create the life I wanted. It became unquestionably clear that I had created my life up to this point. I wanted more time and the financial freedom to do what I loved. I needed to make choices that aligned with my desires. The big aha moment was that NO one was going to save me. No one! No Genie in a Bottle would be left on my doorstep. I needed to take action and rely on myself. I was scared and felt a lot of pressure to hold myself responsible. After leaving corporate, I struggled to cope with all levels of stress. I needed to step up, to act, to look at myself honestly in the mirror and say to myself, "Hey, girl! Get off of your butt and get out there. GO now!" However, this new awareness did not mean I had to do everything alone.

Until this moment, I had been in a state of lethargy.

As Jim Rohn perfectly said: *for things to change, you need to change.* I took that on! I lived a life of fear, yet it was unclear what I feared. I did know a few things: I had experienced a few failed endeavors, and the lack of success put a toll on my relationship with my niece, which I sincerely regret. I was spinning my wheels, seeking extensive training and education for my new business endeavors. As I pressed forward, I remained hopeful that my efforts would pay off. When I say things are happening FOR you, I sincerely mean it. All these harsh times shaped me into the person I am today though I did not necessarily appreciate them at the time. I now live my life passionately, and I am making a difference in people's lives. Taking full responsibility is one of the most challenging yet rewarding lessons I have learned.

So gradually started "getting out there" and contacting people I knew. My confidence returned. I was open to new opportunities and experimenting with what worked and what didn't. And the coaching partnership I had previously created started to grow.

It is easier to sit back and hope things will happen magically on their own, or we will get that lucky break. I believe luck only occurs when you are prepared. You need a positive attitude, and you need to take action when you see an opportunity. Even winning the lottery takes action. You have to buy the ticket.

I began analyzing areas to improve my life and some of the actions I needed to take to shift my life in a positive direction. I was sick of not getting results, spinning around in circles, and feeling defeated. For some of us, it takes getting to this level before we make a drastic move. Acting and relying on yourself is easier said than done. And as a strong, independent, and confident person asking for help did not come naturally to me.

Part of taking responsibility is creating a solid tribe to keep you standing upright and pick you up when you fall. So, I started building that trusting support system, knowing it would take time. I began to meet incredible people who are now an essential part of my life. They have believed in me, supported me, and opened doors for me. I am so grateful for all of them for the quality of the people I have in my life now; some are dear friends. I am blessed. And the more I open up, the more amazing people enter my circle.

You do not have to conquer all your battles alone. What I am suggesting is that you must take the first steps. No one will come knocking on your door saying, "Hey, I need you for this job, or I have this opportunity, or I need coaching." In most cases, you will need to make initial contact with people. Share your experiences, ask for advice or guidance, and listen attentively. Soon opportunities will come your way. It happened to me, and it can happen to you.

I first began focusing on my physical and mental health as I realized I had also neglected to take full responsibility for my health. I kept saying it was my priority, yet it really hadn't been. So prioritizing my sleep, my walks, and eating a healthier diet became an essential part of who I am today.

So, after gaining back some of my strength and cognitive thinking, I contacted some people in my network. One phone call, in particular, triggered me to start teaching at the university and opened a new perspective for me – what I call "facilitating" – I realized this was where I thrive the most: sharing and interacting in front of an audience where I can make a difference to many. How was this possible? After years of being ill, I was given the opportunity to drastically change my life for the better." It took a combination of factors to make it happen. Remember what I said, luck doesn't just happen. You need to act. My experience, education, and personality were leading factors, but most of all, the quality of my relationships with people in my network led to the call that triggered me to teach. They trusted me and my abilities. Then I took a leap. And the floodgates have opened. The more I took responsibility and stood up, the more opportunities presented themselves.

Taking those initial steps wasn't easy, but I soon realized I was the only one who could save myself. And I am thankful every day for that. I still slip, but when things do not go smoothly, I look at my responsibility in each situation. There is always an answer, and then I adjust.

Taking ownership opened up a whole new world for me, and I am forever grateful for that lightbulb moment when I truly understood what the word "responsibility" meant.

And if you are wondering, YES, I did identify what I was scared of… that's for the next story!

Sylvie Plante ~ *Thank you to my wonderful, supportive parents and to Mr. Byron Nelson for being an amazing mentor, believing in me, and introducing me to the most powerful transformational development programs ever.*

One of Sylvie's Favorite Quotes

For things to change, you need to change.

Jim Rohn

MIND Commentary

by Coach Peggy & Dr. Markus

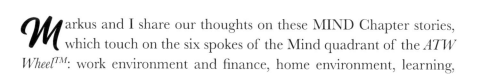

*M*arkus and I share our thoughts on these MIND Chapter stories, which touch on the six spokes of the Mind quadrant of the *ATW Wheel*^{TM}: work environment and finance, home environment, learning, mindset, personal awareness and growth, and habits.

Marshall shows us that we can exceed expectations by overcoming fear in the face of a near-death experience. Another dimension beyond delivering what is needed on time, which in and of itself is rare. The resolve to rescue another at the possible expense of one's own life is one of the highest expressions of love.

JoAnna, you showed power and strength by pulling out of an abusive relationship. Unfortunately, the perpetrator drains this energy to gain and exert control. We are so happy for her and her children. What a great example, and we hope others find inspiration in her lead.

Dennis, you knock it out of the park. The most obvious message of your story: heartfelt joy exists only in giving, not taking. Still, we must recharge to continue providing our skills to others. Unplugging is necessary to be able to concentrate on ourselves especially in our hectic environment. Thank you for this important message. And thank you for building an "empire of giving."

Faith shows how programming instills our thoughts and behaviors. Your internal talk helped us understand how unhealthy "not rocking the boat" really is. We were reminded that our history does follow us. And regardless of the efforts to suppress negative feelings, they will bubble up. We are glad to see you climbed out of the trenches on this and are on a "program" of healing and self-love.

Christopher, without people sharing their own stories, we would not understand what people have been through, nor could we connect with them. We tend to see them in their current human form and forget there is a past that got them there. Growing up in the worst environment makes for a very rough start. When the enemy surrounds you, survival takes all the resources. Finding your own path out of the combat zone requires resources and creativity. Thank you, Christopher, for pointing out that even under the worst circumstances, there is a way to break out. Your story is powerful and shows how we can rewire our minds, surround ourselves with people who believe in us, and thrive!

Ashley, quite inspiring to see how quickly serious issues can vanish when we experiment and find joy. From near suicide to healing, self-acceptance and expression have been quite a journey for you. Finding a connection with our body is not always easy. Your excitement to connect your mind, body, and spirit was palpable in your writing. We are so grateful you shared your story with us.

Alexxa, the word "nurture" kept coming up when we chatted about your story. Accepting ourselves is required before we accept others. Nurturing is the basis for confidence, as you clearly expose. But a lack thereof does not spell doom. A path to confidence and success is presented for those who have been pushed down by societal norms. Thank you for this flare (not candle) in the window. And may your light continue to shine brightly.

Sylvie's message is about trust. Trusting in yourself and taking action even if the goal is "to get out of the funk." It is a great motivator. You exemplify the framework of our book—*Win the Wellness W.A.R. We Are Responsible*. You took personal ownership and responsibility to a whole new level. Your life path is paved now!

BODY CHAPTER STORIES

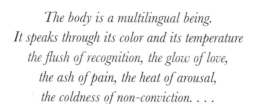

The body is a multilingual being.
It speaks through its color and its temperature
the flush of recognition, the glow of love,
the ash of pain, the heat of arousal,
the coldness of non-conviction. . . .

It speaks through the leaping of the heart,
the falling of the spirits, the pit at the center,
and rising hope.

Clarissa Pinkola Estés

Our Body is a Castle

By Markus Wettstein

I took responsibility for what I determined was broken.

Markus Wettstein
(author, physician)

*M*y studies of the human body began in High School. Along the way, I learned about the structure, function, and interaction of all the systems in the body. I enjoyed studying the biochemical processes. It was only after years of practice that I started comprehending the following:

Every one of us is a collective of roughly 30 trillion cells. They all have their origin in the union of sperm and egg. Yet, brain cells tirelessly fulfill their assigned task every day until the end. The cooperation of all these cells results in our body as is.

In the late 1600s, other cells were discovered. Some of these were responsible for causing disease.

Today, we find bacteria, viri, fungi, and protozoa to be invaders of our bodies.

We are in constant battle with these enemies. We rely heavily on our immune system as our primary defense. Therefore, our individual responsibility is to keep our immune system in top-performing condition.

To be able to do that, all our systems must be performing well. We must step up to the plate, continually assess our health, and make the healthiest decisions possible.

The *All Things Wellness Wheel (ATW Wheel™)* is a self-assessment tool you can complete at any time to see your current state of health and wellness. The tool allows you to determine how you are doing in each quadrant of your life: heart, spirit, mind, and body.

In the body sector, medical care, sleep, exercise, diet, nutrition, and lifestyle are areas for exploration. Balancing the body's sub-sections keeps the wellness wheel rolling smoothly.

To this day, my battle with maintaining enough exercise continues. I struggled for years to embed a consistent exercise routine because I never thought exercise was enjoyable; nonetheless, I realized exercise "outside of the gym" counted.

During the growing season, gardening not only provides organic nutrients but also provides physical activity. It is now at the top of my "exercise" list. And there are always projects to tackle, such as painting and house maintenance. I strive to hit three cardio sessions weekly, but it is often a battle.

My nutrition has improved dramatically over the last few years but remains challenging. The puncture in my wheel could improve. I am reading more and more reports that even the most-balanced diet lacks nutrition. Supplementation appears to be necessary for most of us.

In my practice, I see many patients with Vitamin D deficiency from poor nutrition. This has resulted over the years in the development of osteoporosis. On the other hand, the daily intake of Vitamin D and calcium twice daily significantly maintains bone health in many women.

Another area in the *ATW Wheel*[TM] is sleep. I began using a sleep monitoring app years ago and studied the reports in detail. The most important was finding the hours of sleep I needed each night. Next was to establish bedtime. The app tells me how long it took for me to fall asleep. No 'screen time' 3/4 of an hour before bed was necessary not to delay that. Next, the app tells me how much I snore or cough. It lets me know how much time I spent in the different sleep phases and so much more. I regard sleep as the foundation of the next day, and good sleep is a necessary start.

We need a strong castle.

This helps us to defend against assaults and deficiencies in our external and internal environment.

I am responsible for gathering as much information about my health and wellness as possible. Having an awareness of my current health and gathering knowledge is part of the solution; putting it to work is another. My deficiencies, such as exercise and improving my nutrition, lay on my shoulders.

As I have begun to focus on energy science, I have also worked to reign in areas of excessive energy to create a lifestyle balance. To reel in my stress levels, I now work on a two-week rotating schedule. This has allowed me to remain connected with my patients and balance my personal life. In essence, I took responsibility for what I determined was broken.

The other two weeks are used for creativity. I count gardening as an act of creation with self-sustenance in mind. I am also exploring the bridge between body and spirit. You read more about that in the spirit chapter of this book.

Ultimately, it is clear to me that a regular check-up with the Wellness Wheel is required to maintain balanced wellness and health properly. Fixing the punctures is proactive medicine. We must move away from reactive medicine and Win the Wellness W.A.R.

One of Dr. Markus's Favorite Quotes

A neurotic is a man who builds a castle in the air.
A psychotic is the man who lives in it.
A psychiatrist is the man who collects the rent.

Jerome Lawrence

Learning to Walk Again at Age 21

By Tanner Willms

Don't stop until you cross the finish line.

Tanner Willms
(author, inspector)

*G*rowing up in a small town in Colorado in the 90s seemed horrible as a kid. But, as I look back on my early years, with the status of the world today, and now a father raising my own children, I realize just how blessed I really was.

I was athletic and active, playing sports like football, baseball, and soccer and competitively racing bicycles and motorcycles. Back then, kids could be at the skatepark all day or riding their bikes freely to school or their friends' houses. As a dad, I cannot imagine letting my sons run all over. It's a scary world.

Even though I dabbled in all these other sports, nothing ever compared to the rush of riding and racing motorcycles. At age three, before I could ride a bicycle, I learned to ride a PW50, my first motorcycle. Quickly, I transitioned from riding back and forth between my parents on the front lawn, to the cul-de-sac, to the desert, and then waiting for the starting gate to drop at races. My very first race was the day before I turned four years old. I received my first nickname at that race. At the first turn, I kept going straight, and another ran right into me. My dad came up to check on me, and I guess the first words out of my mouth were, "That guy T-boned me!"

From that day forward, I became T-Bone.

As the years passed, my life was school, practicing, and racing. I raced all over Colorado, Utah, Oklahoma, Nebraska, and Nevada. I racked up dozens of trophies, won a jumping contest at age 10, and state championships. My school friends never really understood the dedication it took to compete or how seriously I took it. It was truly my life.

Until you become a parent, you don't understand how great yours were. They put my brother and me first. They worked several jobs so we could have brand-new motorcycles every year. My mom took care of healthy meals, physical training, and school work in addition to being a nurse. My dad was the ultimate race dad. He took care of everything "bike" related. Because of them, I raced the most talented kids from across the states.

Racing dirt bikes made me who I am today
but also took me to my knees. Literally.

Racing taught me valuable life lessons that rarely come unless you are in a competitive environment, how to fall and get back up. You get out of life what you put in. Don't stop until you cross the finish line.

Our motto was, *Without Risk Comes Reward.*

But with all the wins come losses. It's not a secret that jumping over one hundred feet is dangerous. It is not a question of whether you will get hurt. It is a matter of when. I drank the adrenaline Kool-Aid repeatedly, and I was injured A LOT. My first fracture was my calcaneus (heel) at age six. Later that week, I raced with a big work boot on over my cast. After all, missing one race could cost you the whole season.

Before I even got to high school, I had broken collar bones, heels, and ankles, been in a wheelchair and had a minimum of six concussions. My first time in a wheelchair was in 7th grade, with both legs in a cast.

The growth plates in my feet had so much damage from the non-stop pounding over the years that the doctors decided to put casts on. This was to slow some of the damage and keep me off my feet. My first surgery was on a dislocated shoulder during my sophomore year in high school. My shoulder dislocated, I tore the labrum, and the impact put a 7mm dent in my scapula, causing internal bleeding. I never wanted to quit, so we didn't. If I had high grades, I could race. It is difficult for people to understand how you could keep putting yourself through such extreme risks. It's just in my blood.

After high school, I began working in the oilfield and making a decent living, but I rode when I could. The competitive itch never faded. So, at age 21, I decided to switch things up in a big way. I loaded all my belongings into my Tacoma and a small trailer and headed to Utah. My goal was to immerse myself in my passion. I began working for a motorcycle parts distributor and decided to pursue racing one more time. I practiced on groomed and sanctioned tracks with the fastest guys around. Living and breathing motorcycles again felt amazing.

Ninety-one days after my first day of work, my life changed forever.

Finally, the 215 opened. It was a pro track in Jordan River, Utah. I longed to ride that track, but it had been closed every time I visited. Finally, on October 4, 2015, it was open. My friends and I were over the moon. I couldn't get my gear on fast enough to start laying down some laps! As a trained rider, I know how critical it is when you are on an unfamiliar track to acclimate to the design and ensure your motorcycle is correctly dialed in for the terrain (tire pressure, suspension, wheel spokes, and more). That day, I made the biggest mistake of my career. I didn't double-check the pressure in my forks and was about to pay for it in a significant way.

On lap three, I approached a split-lane rhythm section. You had two choices to reach a huge 120-foot jump ultimately. The right side had a double section before the huge jump. The left side was more complex and faster with a triple jump. Guess what route I chose? I sat down to preload my suspension to help clear a triple jump. I thought I was in second gear but had shifted incorrectly. I was still in third. I sat down on my seat to preload for the large triple jump, but because I didn't shift down, I was moving too fast. I approached the lip of the jump at about 20 mph. About 30 feet into the air, I realized what was about to happen, but it was already too late to brake. I was along for the ride. When I left the lip of the jump, I knew I would overshoot the landing. Unfortunately, my front and rear suspension hit the ground simultaneously, and both completely bottomed out, digging both foot pegs deep into the dirt and breaking the soles of both of my brand-new boots in half.

Both of my ankles exploded.

It felt like someone strapped grenades to my feet and pulled out the pins. I knew right away that they were both broken. The crazy thing is that I didn't even crash. My fight-or-flight instinct kicked in, and I knew I needed to get my feet upright to reduce swelling. I drove to an open area in the center of the track to avoid other riders. I laid my bike down, leaned to my right side, and used my arms to push the bike off me. While on my back, I put both feet in the air and started to unbuckle my boots. Assessing the injuries was next. I felt into my boots to feel for blood or compound fractures. You learn never to take your gear off. Leave it to the professionals. I buckled them back up and began to take my helmet and goggles off so I could cool down.

The shock had set in, and I was white as a ghost and profusely sweating after waving my arms around and trying to get my buddy's attention. Ironically, he had a broken leg from a previous accident and wasn't riding that day. When he got to me, his first words were, "What's up, dude? We just got here?" I replied, "Both my ankles are shattered. We gotta go, NOW!"

It took forever for the track officials to finally stop the practice so they could get me off the track. Everyone kept asking me if I wanted an ambulance. I, of course, denied it because who has the money for that, right? So my friend loaded me and my bike up, and we started driving. Once on the highway, we realized we had no idea where the closest hospital was, so I asked, "Hey, Siri, take me to the closest hospital." I then called my mom, who was at a Denver Broncos game, and told her I had broken both legs and was headed to the hospital, and Kyle would get her the address. Siri didn't know that the small community hospital she sent us could not handle my injuries. The ER cut all my gear off, and within minutes of reading the X-rays, they told me that I needed immediate surgery on both legs. I would be transported via ambulance to the University of Utah, 30 minutes away. The damage report was extensive. My left tibia and fibula were severely fractured. I dislocated my talus in the right leg, and my ankle was turned 180 degrees in the wrong direction.

In surgery, they put an external fixator on the left leg as the swelling was too severe for surgery. A long rod was drilled through each side of my ankle to hold it in a cone-shaped metal device. On the right, they realigned my talus and put two two-inch plates with four screws across my ankle joint to keep it together. Though I was in unbearable pain, I chuckled when I saw the name on the door of my room. Apparently, I was now *Trauma Zodiac*. I arrived without identification, so the staff didn't know who I was. This made it very challenging for my brother and mom to find me when they arrived.

Unfortunately, the bad news kept coming.

When you have extensive trauma in your body, you risk getting compartment syndrome. That's when there is so much swelling from excessive pressure and blood accumulating in your muscles. If the pressure isn't released, the body part can explode. On a scale of 1 to 40, I was 37. I was three points from getting giant incisions down both sides of my left leg to release the pressure. Fortunately, the swelling subsided. So instead of staying in a nearby hotel waiting for surgery on the second leg, we decided I would have the operation on my other leg in Denver. That's where my mom lived. Because her house was eight hours away, we decided to stay a few days with my brother, who lived at the halfway mark. This would allow me to rest before we headed the rest of the way to my mom's.

The trip was one of the most awful experiences in my life. My mom bought every pillow and sleeping bag she could at Walmart to fill up the back of my brother's Pathfinder, where I would lie down for the trip. It was unbearable pain as my external fixator shifted from side to side on the rough roads. I get physically ill when I take pain medication, so I suffered through it.

After two weeks, the swelling decreased, and I had surgery on my left leg. They removed my fixator and added two plates and 30 screws. I now had two legs in casts and spent four months in a wheelchair. I was 21 years old, sleeping on my mother's couch and having to be lifted in and out of the bathtub. Therapy was a nightmare. This experience brought me to my knees, literally crawling on my hands and knees, wearing carpenter kneepads so that I could maintain some independence. Re-learning to walk at an age when you think you can run the world knocks you down a peg or two.

I had been to hell and back.

My mom told me that watching me walk for the first time was exciting but watching me walk for the second time was a miracle.

Months earlier, I had embarked on a journey of freedom with a passion for eating, drinking, and breathing motorcycles. I would never have imagined it all being stripped away forever.

I believe that everything happens for a reason. In hindsight, I suppose teaching me patience, appreciation, and humility tops the list. After all, your pride is thrown out the window when you use a makeshift toilet in your brother's living room. Cut a hole in the seat of a lawn chair, straddle it over a bucket, and there you go.

After I learned to walk, I moved from Utah to Colorado to live with my brother. I could not work for months and spun out of control with depression and anxiety, resulting in severe alcohol addiction.

Through competitive racing, I learned that when you are knocked down, whether it is three feet or 30, as I was, you have to get back up. It's now 2023. I'm married with a beautiful son and one on the way. I am sober and couldn't be more thankful for everything motorcycle racing has taught me. It gave me all the tools I needed to become the man I am today. In the moment, you may feel like you have lost everything, but you've actually won the race.

After my left leg healed, I had another surgery to remove the screws. I still have them in a bag. They don't look quite like all of my other trophies, but they taught me more than the others combined.

Tanner Willms ~ *Thank you, Mom, for always taking care of me during my injuries, and allowing me to make mistakes and learn from them—and always believing in me. Thank you to my wife for sticking by my side through rough times and pushing me to be the best version of myself.*

One of Tanner's Favorite Quotes

Run when you can. Walk if you have to.
Crawl if you must. Just don't give up!

Bear Grylls

The Day I Learned How to Stand

By Evelyn Knight

*Allowing people in also helps you
learn how to receive love.*

Evelyn Knight
(author, speaker, child-care advocate)

9 found myself lying on the floor at my front door, hyperventilating. I could not get myself to turn the doorknob and leave my house. The thought of driving seven minutes down the road to the childcare center that I owned terrified me. It was March 2012, and I was paralyzed in a state of defeat from the events of the last nine months.

It all started when my husband collapsed at work and ended up in the hospital. During this time, two doctors asked me if our affairs were in order. This would be the beginning of my husband's nine-year struggle with a disease that would eventually take his life. Within three months, I also was diagnosed with a disease that would drastically alter my life as I knew it.

**I thought it was stress and anxiety
causing me to sleep twenty hours a day.**

My doctor suspected something neurological was happening, but I was in complete denial. I just assumed I was very depressed. The diagnosis only added to this depression. Not only was I learning to deal with my husband's illness and diagnosis, but now, my diagnosis had defeated me to the point that I mentally checked out.

I left my business in the hands of people I trusted to run my financials. Little did I know that my taxes were not getting paid, and the following month an IRS agent knocked on my front door and informed me I owed over $100,000 in taxes. My business was not making a profit, and I did not know what I was going to do.

I had 150 families that relied on me for childcare and 22 employees that needed work during a recession. I could not let them down, but since I was so overwhelmed with the circumstances of my life, I froze. I did nothing. I hid in my house, and I slept. I embraced the neurological disease that had hijacked my life and allowed it to control me completely.

This wasn't the first time I found myself lying on the ground by my front door, trying to leave my house. It had been happening for about two months. Up to this point, I had stopped trying to, and I just slept the days away, but this time something inside me wanted to fight. However, I was scared.

I got up off the floor and made an appointment with a psychologist.

My husband drove me 45 minutes from home to the first available therapist the following week. She quickly diagnosed me as agoraphobic. She explained that the insecurity from what was happening to me because of my neurological disease and other traumatic experiences I had been through was causing me to have a crippling anxiety that did not allow me to leave my house without my husband. I had become terrified to be in public. With how she spoke, it sounded like my only hope was to adapt to this paralyzing condition.

I could not accept that! I am a mother, a daughter, a sister, and a wife. How could I show up for my family if I was tied to my house? I am a business owner and educated woman with ambition and a clear vision for my life. How would I fulfill my God-given purpose if I was bound to my home? I knew I could not allow this situation to become permanent. I had to fight.

The next day I took out a notebook and journaled through a few very important questions. I asked myself what my life would look like if I owned my two new diagnoses. What would my life look like if I allowed narcolepsy and agoraphobia to define me? For a while, I argued with myself. What choice do I have? That question led me to ask myself a critical question that would change everything: *What part of these two illnesses was completely out of my control?*

The results were shocking. That question made me realize that I was allowing my conditions to dictate my future. I was so focused on the negative ramifications that I wasn't even looking for a way to adapt and thrive. I asked myself two more questions: What do I want my life to look like, and why can't I live this life?

Initially, I chose to answer with blame. How could I live the life of my dreams with this neurological disease? So, I asked myself what exactly about the disease was stopping me. I kept asking myself different questions until I realized that my perception and mindset, not the disease, were the things that were holding me in place. The next questions I asked myself would set me on an entirely different course. I had to step outside the box I had created and start looking for opportunities and adaptations.

Through this process, I have come to a new realization that I now use in every aspect of my life. I now realize that no matter what happens, I choose how I will react. I get to choose whom I will show up as and how each situation will impact me. I realized that every day I am creating my testimonial, and I get to choose how it plays out. I knew that as long as I was willing to do the work, I could find a way to adapt and live the way I wanted to live. I had to make a decision. I realized that I could do the work and find a way, or five years from now, I could be locked inside my house with my conditions absorbing me.

I am no longer considered agoraphobic and have learned how to adapt my life around narcolepsy. Not only did I find a way to pay the IRS, but I also completely turned my childcare business around and now teach childcare center owners how to be successful in the industry. I have also gone on to start a podcast and opened a second business that has proven to be even more successful than my first. I found ways to adapt to my condition that may not seem very conventional and, as an employer, almost unrealistic. I take two naps most days, watch my diet closely and exercise religiously. I now look for adaptations and opportunities in every situation I face. I constantly ask myself, *"how can I make this work for me?"*

Everything changes when you realize that life does not have to happen to you, but you can make it happen for you. You can turn the darkest moments into victories. This isn't always easy, and it takes work! Some life events are so significant and painful that it is hard to find a way to make them happen for you.

In 2021, I lost my husband and life partner of 29 years.

This would prove to be the biggest challenge I've ever faced. I have built two successful businesses and accumulated a comfortable life between the events of 2012 and 2021. Our 30th anniversary came seven months after his passing. That day, I looked at my life. I knew I could sell my companies and never work another day. I went back to the questions I asked myself in 2012, but this time they were much harder to answer, so I came up with new questions.

"What do I want my testimony to be at the end of this?" "How do I want my children to see me one year from now?" These new questions I asked myself were deeper and more challenging to answer but asking them was not the point. In 2012, I had an awakening. I realized that I could control the thoughts that go through my mind. I can control the darkness by questioning and reframing how I interpret the world around me. In 2021, I had a new epiphany that has proven to take me to an even higher level: I need the help of other people.

This realization took longer to come to or maybe to acknowledge. My husband had been terminal for three years before he died. I was the CEO of one of my companies and the co-director of the other, and I now had to become my husband's nurse. I learned to lean on others to help me during this time, although asking for help was so painful. It made me feel weak and like I was a bother to them. Through this experience, I learned that people want to help and often are hurt when not given the opportunity. To rise to the next level in any aspect of life, I need help.

I leaned on my family, friends, and staff. I learned to trust them with my businesses and, most importantly, my vulnerability. I also got professional help. I enlisted the help of a life coach, business coach, and therapist. Watching the person you love slowly die over the course of three years is an awful experience that I could not have done alone, no matter how positive I tried to be. Without help, I could not reframe my thoughts or see the light at the end of the tunnel.

I now teach others the importance of having people to help you see through different eyes. You see, each of us lives in a metaphorical fishbowl. We cannot see outside our fishbowl and often don't even realize there is an outside. The people that come alongside you can be your eyes outside the fishbowl. They can help you see things you weren't even capable of seeing.

Allowing people in also helps you learn how to receive love. I have always been someone who loves to pour love into people, but I struggle receiving it. During my husband's illness, I had no choice but to receive. It is crazy how hard it can be for some of us to merely receive without question. I could tell you story after story about times I felt hopeless and lost without realizing someone was there wanting to guide me and give me hope. I could not see this from inside my fishbowl, but I could work through it with the help of the professionals I hired.

With all of the struggles I have experienced, I realize, above all else, that I have a choice – will my life's struggles destroy me, or will I stand up? It is my choice to stay on the floor or learn how to stand.

One last note… Some life experiences do require professional help. Our life events can cause traumas with hidden ramifications that may affect our quality of life. There are some things and situations that we cannot *will* ourselves through. I am writing this as a victor 18 months after my husband's death because I got professional help. There is no shame in needing help. You are not weak for needing help. We were not meant to walk this life on our own. Getting help was how I chose to stand this time around.

You, too, can *Learn to Stand*.

Evelyn Knight ~ *I dedicate my stories of resilience to my children Bronson and Ronin Knight for always giving me a reason to fight!*

One of Evelyn's Favorite Quotes

For God did not give us a spirit of Fear
but of power and love and self-control.

2 Timothy 1:7

Surfacing

By Cyndi Wilkins

I felt grateful to be alive for the first
time in over thirty years.

Cyndi Wilkins
(author, bodywork expert)

I have always been fascinated by the manifestations of chronic pain
and illness and the behavioral patterns that often lead us into a
lifetime of struggle with chronic disease.

Over many social platforms, I have shared my thoughts on how we
can create shifts in the mindset of disease and reset the circuitry of our
brains to set us on an open course toward wellness.

I must note here that my thoughts and opinions are purely my
own and based on personal experience. I am one of the many who has
struggled with the addictive behaviors that can put you on a collision
course with chronic pain and illness.

After years of dredging the bottom of my own emotional well, I finally
managed to rise from the depths and reflect upon the past, recognizing
the behavioral patterns that swept me away into a deep undercurrent of
chronic pain, anxiety, and depression.

This is not about assigning blame or judgment. This is about assuming
responsibility. "We Are Responsible" for the outcome of our mental or
physical conditions. I believe that the conditions we have created are
a direct result of the choices we make every day due to the behavioral
patterns set in motion by the energetic charge of our emotions.

Those with conflicting opinions fiercely defend their positions and/ or conditions, and it is not my intention to undermine the sufferings of others.

Tapping into these energies rattles cages for a reason. A great deal of fear and anxiety accompanies the deeply embedded pain of trauma. This internalized fear keeps us from BELIEVING we have any power over our conditions.

Coping mechanisms for stress management are basic life skills we should teach our children in grammar school. Instead, we have conditioned ourselves for the use of pharmaceuticals as a first line of defense for everything that ails us. From the bumps and bruises of everyday living to the severe chronic pain and illness that can result from the overuse of medications, we have avoided confronting our pain by numbing it.

However, the bottom line is, whatever the conditions are playing out for us personally, our lives are a product of our own choices, intentions, and attitudes, whether we are aware of it or not.

The beauty of life and all its difficulties is that we have within us the power to choose our own thoughts and actions. No one can ever take that from us. If we do not like what we see or the way we feel, we can consciously choose to 'think differently' in any situation, no matter how dire it may outwardly appear.

When we understand how energetic resonance works (output of thought and emotional energy) and how it affects us and all that we interact with, we will no longer flounder our way through a life of pain. Nothing, and no one, will ever have the power to debilitate us again.

But first, to understand the true nature of our pain, we must understand its origin. In this case, I am speaking primarily of post-traumatic events and the chronic pain and illness that can result. Be it physical or emotional, if left unchecked, it can and will manifest in the body and mind.

Past trauma is exactly that. It has passed. My intention is not to dismiss the traumas of those who have suffered, some more horrific than others. What I am suggesting here is that the pain from our past we are dragging into the present is our own responsibility to address in the now so that the wound can heal from within.

When we are hurting, we can become incredibly angry and resentful. Unless we address our pain in the present moment, we will repeatedly bury it until it becomes a thickened sludge at the bottom of our 'not-so-well' past.

With every emotion, every perception, and every experience of pain that follows, that sludge begins to simmer at the bottom of the well. With enough heat (anger, fear, frustration, resentment), it will eventually erupt to the surface.

With each uprising of this energy, we have an opportunity to address or ignore it. Unfortunately, the longer it sits in the bottom of the cauldron, the more difficult it becomes to address because of our continual recycling of its energy.

We build layers upon layers until, eventually, we have walled ourselves off from the rest of the world in a desperate attempt to protect ourselves from feeling any more pain. This process does not spare us pain. It prolongs it.

For me, that repressed pain manifested as severe chronic migraines. I lived most of my adult fearing this constant, lurking threat. When the darkness came, I knew the pain was nearby, creeping up on me like a predator about to pounce on its prey.

Here, I share with you a glimpse into the eyes of "The Monster."

I awaken in the night. It has crept in under the cover of darkness, catching me unaware. It claws at my eye while ripping the flesh from my face. It tears a vicious path to the back of my head, screaming in my ears. The sirens are blaring, but I am powerless to stop them. " Do not move, " it warns.

I desperately reach for something to dull the pain. I know NOTHING will quiet the beast, but I try anyway. Nausea washes over me in a merciless wave. Now I have made it angry. "IT" is a migraine, the monster of all headaches combined.

My jaw is clenched so tight I can barely open my mouth. My teeth are aching with every beat of my heart. I plead with the beast, but it scoffs at me. I am immediately aware that the pain will become far greater before it is over. I surrender as the intruder settles in.

"Let us clear your schedule, shall we?" It is mocking me. " I will be staying for a while."

I am a prisoner now, shackled by the power of its brutal force. The beast will not kill you, but it will make you wish you were dead. It knows its power, and it can destroy lives, leaving in its wake the ruins of careers, relationships, and anything else that dares get in its way.

Many have run away, unable to face you. I am forced to stay, unable to escape you. There are loud noises in my head, although I am alone, paralyzed in a dark and quiet room. A huge cracking sound startles me, followed by a piercing, primal scream that causes me to moan softly.

The sound of my own voice is like thunder in my ears. I am breathing very shallowly now. I feel the presence of my mother. She suffered at the hands of the beast as well. Suddenly, I am missing her terribly. I begin to cry.

"No, no," she whispers. "Crying will only make it angry. Just breathe."

I am grateful for brief moments of sleep. I dream I am floating in a room full of brilliant colors. The light dances with life as I reach out to touch it. The energy surges through my fingertips, my hand tingling with delight. I am not in any pain, just in the presence of comfortable peace.

I know this is just a visit, and I cannot stay. I do not feel my body's weight, just my soul's presence. I wish never to leave this place, but I am encouraged to return. I am in restful sleep, but the beast will wake all too soon.

I fade in and out of tortured sleep as it continues a relentless assault on my entire body. I am aching from the stillness, terrified to move. That will just make my heart beat faster, surging the tides in my head. It has been fourteen hours now, with no end in sight.

"Hello?" A little voice whispers in the darkness, " Mom, are you ok?"

It is my ten-year-old daughter. She kisses me gently on the cheek.

"I brought you some ice cream to help you feel better."

I see myself, so many years ago, doing the same thing for my own mother as she struggled in the clutches of this beast. I try not to cry. She is so sweet. I am so lucky to have her.

Twilight comes again. As I awaken to the dawn of a new day, the beast has loosened its grip a bit. I sneak down some crackers and medication. I notice the subtle turning of the tide in my head. A mere twenty-four hours this time. How fortunate, I think. It has been known to hang around much longer.

"Do not get complacent," the beast growls. "You and I have a long history."

"Yes, we do, beast, and I have the utmost respect for your power. But I have a life to live, and it is time now for you to go."

The beast scowls at me and decides to linger for several more hours. It allows my body to function while continuing to throb at the back of my head, reminding me of its presence.

For now, it is leaving me, but I know in my heart that we will dance again one day.

Sometimes, we just do not know how strong we are until something breaks us, shattering the collective pieces of our hearts and minds into a fragmented puzzle that only we can reassemble. It is quite daunting to step up and reflect upon the things we would rather forget.

These moments haunted me, rattling the cages of my subconscious mind where I had imprisoned them for decades. They were angry, in pain, and begging for release. I had kept them quiet for so long, but the beast outgrew its cage. When I was finally ready to reflect upon these moments, a beautiful space was created for a new me to emerge, freeing me from the ghosts of the past.

Humpty Dumpty sat on a wall, Humpty Dumpty had a great fall; All the King's horses and all the King's men couldn't put Humpty together again. ~Lewis Carroll

Yes, I was Humpty Dumpty, and to put myself back together again, I knew I would have to start digging. Only I knew where all the bodies were buried, deep within the well of old bones. The pieces were buried so deeply that I found it difficult to breathe. They choked me when I went diving for them, so angry at being left for dead.

I spent years dredging that well. First, I had to clear a path through the emotional residue floating on the surface. The deeper I went, the harder it was to breathe. The sludge became so thick I could barely see. Eventually, I found her. In the dark corners of my mind, a frightened eleven-year-old girl was left alone for decades at the bottom of a cold and dark well.

I knew her story. She tried to tell them of the assault but was silenced by the ones she trusted. No one would believe her, they said. Besides, adults do not do those things to children. She was so ashamed, feeling she had done something wrong. She kept the pain hidden in her heart and never told a soul until now.

With each conversation, we slowly rose from the depths. It would be another decade before we would catch even a glimpse of the light. The beast remained hot on our trail but soon lost sight of us in the sun's glare. We were finally surfacing together as one, collecting all the old bones along the way.

As I crashed through the surface, shaking free from the pain of the past, I felt grateful to be alive for the first time in over thirty years. Love was the antidote. My love for myself, and a little girl, would never be left alone in the dark again.

Cyndi Wilkins ~ *This book is so much more than a compilation of stories... It is an experience set in motion by some of the world's greatest teachers!*

One of Cyndi's Favorite Quotes

If we are willing to do the mental work,
almost anything can be healed.

Louise Hay

Becoming a Badass

By Peggy Preston

———————— ⭐ ————————

We must be kinder, more forgiving, and more open.

Peggy Preston
(Author, Pastry Chef)

I am a Wife, Mother, Friend, Aunt, Sister, Co-worker, and more. I am a strong, able-bodied woman who takes no shit from anyone and works hard daily. I am in control of my life and manage a million things, from home life to work life. I like to be in control and independent. I want no one waiting on me or doing things for me. I…I…I…

My husband and I love to golf, among other activities. It was a Tuesday in May, and we had a great round of golf. The next day we were joking about the first day out golfing— we felt the aftereffects in our bones… my back and legs were killing me, and he was sore all over. I was leaving for Atlanta the next day for a trade show and thought if it didn't improve, I would see a chiropractor. It felt like it was sciatica.

In Atlanta, I noticed that my left leg felt heavy, forcing me to stop and rest periodically. The pain intensified. After making it through one of the industry's largest trade shows, I arrived home and realized my soreness was not due to our first golf game of the season.

I saw my general practitioner, and he immediately sent me to a vascular surgeon. My gut told me something was wrong, but no one else was. I was scared and pissed! My husband could not leave work to be with me, so I was alone.

I have never felt so alone.

I heard my doctor talking in the hallway, "She is 44 and has no health issues. I have never seen a case like this before. I think I need some reinforcement." The doctor walked back into the room, and the look on his face gave me a lump in my throat.

The words, "You are lucky to be alive," came next. You have an aneurysm underneath your heart, and it has spawned a blood clot behind your knee. With the most serious look and heavy heart, my doctor said I needed to go to surgery immediately. He followed it with, "I have only seen two percent of these cases survive. Typically these clots travel directly to the brain, thus being fatal."

I burst into tears, started cussing, and my body trembled at the sheer thought that, at any minute, I could drop dead. WTF! How did this happen, when, why, and where? I did not have the time or energy to deal with this shit. I was so pissed and confused.

On July 2ⁿᵈ, I was admitted to the hospital to have a bypass of the leg to fix the aneurysm and blood clot. One surgery, in and out! I prepared my home for recovery. I remember driving to the hospital with my husband in our Camaro (cool ass Camaro, I might add), and we were jammin' to Fall Out Boy. I don't remember much after that except waking up from surgery and hearing the ultrasound machine on my foot, and it sounded like healthy blood flow to me. Let's get this recovery started. I've got things to do!

A few hours later, it felt like a brick had fallen on my foot. The pain was nothing I had ever experienced in my life. I remember vaguely screaming and swearing so loud that my friend Dan took my kids home so they did not have to see me in that state. I remember grabbing the sides of the bed and gasping for air because I thought I was dying. No amount of painkillers can decrease the pain of no blood flow to your foot. The surgeons quickly determined I needed to go in for another eight-hour surgery or whatever it was. At midnight, they wheeled me back in and performed another bypass.

And...again, the pain was unbearable.
And...again, the surgery was unsuccessful.

They decided an epidural was the only way to give me any relief. Except for a few flashbacks—intense pain, my continued screaming, and the steadiness of the ultra-sound machine, I remember little else. However, I vividly remember the part that changed my life and my family's lives forever.

My husband was sitting next to me when the surgeon walked into the room with a look of death on his face, he spoke. "Peggy, the surgeries were not successful. We have to save your life, and the only way to do that is to amputate your left leg. And until we go in, we don't know if it will be below or above the knee."

You would think at that point I would break down or cry and scream, but I calmly said ok, let's do it. I am sure the number of painkillers and anesthesia from two long surgeries back to back kept me in check. It was simply a matter of trusting the doctors. That next morning, I headed back to surgery, and my life changed forever.

As I was wheeled into the operating room, I heard, "We are going to give you a local anesthetic." I about lost my shit! "Nope, you will knock me out for this!" Thankfully, I won the argument.

All I remember post-surgery was being transferred from the bed to the chair. It hurt so badly that I wanted to die, and I thought there was no way I would ever handle this recovery.

The first day standing on one leg was excruciating. When my residual limb hung down, the pain was unbearable. Turns out, yep, guess who had an infection...this gal! After two weeks in the hospital, I thought I was headed to the rehab hospital, but I was on my way back to the operating table. OMG, you guys, it sucked! I have not relived this since it happened, so excuse me if my words got crazy! This incision was to the bone, deep, large, and gross!

After the infectious disease doctor released me, I was moved to the rehabilitation hospital. A little piece of information I left out at the beginning of this story was when I was admitted, I was told I was anemic due to the clot in my leg and an undiagnosed blood disorder they think I have had from birth. My hemoglobin was at dangerous levels, and guess what happened next? A complete blood transfusion.

After 60-something days in the rehab hospital and extensive physical and occupational therapy, I improved. Imagine cooking while on one foot, trying to move things from one spot to the next, or reaching into a cabinet while standing on one leg.

I felt like I was five years old and did not like it one bit!

I had some terrible ups and downs and experienced a plethora of emotions, day in and day out.

This was my first experience with depression; it consumed me. During the day, I felt strong and courageous, but then back in my room, I would have these ghastly bouts of tears and anger. I'd scream, "I just want my foot back," only to burst out in laughter because I only needed one shoe.

My thoughts ran rampant. Surely my husband would leave me, and I would be a vegetable in a wheelchair living at some facility. Certainly, I would lose the job I loved so dearly. I'd be alone, and my kids would stop loving me. Life was over! I was now a burden to everyone around me, and my life no longer mattered.

While my husband assured me I had nothing to worry about, I still wallowed in pity.

Returning home after about 80 days in the hospital was one of the most emotional days of my life. Leaving the comfort and security of the rehab hospital terrified me even though my husband shared pictures of my family, co-workers, and friends flipping our house on its head and making it accessible so I could come home; that filled my heart.

I ugly cried the first time I wheeled myself up the driveway and onto my newly constructed ramp. We lived in a two-story house, but my team of angels had moved our bedroom to the dining room downstairs, but I still had to shower—it was 14 stairs to the second floor. But it only took me a few weeks to master the obstacle.

The world of prosthetics was foreign to me. Several Prosthetists visited me in the hospital. Most of them were like used car salesmen and did not want to spend time explaining the process to me or what it meant to my future. Until one day, Dan walked in. He spent hours getting to know my family and me, and he allowed me to vent and ask questions from A to Z. He visited me daily, knowing that due to the size of my wound and that I was on a wound vac machine, I might be a year out before I could wear a prosthetic. Dan made me feel valued at a time when I felt like nothing. To this day, he is my "leg man" and part of our family. We are forever grateful for his love for helping others.

Imagine trying to get out into the real world.

Imagine going to dinner and using a public restroom (which I am notorious for), but your wheelchair doesn't fit into the stalls, and you only have one leg! Or attending an outdoor function, and there are no accessible outhouses! What about parking at the grocery store in the dead of winter, and some young, lazy punks sit in a handicapped spot laughing at you? My husband always says I will get myself shot because I cannot keep my big mouth shut.

Imagine EVERYONE staring at you and your missing leg or your prosthetic. After eight years of dealing with the looks of fear and the laughs, I have concluded that Adults are RUDE AF and children are just curious.

Wearing shorts in the summer brings many questions. Little kids ask their parents, "What happened to her leg?" or "Look at her leg!" Many parents respond, "Don't talk to her or stay away." Some parents allow their kids to approach me and ask questions. Then they thanked me for sharing my story with them. To those parents who don't even allow their child the opportunity to learn about disabilities and how we are the same as others, a big FU to you!

My husband, my rock, my everything.

My husband hurt so deeply inside, but he stood tall and strong for me! EVERY DAMN DAY he showed up, EVERY DAMN DAY he sacrificed for me, and EVERY DAMN DAY he loved me hard! He encouraged me and told me when to stop being a damn baby and suck it up. When I had a panic attack, he made sure he took me to places that calmed me. He is and always will be one of the reasons I am still here today. He made me remember just who the F I am! I love you, baby. Forever and always!

We must teach others that the world is diverse and that inclusion is real! We must be kind, forgiving, and open to what makes us a great society. We are all equal!

Being an amputee has helped me find purpose, given me killer discipline, and has given me a new appreciation for the little things.

My appearance changed as a professional—no more heels—yay. But my clothes didn't fit properly on my amputated leg. Feeling beautiful didn't exist until I realized that "status" no longer had meaning in my life and that true beauty existed in my heart, mind, and soul; physical beauty is irrelevant.

I have learned that those who love me really love me and accept my new self. Inspiring others, being kind-hearted, and overcoming adversity are my gifts.

**Loving myself through this experience
has been the most significant gift of all.**

To the folks who snicker or roll their eyes at me, I must say you make me work harder and want to raise more awareness. I won't allow you to make me feel less than the powerful woman I am! You motivate me to be a badass every day!

Eight years later, I am thriving like crazy! My life is wonderful! I am so grateful for overcoming these challenges, which have given me valuable lessons. Along my journey, I will continue to touch hearts and souls through my experience.

Be Kind to each other! We can learn to love each other one leg at a time!

Peggy Preston ~ *My husband, My rock, My life- Thank you for sticking by my side through it all and loving my whole self, even when I wasn't complete. My boys, you protected me, hugged me, and never let me quit!*

One of Peggy's Favorite Quotes

Your time is limited, so don't waste it
living someone else's life.
Don't be trapped by dogma – which is living with
the results of other people's thinking.

Steve Jobs

Sweet Surrender

By Jesica Henderson

It wasn't about losing weight and eating healthy.
It was, but it was more than that.

Jesica Henderson
(author, host, producer)

*I*t starts as an intimate process, separating each into flavor categories. This creates a beautiful rainbow of colors and designs. I have little piles displayed before me on the ottoman. There are vibrant hues of purple, lime green, deep cherry red, sky blue, and yellow. It is almost like a game to see how many I have in each flavor and decide where to place the piles. Then I take a deep breath, carefully moving the pieces around, matching complementary flavors together. This work of art moves the less desirable flavors to the side to "throw away" because they are not as pleasurable as the rest.

Once everything is nicely laid out in front of me, I take a moment to examine my masterpiece. I can already smell the sweetness left behind on my fingertips. I carefully contemplate where I want to start. Which flavor will be my first? More importantly, which flavor will I save for the very last? This process takes patience, thought, and a level of mindfulness to get it all just right.

The decision is made. I'll start with one of my favorites. Then I begin moving through the flavors to the "lesser than" but saving at least one or two of the best for last. Here goes the first one. The second it hits my tongue, I feel a rush. It's sweet, almost too sweet. It makes my mouth water and tongue tingle. I waste no time going for the next.

It isn't long before I've abandoned my entire process.

Now I'm tossing back multiple flavors, not really thinking about any particular order; I need the sweet hit. Five minutes go by, then ten. I'm still going. It is just so good. My stash is dwindling, and I feel a slight hint of panic. Ok, slow down, savor what's left. "You are down to the final few handfuls," I tell myself.

As I reach the end, I am snapped back to reality. My stomach is starting to hurt, and the sweet serenity has become an uncomfortable numbness in my mouth. Not to worry, I know the solution. I need some salt to cancel out the sweet. Not a problem; I live less than a block from the store. I'll walk over and get some chips to even it all out.

While I'm there, I might as well get another pack of the sweetness; why not? That way, I won't have to make another trip next time I want some. I'll keep them in the cupboard. I get home, unpause my Netflix, and work on the salty goodness to counteract the sweetness. The crunch, the salt, now I'm at a new level of pleasure. It tastes so good. The numbness of flavor left by over sweetness is now replaced with a mouth-watering mix of salt and garlic. "Once you pop, the fun doesn't stop," as they say.

Minutes into demolishing my salty snack, I realized I'd taken it too far. I felt sick. The bitter taste left in my mouth is not only physical because I'm nauseous but metaphorical because the reality of what I had just done sets in. This isn't the first time. This is actually day three of a series of my many binges before. And more to come? I know better. I've been to a dietician before. I have experienced the gain and loss cycle many times in my years on this planet. It started in 8th grade when the "ah ha" moment of gaining weight and entering puberty changed my entire perspective.

My next move is the only logical one I can think of at the moment. I need to get rid of the new bag of jelly bellies that I just bought. So I open it up and get to work, tossing back handfuls at a time. I tell myself this is the best thing to do. My teeth and jaw hurt from chewing so vigorously. I can't have it in the house, so I might as well eat it all now. About halfway through the bag, I'm so sick I can't move. I toss the rest of the bag in the trash.

The next day, I'm feeling motivated to make better choices. I start my day with a healthy breakfast and intend never to let myself do that again. Yesterday is behind, and I'm a new woman. By lunch, without even a pause, I'd carefully retrieved my bag of jelly bellies from the trash; thank goodness most of them didn't fall out into the gross leftovers from the previous day. That would be a new level of rock bottom. As if pulling food out of the trash isn't already rock bottom, regardless of whether it is in the container or not.

A quick flashback to high school popped into my head when I pulled a fudge bar out of the trash that someone had already taken one bite out of. Everyone said that it was disgusting and hilarious, which was kind of my MO. At that time, it was more for the reaction than the "need" for the fudge bar. In contemplating this years later, I wonder if there is more to examine here…

Flash forward to where we left off, day four of my sweet, salty, sweet binge pattern. This is a cycle I got to know very well. It wasn't always the jelly bellies to chips routine. I would switch it up with dove chocolate to pizza bites or ice cream to pretzels. I like to be creative with my binging. Doing the same old thing gets tiring.

Citrus Pectin, Sodium Citrate, Confectioner's Glaze, Blue 1, Yellow 5, Yellow 6, Red 3. Yummy, don't those sound delicious? It is an amazing trick I learned from my grandma. She taught me to separate the ingredients and think about eating them individually. It slows down the craving and gives more of an opportunity for a conscious decision, I suppose. She used to do it by picturing eating a stick of butter or a cup of flour when she wanted to eat a cookie. This is all good, except it still requires a level of mindfulness. When the need for your next hit blinds you, you are not always thinking logically or mindfully.

One day while reading my women's health magazine, I got my first dose of almost admitting I had a problem. I was casually flipping through when I was stopped by a headline that I couldn't ignore. "The Truth about Sugar Addiction" stared me right in the face. I started to read about dopamine production in the brain when someone eats sugar. They wrote about a spike so significant and so intense that it was a similar response to those who use heroin or cocaine. Reading this left me with a pit in my stomach and a heavy heart. Sprinkle on some denial, and you have a perfect combination for another binge. That is precisely what I did. I was out to prove something, though I didn't know at the time what that was. I wasn't an "addict." There was no way that could be true. I make healthy choices, I work out, and I eat salad. All these thoughts kept spinning as I put down another round of jelly bellies.

Insert a husband (then boyfriend) diagnosed with adult-onset type 1 diabetes. This changed a lot about how we ate and exercised. I got myself on track unintentionally during that time because we cut a lot of unhealthy habits out. He was now insulin-dependent, and I wanted to support his journey. So naturally, I started hiding my treats and consuming them in secret. I went as far as "going to the bathroom" and taking my jelly bellies with me to get my fix.

Eventually, the newness of his diagnosis wore off, and I got more relaxed about what I ate and when. Through all of this, that article stayed with me in my subconscious. It would make a little appearance in my mind once in a while, usually when I was on the "Wellness Wagon," as my coach put it. It catalyzed a wellness journey I didn't yet know I was on. Nearly four years after I read that article, I finally decided to make a drastic change.

I happened across a wellness coach because of the work I do. Also, because of my job, I come across a lot of personal development and self-help people. My job is to seek these experts and share how we can help elevate their message and business through our positive media company, The Transformation Network.

One day after she said yes to working with us, she asked me a simple question. I don't remember the exact question, but it was somewhere along the lines of "Are you doing ok with your own wellness?" Followed by a "you look tired" comment. Something about her sincerity and the trust I'd already begun to build made me want to work with her. I'd put off working with anyone in that field for years because I already knew everything they would tell me, and it would be a giant waste of money. This time felt different, so I dove in. I didn't know what to expect, but I knew I had to commit if I was going to pay for someone to tell me to eat healthily.

This journey was not what I expected. It wasn't about losing weight and eating healthy. It was, but it was more than that. I went on a journey of self-discovery, self-love, and, ultimately, self-forgiveness. I started to uncover the "why" behind my binging. Once I knew the why, I could make different, conscious choices. Sounds simple, right?

Well, it turns out my why comes from multiple reasons.

I started to make a conscious effort to understand when the binging was the worst. I had to get out of my comfort zone to log my food and emotions. After doing this for a couple of weeks, I was shocked to discover that almost every emotion was triggering a binge in some way. If I am happy, I celebrate with food. If I have a hard day at work, I self-soothe with food. If I am home alone, I cure boredom and loneliness with food. That dopamine hit is something I crave in the good and the bad parts of every day. This is a daily battle in an ultimate wellness war. I've come a long way with this journey. I've had one major jelly-belly binge in the last three years, which feels like an enormous win. I still catch myself pacing around the house, looking for something to get my hit. I had an honest and vulnerable conversation with my husband about how he could support me—knowing that it is a sensitive subject, we had to turn it into a game to lighten my energy around it. The deal we made is that if we have any treats in the house, he locks them in a file cabinet and takes the key with him. I won't pretend I haven't pulled on that drawer, hoping he forgot to lock it. He knows I try, which is now part of an ongoing game we play to see how many times in a week I try to get in, knowing it is locked every time. Or better yet, he will leave it unlocked on purpose with no treats inside to see if I try to open it.

Wellness is a journey. The sweet surrender is knowing that it will always be a journey. Surrender to the process. Surrender to knowing when you need to reach out for help and surrendering the guilt of trying to make a change for the better. Today, reflecting on where I am on this journey, the good days outnumber the bad.

I have worked hard to form new habits, especially in celebrating. I have become aware of my red flags and filled my toolbelt with ways to cope if I need that soothing dopamine hit from a bad day. My go-to is no longer sugar. Fun Fact: guess what else fires those dopamine triggers? Exercise!

My self-discovery is never-ending. I continue to investigate my whys. I use my creativity to find new strategies and solutions. At times, I feel myself on the balance beam, teetering one way and then the other, but I am able to find my center. Once I find my center, I return to the sweet surrender of acceptance and progress.

One of Jesica's Favorite Quotes

We cannot solve our problems with the same thinking
we used when we created them.

Enough is ENOUGH

By Michelle McDonald

It was dark, cold, and oh so ugly, but I had to face every aspect
of my prison cell.

Michelle McDonald
(author, mental health therapist)

9 was 38 years old, angry, and bitter.
I spent hours and hours obsessing about everything I had missed out
on and feeling like the world had left me behind. My anger consumed me
99% of the time. It was like an infection that had spread into every area
of my body and my life. I had finished Grad school but wasn't working in
my field, and I felt like a failure. I couldn't get out of my own way.

Being extremely overweight my entire life kept me from doing what
I wanted but couldn't. I had the heart of an athlete but the body of
an elephant. Spending years hiding away and trying to find my place
in the world only led to decades of pain and suffering. There wasn't a
room I walked into that didn't include stares, laughter, and mocking. I
still have PTSD when I hear the song "Old MacDonald Had a Farm."
When you are overweight with a popular last name to match, well, let's
just say kids can be cruel. It has taken decades to move past these childhood heartbreaks.

I have nightmares of going to the doctors just to be told that if I were
"their" child, I would be at a fat farm. It was a lot for anyone to handle,
much less a child who was just trying to find acceptance and a place in
the world.

I never felt enough. Not enough for my dad, who left us and made a new family; not for relatives, who looked at us with pity because my dad had left; not for any sports team because I was fat and slow; not for friends, because they needed a butt to all their jokes. Not enough. My siblings moved on with their lives, and I desperately tried. But deep down, the same narrative consumed me and repeatedly played in my head.

I would never be enough.

Self-hatred consumed me. My reflection in the mirror disgusted me, and I questioned my existence. Having no value in myself gave me little hope for what life had to offer. Getting out of bed was a struggle because I didn't want to be alive and fought with suicidal ideation most days of the week. No one was ever going to love me. My showers were filled with tears because I was so miserable. Luckily, I was too chicken to end things, yet I lived with the guilt of wanting to do it. Not wanting to hurt my parents and, more importantly, my grandparents likely saved me.

One night I watched my nephew, and while trying to pick up his toys after he had gone to bed, I realized I couldn't do it. Getting down on the floor and scooting around was humiliating and exhausting. I leaned against the couch and cried. This was the straw. I was tired of not being a part of my own life. In this moment, I realized it was time to stop being a victim and take back my life.

I joined Fit Body Boot Camp a few weeks later. I was scared out of my mind. Repeatedly, I recited excuses in my head. Don't go! But the first day I walked through that door, I knew it was one of the most life-changing decisions I had made in my life. Five years later, I still walk through that same door. Choosing to take a risk and showing up that first that day was empowering. But walking through those doors was just the beginning.

Three weeks into my "new" life, my grandpa passed away. My grandpa was my person. He had been one of the only constants in my chaotic life. It hit me hard, but I leaned into my coach, and he encouraged me to keep going. I did, and my training never derailed. I showed up every day to every workout and measured and weighed all my food. And slowly, the weight came off.

Losing weight wasn't what my journey was really about. So, as the number decreased on the scale and around my waist, I started to put in the internal work. It was time to find myself. During these challenges, questions popped up, and while responding to those questions, I began to process and explore my mindset.

I needed to break out of my prison.

It was dark, cold, and oh so ugly, but I had to face every aspect of my prison cell. I am still working through some of those spaces. My biggest ball and chain was the narrative I had told myself and the excessively damaging words from those in my past that held me back for years. Breaking the chains has not been easy. Much of my self-discovery has been about boundaries and not giving power to others.

When I realized I was the driver of my own bus, I couldn't decide where I wanted to go. And let me tell you, I was done driving into the negative forest of no return. Every day, I uncovered and constructed my new truth. Instilling a sense of badassness kept me focused. When I took responsibility and regained my power, I realized I could be whomever I wanted. Being a badass kept me focused on my present and my future. The challenges were embraced!

I wanted to be the aunt who played with her nieces and nephews and was present in their lives. Playing on the floor with them, running around effortlessly, and taking them places are a few of my driving forces. It was also crucial for me to be the friend others deserved.

Embracing life to its fullest was something I worked on daily. So the pandemic was another blow to me. When life shut down, so did my gym, where my journey started years ago. My sanctuary. COVID threw many people off their rails. But, despite the uncertainty, it did not shake me. I still showed up for myself every day. Was it perfect? Hell no, but I kept moving forward. I looked around and realized I didn't have to let obstacles stop me from living—pivot, adjust, and keep moving forward.

Commitments to myself are non-negotiable.

The gym offered us tons of videos. Many coaches also worked out with us via Zoom. It wasn't easy or ideal, but I was so attached to my goals that I kept doing the work. One of my favorite shirts says, "My commitment to myself is non-negotiable." That's my mantra! I also pushed my sister and friends to work out virtually. Having virtual dates with my friends kept us all connected and focused.

It has been a challenging experience rewriting my narrative. Realizing I own my story, and it cannot be told by anyone else. Creating boundaries was a bit difficult. One of the most eye-opening shifts was not allowing people into my circle who might steer me from my positive energy. Learning that it is not selfish to put yourself first was another big aha. It doesn't mean I don't value others because, trust me, I do. However, my self-care needs to come first. As they say, in order to love others, you must first love yourself.

Digging deep into my values helped keep me on track. Those promises I make to myself are the center of my being. Living a healthy life was the first step to creating that value. Perfection is not attainable. I tried that for years. I now have the resilience and determination to keep going, and I know I will conquer whatever comes my way.

Building a solid support system has also been essential. My gym tribe, whom I love dearly, understands me. I spent my whole life trying to fit in and find my people. Little did I know I would ever find them at the gym. We are all different ages and walks of life but we love and support each other fiercely. I have never experienced friendships like this. This crew gave me what I always craved. We all found each other because we have a common goal—to live healthier lives. We can be a hot mess sometimes, but I wouldn't trade any of it. My three parents would drop anything for me. I am close with my sibling, and my sister-in-law is one of my best friends. And I now have many friends, which is the opposite of my younger years. In this phase of my life, my support system is its strongest.

There was a lot of hurt and pain in childhood, but as an adult, I realized things you could never understand as a kid. The people who bullied me and didn't accept me for me are no longer part of my life. There may be a few along the sidelines, but they have also changed and grown, so I don't push them completely out.

Now that I am focusing on my health and wellness, I feel free and no longer stuck in prison with no hope or future. I think more clearly when things come my way and don't dwell on the negative or let unfortunate circumstances set me back as long as before. Being healthier and happier has made me a better therapist. Taking care of myself has given me the capacity to help others.

I am not jaded by life and am not biased by negativity.

Saying you are worthy or enough is only part of the battle. Truly believing it is another. Being "enough" is subjective. Each person must dig deep and discover who they are in order to write their own narrative about being enough.

I am just me, and that makes me valuable! And I am ENOUGH!

Michelle McDonald ~ *Proudly, I want to acknowledge myself. Thank you for deciding you were enough and that you deserved to live life to the fullest.*

One of Michelle's Favorite Quotes

If you are serious about changing your life,
you'll find a way. If you're not, you'll find an excuse.

Jen Sincero

Mind and Body Connection

By Carolyn Lebanowski

———— ★ ————

I did not know high blood pressure was a "silent killer."

Carolyn Lebanowski
(author, strategic leader)

It was a beautiful sunny Monday morning in Houston, Texas. My husband and I were driving separately for our routine annual bloodwork. It was just another start to an amazing day – or so I thought.

After three attempts to take my blood pressure, the tension in the room began to rise. The medical technician was looking at me but <u>not</u> looking at me; something felt very off. The silence was broken when he nervously said he had no option but to call an ambulance to take me to the hospital. My blood pressure was elevated at a dangerous level that could not be ignored.

How could this be happening? I have created a healthy lifestyle with regular exercise and good eating habits. I have worked too hard for too long to maintain my weight, my health, and my mental wellness. In the calmest voice I could muster, I told the technician that his blood pressure machine must be broken and there was no way I am going to the hospital.

My husband was calm yet clearly concerned and drove me directly to our own doctor, who fit me into her schedule. Surely, she would see that nothing was wrong with me and that it was all a mistake.

It was not a mistake.

I did not know high blood pressure was hereditary. I did not know high blood pressure was a "silent killer." I did not realize that untreated high blood pressure increases the risk of heart attack, stroke, and other serious health problems.

It just never occurred to me that my heart may be compromised. I had very little information on my family history and had no idea of possible potential risks. But more than anything, I could not imagine seeing a cardiologist when I felt fine.

There was a sense of urgency that was unnerving and unsettling. The space around me became cloudy, thick, and sideways. I could feel myself sliding into fear. This was not helping my blood pressure.

I was referred to one of the top cardiologists in Houston. And a new relationship began between this new physician and my own heart. As a standard and safe protocol, she prescribed heavy doses of medicine to try and level the readings. I was beginning to understand the seriousness of a diagnosis I knew nothing about. She requested that we purchase a blood pressure machine and record my readings three times daily, and report back weekly.

At this point, I knew something had to change. I wanted to be the owner of my own mental and physical health without medication - if possible.

Although I worked out regularly with weights and elliptical equipment at the gym, there was a deep desire to dive deeper outside of my comfort zone. So, I did the unimaginable and walked into a yoga class - cold turkey. Anxious, scared, and yet weirdly comfortable, I trusted myself in this moment. There was no attachment to any outcome because there were no expectations. I just knew I needed to be there.

The class started with three minutes of breathing—just breathing. Sitting in an abyss of ignorance, I thought this would be an easy exercise, but I was wrong…again. This was my opportunity to learn a new way of breathing life into my body and mind, not merely to survive.

I began learning mindfulness, focus, and humility. I started managing my monkey mind, thinking about 100 other things I needed to "do in the moment." It was heart-wrenching that I could not stop my brain from moving at such a fast pace. I could not even focus on one simple thing—breathing.

As we moved into the actual practice, I realized that yoga is about flexibility, strength, balance, and mindfulness. I had no idea what I was doing, yet I was completely committed to finishing the class with integrity for the effort I made.

The class ended in Savasana: a practice of gradually relaxing one body part at a time, one muscle at a time, and one thought at a time. This is where I became uncomfortably comfortable. I wanted it, but I could not find it. I resisted the urge to move, think, do, or be.

Sadly, I could not permit myself to relax.

Highly competitive, I was now competing with myself, for myself. I could not understand why this was so difficult. Trusting there was some gift on the other side, I was committed to keep trying and practicing as often as I could.

Slowly, I began to settle into the practice and into myself. I was learning that yoga brought a new awareness to my body, breathing, and thoughts. There was a keen connection between the three, and I began to understand how the body affects the mind and vice versa.

"The yoga pose is not the goal. Becoming flexible is not the goal. Standing on your hands is not the goal. The goal is serenity. Balance. Truly finding peace in your own skin." —Rachel Brathen

It is said that the mind-body connection relates to how the brain and thoughts influence the body. The health of the mind is directly correlated to the health of the body. Practicing a mind-body connection can improve health, such as relaxation, meditation, and yoga. The science of yoga does not see the mind and body separately. Yoga means "union," which is a way to integrate the mind and body.

Early in my practice, my teacher would begin each class with this instruction: this is your yoga class; this is your mat. There is no need to look at anyone else in comparison to what you are doing. There is no competition in this room. All egos must be left at the door. This is your yoga class; this is your mat. Focus inward, not outward.

This was the moment of clarity when I began listening with my heart and no longer to my head. I would practice with a new sense of the internal work that was required. I realized that yoga is a very personal and sacred experience requiring deep self-awareness and pure focus. I learned that the mind and body are intrinsically interwoven. You work the body to quiet the mind. You work the mind to free the body.

Off the mat, my body was getting stronger. My sleeping improved, and I felt more control of my emotional responses. I was learning to observe my thoughts and not give them the energy that would cause me stress. There was a sweet current of "calm" that felt like a warm blanket on a cold night. Something was shifting, and I knew I was heading in the right direction. I was far from out of the woods, but I felt I was beginning to manage my life versus my life managing me.

My daily blood pressure was still higher than normal, even with medication. This was confusing and frustrating at best. Sitting on the edge of uncertainty, I began to question everything. I felt healthier, stronger, and more grounded than I had been in years. It just made no sense. The cardiologist ran more tests with no definitive results. The only action was to prescribe higher doses of medication.

Reluctantly, it felt like my only choice.

After three days of increased medication, I felt like I was dying. I was losing energy and interest. I was losing my life…I was losing myself! My blood pressure was now seriously too low. The doctor told me to stop taking the medications to let my body level off, and we would reassess in a few weeks.

At this incredible low point in my journey, I became more committed and driven to heal my own body without medication—if I could.

I increased my yoga practice with more intention. I expanded my meditation approach with more awareness. I practiced different breathing techniques with more focus.

My wellness journey intensified when I began studying and consciously practicing diaphragmatic breathing daily on and off the mat. On the mat during yoga, off the mat while driving, waiting in line, on hold on the phone, and during the night if I was restless.

Diaphragmatic breathing regulates and balances the nervous system and supports physical, mental, and emotional health and well-being. Simply, it is being aware of your breath and how you are breathing. It is conscious breathing with attention to your inhales and exhales in a way that expands your diaphragm and allows more oxygen into your blood, translating into healing properties on many levels.

This new awareness of my breathing and consistent yoga practice made a difference. I continued to find new layers of confidence and calm in my daily life. It was like building a muscle; it needed to be worked daily.

I continued to take my blood pressure daily, and I began to see the changes occur slowly. Days and weeks passed without medication, and I remained steady and in a normal range. When my cardiologist called to set another appointment, I shared my progress and told her I would continue to monitor and schedule an appointment if needed.

I never saw her again.

It has been four years without medication, and I continued to take my blood pressure weekly. It is a constant reminder that life is precious, and we own the power and responsibility to pay attention.

I have learned so much on this wellness journey. We are perfectly imperfect humans living in a world of complicated uncertainties, personal truth, and choice.

We will all face scenarios that need medical intervention. That goes without saying. But for now…

I have learned when to take control and when to surrender, when to push, and when to let go. I am learning to trust my thoughts, own my body, laser focus my thinking, and just breathe— really breathe.

Grateful for this life, this day, and this moment.

Carolyn Lebanowski ~ *My husband, Wayne, for his unconditional and unfaltering support in my journey. To my yoga instructors who gently pushed, encouraged, and inspired me along the way. I am forever grateful to Marizol Cabrera, Larry Thraen, and Harris Hammer.*

One of Carolyn's Favorite Quotes

*Yoga is a dance between control and surrender —
between pushing and letting go — and when to push
and to let go becomes part of the creative process,
part of the open-ended exploration of your well-being.*

Joel Kramer

Goodbye, Momma

By Martiné Emmons

*I expected my mom (especially my mom)
to be strong forever.*

**Martiné Emmons
(author, host, entrepreneur)**

"**M**omma, oh, Momma." I couldn't believe my sight. "Momma, it's me. It's Martine'." My words were met with a somber stare. My vibrant, healthy momma was "gone." I thought I had prepared myself for her declining health, and clearly, I hadn't.

Ultimately, my mom was diagnosed with a psychotic form of dementia. Sounds scary, I know.

Her physical and mental changes seemed to appear after a car accident. My dad's injuries were minor, but she never recovered.

My mother was a vibrant, loving, and compassionate person. People were naturally drawn to her. People at the grocery store, church, or retreats she attended all loved her. Although a stay-at-home mom, she was fiercely powerful, independent, and never hesitated to speak her mind. She also had a kind and compassionate heart. She exuded love.

In June 2013, my dad called. "Martine', I can't care for your mother alone anymore. Can you help?" I said, "Of course, Dad. I told Mom I would always be there for both of you, but I can't move back to California. Can you come here?"

A year earlier, I had remarried and moved from California to Michigan with my husband and children. It was hard leaving for many reasons, one being that my mom's memory was declining more and more every day.

We all picked my parents up at the train station in Chicago. I was so excited to see them. As I waited, I prepared myself for a few changes as I hadn't seen my mom for a year. But shockingly, she simply wasn't "my mom." I was devastated and guilty because we had moved halfway across the country, and I should have been there for her and my dad.

My dad called me within ten minutes of arriving at the hotel, where we planned to stay overnight. He asked me if I could help bathe my mom. And so the care began. While bathing her, I was filled with regret, sadness, and FEAR. How would I take care of her in addition to my three kids, work, and ... sigh ...

"Momma, what happened?"

In the past, I had taken care of my former mother-in-law when she was in the end stages of cancer. A significant difference in her case, as I was not the only caretaker. My former sister-in-law and I shared responsibilities for her personal hygiene and getting her dressed. My ex-husband and other family members took on the food preparation and other things needing to be done.

But caring for my mother became a solo job. To complete their move to Michigan, my dad returned to California to pack up and sell their home. So my mom moved into our home. One is never prepared to care for their parents. It's scary, humbling, and very difficult. I expected my mom (especially my mom) to be strong forever.

We made temporary adjustments in the small home we rented and began searching for a larger house to accommodate the expanded family—my parents and our five kids. My husband had two boys from his previous marriage who lived with their mother most of the time. From a previous marriage, I had two girls and a son. His boys and my girls were the same age. My son was seven years old.

Two months later, my dad finally returned from California. He said it felt like he had slept a month. He was not only exhausted from the toll of caring for my mother, but he and other helpers packed up years' worth of belongings, including my grandparent's estate. My dad put most of their belongings in storage and packed the rest into an old school bus, and he left California.

In hindsight, my mom's memory had declined for about a decade. It was subtle in the beginning. She would forget how to do the simplest things that used to be part of her daily routine. And she would say something that didn't sound like her. For example, my mother was very proper, and though the "new" things that came out of her mouth were funny at first, it gave me pause to think something was not quite right. Eventually, she stopped doing the things she usually loved. Most notable was her relationship with her girlfriends. Many of them had been friends since elementary school (she called it grammar school), and they got together yearly. After she declined to meet with them two years in a row, my dad and I knew something was really wrong. She loved her friends so much.

I remember the day our phone calls changed. I quickly realized our calls needed to be fun though they felt so superficial. My momma, the one who could soothe anything with her warm, calm voice and hugs, was no longer available.

By the time my dad arrived back in Michigan, a lot had changed. We had made an offer on a larger home, and my mother no longer resided with us. We had to put her in a safer environment. And by safe, I mean for the kids and us. Her dementia was worse - confusion, memory loss, disorientation, and limited mobility.

One morning at our rental home, my mom woke me up at 4 AM, telling me to take her to my brother. By this time, I had learned it was best to "go along with" her. I no longer corrected her. Even though my brother lived 2,500 miles away, I told her that we would make plans in the morning and that she should go to bed and get some sleep. She cooperated. By 6 AM, she was banging on my bedroom door and was "ready to go again," which meant her clothes were inside out and her bra was on the outside of her top. I told her it was still early and to relax. I had to get the kids up and ready for school. And thank goodness, I got them out the door.

By this time, she had become quite violent.

It's amazing how someone with dementia can be so feeble and pleasant in one instant and flip a switch and become excessively strong, determined, and forceful. She grabbed me by my breasts and told me to take her to Stephen, my brother. I broke away from her, locked myself in the mudroom, and called 911. As I called for help, I heard her leave and take off down the stairs. Mind you, she was dressed in disarray and did not have her walker or any form of assistance. Emergency personnel, my husband, Eric, and I desperately searched for her. Finally, she was found at a church by the dispatched officers. She told them, "People are trying to harm me." At this point, we determined that she needed an evaluation. During her hospital stay, the mental health professionals diagnosed her with dementia with psychosis. After that, she never returned to the house.

Her disease progressed rather quickly. Just before her church escape, we had enjoyed picnics, and our conversations were somewhat normal. There were still snippets of my "normal" mom. I am forever grateful those moments are captured with photos.

We moved into our new home with my dad and took turns visiting Mom. One morning, she fell out of bed and broke her hip. During one of my dad's visits after her fracture, mom told him, "Let's go to lunch." He said he would love to take her out, but she had broken her hip and couldn't go out for a while. She replied, "I did? No one told me."

About three weeks before she passed away, my sister, brother, his wife, and their son flew in to visit Mom. They were devastated by the changes in her since they last saw her. My brother took it the hardest. He had always been her favorite, and he loved her so much.

On January 9, 2014, about six months after moving into the nursing home, Mom passed away while holding my dad's hand.

Everyone flew in again for the service. Mom was cremated, and we had a service at the local Catholic church. It was a small gathering as they had not lived in Michigan long. My mom was such a loved woman. The church would have been packed if the service had occurred in California. Instead, my dad sent her ashes to Nevada, where she was buried with her parents.

I missed my Mom so much. I still do! Mostly, I was glad she was free of the illness that had taken the last ten years of her life. She taught me to stand up for myself and to lead my life with love.

The kids took her passing pretty well, as their grandma hadn't been the same in so long. My oldest daughter missed her the most as she had experienced the best part of her. When she was born, Mom was still full of life.

Though my father missed her immensely, he was exhausted from his caregiving role. And he knew she was at peace. So for those of you that have been in a caregiving role, you understand. You miss your loved one so much, yet you are drained.

From my heart to yours, friends, please take the time, no matter how inconvenient or how much work you have to spend time with those you love. You NEVER know how much time you have.

About one month after my mom passed away, my dad traveled to Washington to explore. He had always wanted to live by the ocean as it was where he grew up. He returned two weeks later and told us he had bought a home and was moving there.

One month later, I was diagnosed with colon cancer. I hadn't felt well for a while and suspected something was wrong. I had terrible stomach and intestinal pains but thought it would pass. As a woman, we get a lot of little pains, and sometimes as in my case, you are unsure if it's a female issue or something else. But, we also care for everyone else, and time passes, or we minimize what we are personally going through. I had three of my own children, cared for my stepsons when they were with us, worked, and spent time with my husband ... just so much to balance.

I finally went to the doctor, and they suggested pain medications. That didn't sit well with me. I asked a friend in the medical field what I should do, and she suggested that I see a gastrointestinal physician. It scared me, but I knew I needed to go. The doctor's office said I had to have a colonoscopy before the doctor would see me. After I completed the procedure, I went to the doctor's visit. I remember him saying, "Don't worry. It's probably just IBS. You are way too young for it to be anything more serious." After I came out of the procedure and the anesthesia wore off, the doctor was there, and he looked pretty solemn. He said he was so sorry but needed to do a biopsy and was 99% sure I had colon cancer. I tuned out and let my husband finish the conversation. He called me two days later, confirming I had Stage 3 colon cancer. He recommended a surgeon, and we got started. The very next day, in fact, I was on the treadmill with a plan. I already had an exercise regime, and I would continue!

I would beat this!

Believe it or not, both of my siblings had had different types of cancer. It was hard to comprehend that all three of my parents' children had cancer. Really?! I think this is part of why I tuned out—how could this be? Other than my siblings, cancer had never been in our family. We come from a pretty healthy line.

I met with the surgeon, who was very kind (and oh so NICE to look at). He told me I was young, healthy, and would have a great outcome. We did the surgery, and two weeks later, I began six rounds of chemotherapy. I was very blessed during this time because I could mostly care for myself. Though it was hard, it wasn't as difficult as asking for help. Neighbors and friends took my kids to school. People brought us meals. Friends and my mother-in-law took me to treatments while my husband balanced everything.

My mother's demise and my unexpected battle exemplify how short life is. You never know from one day to the next what will happen. Take that trip you have been putting off and visit the people you love. DO what feels right for you.

My sister died one and a half years after my mom passed away. Stay tuned for that story in Book 3 of this *All Things Wellness* series.

Martiné Emmons ~ *I wish to thank my mom. She was always a loving presence. She showed me strength and deep love. I will miss her always.*

One of Martine's Favorite Quotes

There is always light. If only we're brave enough to see it.
If only we're brave enough to be it.

Amanda Gorman

Am I Typhoid Mary

By Renee Gideon

What can I change? What can I accept?
When do I need to talk to someone?

Renee Gideon
(author, caretaker)

I wanted to write a story for the first book of this *All Things Wellness* series, but I was coming through a difficult time and losing my sister. My story was too raw to convey my message correctly. I want to take a moment and set the background of where I came from and how it all began.

I am the youngest of eight children. There are 25 years between my oldest sibling and myself. Seven years between myself and my closest sibling. So, growing up, one might think of me as "the baby," however, my youngest brother is not the sharpest tool in the shed, and I say that playfully! So the brother, just older than me, might seem to be the youngest. Nevertheless, he and I were very close. I was also close to my next older brother. My parents were always the oldest parents at my school functions, which is not always a bad thing. At least they were mature enough not to make fools of themselves!

My parents' elder care fell to me.
So now the story begins.

My mother was an emergency room worker and developed uterine cancer when I was only six. She underwent chemotherapy and never missed a day of work. She hid her illness from everyone except my oldest sister. Luckily it was the 70s, so wearing wigs wasn't that unusual. She recovered and fought many different cancer battles throughout her life, ranging from superficial skin cancers to more aggressive types such as advanced basal cells. I would fill a whole page if I were to list them all. Ultimately, she lost her battle with lung cancer.

While fighting lung cancer, I was her primary caregiver even though I had a business to run and lived 300 miles away. I spent endless hours on the road with many hours to process. I pondered why my siblings, who lived much closer, couldn't or wouldn't take the lead on her care. I was devastated to think that no one else had the same bond I did with her. My caregiving eventually included my elderly father, who was, for all intents and purposes, legally blind and not the easiest person to relate to. But, for the most part, I had a great relationship with him. During the last weeks of her life, I stayed with my parents and operated my business remotely. After she passed, I upheld the promise I made to her. I took care of my dad. He moved in with me, leaving their home and all of his friends (not the smartest move I have ever made). I did not take a moment to grieve or reflect on the loss of my mother.

This was the beginning of another disaster.

I loved my father dearly; however, I had no idea what I was in for. I was up and down numerous times during the night with falls out of bed, causing severe skin tears, or he would aimlessly wander because he couldn't find the bathroom. He had repeated visits to the VA hospital. The extensive care he needed eventually led to the breakdown of our relationship. He moved in with my older brother, but he died less than four months later, a very lonely and broken-hearted man. I felt so responsible for sending him away that it was nearly unbearable when he passed. I vowed never to turn another person away.

I continued to care for several other loved ones and friends battling cancer, many of whom I brought into my home. My husband began to think I was obsessed with dying people, and I wondered about that myself. Each time I strived to become a better caregiver and take care of others, I became a shell of a person.

The next on the list…My husband and I befriended a carnival worker who moved into our home and worked for room and board during the winter months. It was the third winter he came to stay with us, and he developed severe back pain. We insisted he go to the hospital, thinking he had an injury. Instead, we discovered he had liver cancer that had spread to his bones, mostly affecting his spine. There I was again—caring for someone who was ill.

This man had no family, and I couldn't let our friend die alone. My husband was so supportive and helped with his care and was at his bedside when he passed away. At this point, I began feeling like Typhoid Mary. Would everyone I came into contact with develop some cancer and die? I became quite reclusive, pulling away from my friends and family. Was I contagious? But the cycle began again.

My brother-in-law became terminally ill. My sister asked me to help her "walk him to the gates of heaven" (not my words, but hers), and I accepted. As a perpetual caregiver, I worried about my sister taking on this role as she wasn't the healthiest and was legally blind. Our family had not supported her self-care, and now she needed to care for someone else full-time. My brother-in-law passed away after months of extensive care by my sister and me. Now it was time to care for my sister.

I made several monthly trips to take her to appointments, and months later found out her finances were in shambles with maxed credit cards, and her home was in ruins. She lived in a 16x19 room, and everything she owned was stacked in that space alongside her sleeping area. There was only one way in and out. God forbid there was a fire. I was furious and disappointed, to say the least. My wonderful husband suggested she move with us, and we built her a space in a shop we planned to build. This leads me to the next chapter of my dilemma.

We were blessed with four years before she became diagnosed with ... you guessed it, cancer! She was diagnosed with multiple myeloma, which went misdiagnosed for nearly a year thanks to Covid-19. She had a large tumor on her mid-shin, which several doctors thought to be Gout. We went for a second opinion because I knew Gout would never show up outside of the joints. We found a doctor who agreed with me, and he referred her to a dermatologist. After a biopsy, it was determined that she had a rare form of lymphoma. After extensive treatment via radiation and chemo, she passed away.

And here I go again.

My brother had suffered a stroke 13 years earlier, was wheelchair-bound, and needed assistance with his personal needs and getting in and out of bed. Truthfully, he needed skilled nursing care. His son, who had suffered from advanced kidney disease, could no longer care for him. After my sister passed away, the apartment that my husband and I had built was empty. My brother, who lived in Oklahoma, asked to come live with us. And, of course, I agreed. His care was exhausting. Someone had to be available 24/7 for assistance. Thank God my two daughters and niece were here to assist with his care.

Shortly before Christmas 2022, he passed. Although his health had been questionable for some time. He was remarkably healthy right to his last breath. He had a fantastic day watching football and had a wonderful dinner. We put him to bed, and he never woke up, dying sometime in the early morning hours. I found him with the most pain-free and serene expression on his face. I wondered if I had somehow missed a significant indicator of something wrong. But he did it on his terms, without someone to comfort and hold his hand. When it is my turn, I hope I can do it his way.

As I became aware of the title of this book, *Win the Wellness W.A.R. (We Are Responsible)*, I realized that it was time to share my story. I help others *win their wellness wars*, and though it can be exhausting and emotional, I am blessed to take *responsibility* for "walking people to Heaven's gate." I do remain curious about how they seem to find me! Fate, perhaps. Regardless, we are responsible for accepting the gifts we have been given, even if it's a gift we don't initially understand or want.

We all take something away from our experiences. Until recently, my takeaway was hurt and pain. I have learned that self-care and mindfulness are the way to peace and harmony in my life, especially after a loss—after several losses. Sometimes, self-care can seem selfish, but it's ok—be selfish sometimes!

Breathing exercises allow me to focus on myself. When I first lay down to sleep, I do some breathing exercises in through my nose and out through my mouth. When I concentrate on these deep breaths, so many things fall out. For example, there are times when I realize I am feeling a bit depressed or anxious. Focused breathing allows me time to deal with emotions and feelings. During *my time*, I don't have to explain to anyone how I am feeling or what I am thinking! It allows me to put things into perspective, what I can change, what I need to accept, or if I need to talk to someone to help me put things in order. I take the time for myself, whether for a minute or an hour!

Meditation and mindfulness are essential parts of what I've learned in my journey. I had no clue what either was until recently. I thought I was handling things okay until I met my friend, and he helped me understand the importance of breathing. He explained it in a way I could grasp. I then began practicing it. We should all learn some self-care not only in the emotional and mental sense but in the physical as well! God Bless you if you are a caregiver, for it is the most challenging and demanding job you will ever have. However, it is one of the most rewarding!

Just don't forget about YOU along the way!

Renee Gideon ~ *Thank you, Markus Wettstein, for helping me understand the true meaning of self-care and how selfless it truly is. Thank you to my husband,*

Richard Gideon, for his patience and understanding. And my daughters, Stephanie and Jessica, and niece, Donna. I would never have made it without you!

One of Renee's Favorite Quotes

For each Thorn, there's a rosebud.
For each twilight-a dawn.
For each trial- the strength to carry on.

For each storm cloud, a rainbow.
For each shadow-the sun.
For each parting-sweet memories when sorrow is done.

Ralph Waldo Emerson

My Unexpected Crucial Test

By Hepsharat Amadi

Sometimes we need to trust our gut, pivot,
and find other solutions.

Hepsharat Amadi
(author, physician)

I told my children to always be open to learning because you never know when the knowledge you attain might become crucial or when life might spring a test on you!

I am a conventionally trained family practice doctor who always understood that conventional medicine while working well for emergencies, was not capable of helping an already healthy person become any healthier. So I understood, before going to medical school, that my purpose in attending was more than just laying the foundation for my medical knowledge but would not be the sum total. Little could I have imagined when that extra knowledge would one day save my oldest child's eyesight and health.

My aspirations were higher than just managing my illness by using drugs and surgery. I wanted to help people get healthier and educated enough to minimize or limit their need for medication or emergency services. That was why, a few years after graduating from SUNY at Stony-Brook medical school and completing my residency in family practice at Bronx-Lebanon Hospital, I began studying many different holistic health techniques, including earning my license in acupuncture and Chinese herbs at night and on the weekends, while continuing to work full-time at an outpatient clinic during the day.

My search for more knowledge about how to improve peoples' health naturally continued.

While attending yet another health-related seminar, I met a colleague who was also holistically oriented. He introduced me to a quantum bio-feedback machine. It changed my life.

Imagine a machine that consists of a laptop computer to which a box is attached. The box has leads that can be plugged into it and attached to a person's head, wrists, and ankles, and it acts as a transducer that detects the electronic magnet activity of the entire body. The most familiar analogies I can give you in conventional medicine are the EKG machine for the heart or the EEG machine for monitoring brain waves.

Now, imagine that, instead of just printing out squiggly lines that take specialized training to interpret, the quantum-biofeedback machine prints out its information in English and numbers! And imagine that instead of only measuring and monitoring the electromagnetic activity of the entire body, the machine could also run therapies for improving the health of the body. How awesome would that be?

That is the nature of quantum biofeedback, assessment, and treatment, and once I saw all the information that could be learned from utilizing it, had on me, I was hooked!

I decided I had to have one of these machines. and treat me, my family, and my patients.

I was introduced to the quantum biofeedback machine in January 2003. In May, I attended a convention in which I learned more about all of the different things I could do, and by August of that same year, I had bought my first quantum feedback machine and started learning how to use it. I turned 47 later that year. While I learned more about using the machine, I attended some other seminars about bio-identical hormone therapy and implemented bio-identical hormone replacement for patients in my practice.

I began taking bio-identical hormones myself when I was 48. It was the confluence of all these circumstances that allowed me the opportunity to help my oldest daughter when she was confronted with a major health challenge in January 2008, five years after I first got the machine.

Around the first week of January, she began complaining of headaches and seeing flashes of blue light. My husband took her to the ophthalmologist ASAP, who called me to tell me that my daughter was having retinal detachment in both eyes and that she was going to refer her to a retinal specialist. I was shocked, horrified, and very frightened! I knew that if retinal detachment was not treated quickly, it could lead to permanent blindness. She was referred to a retinal specialist who confirmed this diagnosis after examining her eyes with a scan called an OCT. In order to treat her retinal detachment, they wanted to put her on a high dose of steroids.

I knew that could have an adverse effect on her in the long run such as making her gain a significant amount of weight and compromising her bones and immune system. I was determined to attempt to treat her naturally before I resorted to such a drastic solution as Prednisone.

When I began assessing her on the quantum biofeedback machine, it told me that I needed to find a granular solution to her health problem. So, in addition to increasing her nutrition and exercise, I also used the quantum biofeedback machine to not only treat her but also to find out which bio-identical hormone she needed each day so that I could give them to her. Within the first two to three hours of this treatment, her headaches and flashes of light stopped, and she began feeling better! I took her back to the retinal specialist several times over the first half year of that year so that they could examine her. By the time we made our last visit, five to six months after the whole crisis started, they repeated her eye exam and her OCT, and they were both absolutely normal, without her ever being on Prednisone!

I knew then that I had succeeded and passed a crucial test life had set for me. I met the challenge of her condition by having enough knowledge to save my daughter's vision and health, naturally.

Conventional methods are not always the solution to improving our health. Sometimes we need to trust our gut, pivot, and find other solutions. My willingness to experiment with new methods was a risk, but one I was willing to take. And I am grateful I did.

Dr. Hepashart Amadi ~ *I would like to thank Desire Dubounet, the inventor of quantum biofeedback, and my oldest daughter for teaching me so much.*

One of Dr. Amadi's Favorite Quotes

We are energy.

Hepsharat Amadi, MD

The Birth of B.E.S.T. Living™

By Rachelle Simpson Sweet, PhD

*I vowed I would make changes by learning to take time
to fill my cup with beneficial activities for my health.*

Rachelle Sweet, PhD
(author, neuropsychologist, coach)

*R*ecent research has shown that as many as 50% of the three million annual deaths in the United States are entirely preventable. In America, most deaths are caused by cardiovascular disease as a result of lifestyle choices. Surprisingly, even cancer could be prevented in about 50% of cases.

Dr. Jeffrey Bland states, "Chronic illness results from an imbalance in one or more of our core physiological processes. This imbalance derives from the interaction between our genome and our lifestyle, diet, and environment. The imbalance alters our function over time. That altered function is evidenced in the signs and symptoms we collectively label a disease. Changing lifestyle, diet, and environment can bring our core physiology back into balance."

Why don't people take responsibility for their health?

I am as guilty as the next person. Personal responsibility means taking ownership of one's thoughts, behaviors, and outcomes and recognizing our role in creating our own experiences. When individuals take personal responsibility for their lives, they are better equipped to make positive changes, set and achieve meaningful goals, and ultimately thrive.

In the first book in this series, I told the story of the trials and tribulations of yo-yo dieting and my eventual transformation and began my journey to healthy! It was a challenge, and it continues to take mindfulness to stay on track.

I soon realized that maintaining health is more challenging than achieving the initial goal, like losing 30 pounds for the first time. The billion-dollar "diet" industry proves this year after year. Thousands of people lose body fat, yet many cannot maintain that loss. I did this for decades. Sometimes, we try the same thing repeatedly, praying to get a result and often running around looking for external answers to an internal challenge. We look to the next shiny thing as the cure. We do this with our health and other areas of our life. Returning to past habits is much easier than maintaining those that are not ingrained yet. Sometimes, we revert to comfort foods to soothe our frustration or sadness, not realizing we are continuing the downward spiral. Maybe it is because others in our life are not supporting our change or don't like the idea of our newfound path.

We fill every waking moment with external noise and ignore our internal voice. We become time-starved by our schedules. It is much easier to pick up convenient food that may not be as healthy than to spend time prepping and cooking healthy food. Our jobs have become more demanding and sedentary as we must sit in front of computers most of the day. Many are in environments that restrict natural light, such as being in an office during the most crucial parts of the day.

For me, there was an ever-nagging voice to become healthier, yet balancing life while earning an income felt impossible. By default, we live on autopilot. We rush from our house to our job, to school for the children, to functions, trying to fit in as much as possible. As a result, most of us are not thinking about our health or what is happening inside us. People often do not believe that disease or infirmity will be part of their future, but the truth is that the more we neglect our health, the faster it will catch up with us.

I watched a documentary about a man who lost significant weight by drinking green juices. He interviewed people at restaurants about what they ate. My revelation was that people understood the types of food they should eat and that if they didn't change their behavior, it could lead to premature death. The show host interviewed a gentleman eating. His son was sitting with him at the table, and it was clear from the son's face that he was shocked to learn his father had this knowledge yet made unhealthy choices. Why would his father continue to make these choices when he knew he might die prematurely and their time together might be reduced?

Most of us do not think about how we will spend our later years, especially the last decade. As I age, I have started to think about my parent's age. As I get up from a chair with minor aches and pains, I often wonder what it will be like when I'm 60, 70, and 80. Will I be able to move the way I want to in the future? How decreased will my ability be?

Ultimately, it is up to me.

The actions I take today are for my future self. Therefore, the last few decades of my life start now. Yes, maintaining my health now allows me more freedom to enjoy life in the present. However, that carries over to the subsequent decades of my life.

Everything lives on a spectrum. Our level of responsibility lives there, too. Each choice we make comes with an outcome. The saying, "If it is to be, it's up to me," motivates me, but it has not always been for the positive and has been a detriment to my long-term health. I was fortunate to have many different experiences in my life, which have given me areas to improve. My drive has rubbed up against finding balance in my life. I often thought everything was a priority. And when it comes to our health, many of us think we can put it off until later.

All we have is right now, this present moment. There is no "later."

For about a decade, I managed a hotel. The job was very demanding and required long hours. It was a small hotel, which required much of me, as it did not produce enough income to allow staff to cover everything needed. I am unsure if it was distrust or my insecurities that things would not get done, so I rarely delegated to others. During the peak season, I worked up to 100 hours a week, attending to guests' needs.

The physical strain kept me awake at night. During slower times, I found time to exercise, walk, and enjoy the beautiful scenery, but many of those benefits were offset by the busy times of extreme stress and anxiety, ensuring everything got done correctly and that the business was profitable,

My inability to respect my limits and set boundaries ultimately caused negative health consequences. This caused physical and emotional exhaustion, detachment, and lack of motivation leading to burnout. I lived in a beautiful setting, a postcard in many ways, yet I wasn't enjoying it. People who visited the hotel used to say to me, "You must love living here so much." In many ways, it was true, yet the responsibility of the job clouded it. When taking on more responsibility, you may neglect your personal life and proper rest. While I was doing many things on the outside to be healthy, I could not see how much stress and strain this was taking on internally. I had emotional, physical, and mental exhaustion.

Burnout can significantly impact mental health and well-being.

It seemed nearly impossible to step outside my norm. My usual mode was to push myself to work harder and longer. Research shows that working beyond 55 hours a week diminishes productivity. Much like the lumberjack cutting trees that never sharpens his ax, there comes the point when you can no longer do the work you once could. My breaking point came with a life-threatening illness and emergency hospitalization. I was forced to stop. It was so stressful. At one point, I told the doctor he had to let me out because I needed to return to work. The staff thought I was absurd. Once I was discharged, I returned to work immediately. My body didn't agree with that tactic, and it actually prolonged my recovery. Despite my insanity, I vowed to make changes by learning to fill my cup with beneficial activities for my health. It is one thing to be responsible. It is another to think you can be responsible for EVERYTHING!

Simultaneously caring for myself and all of life's demands proved impossible. Being comfortable in my routines and accepting that I was "rightfully" exhausted caused me to skip physical activity and beneficial rest. These crazy demands also increased my consumption of comfort foods high in calories, sugar, and unhealthy fats. Believe me, this one is hard. I love my comfort foods, and while comfort may temporarily relieve stress, relying too much on comfort can lead to apathy, disengagement, and depression. I knew intellectually that my thoughts and behaviors would likely lead to weight gain and other health problems. And the risk of heart disease, diabetes, and other health conditions was not lost on me either. By trying to control every situation and not thinking there was an alternative.

My lack of mindfulness kept me on "autopilot."

I know you can relate. This "autopilot" state often refers to a state of mind where an individual is not fully engaged in their surroundings and instead thinks about other things or is mentally disengaged. I was actively engaged, but mostly with work. My life was terribly out of balance. Here's the thing about stress. It is a U curve. No stress; being sedimentary and not engaging in life is as unhealthy as too much stress. Living at either end of the spectrum is unhealthy. But, like the coal under pressure to produce that beautiful diamond, some stress can be beneficial. A mentor once told me, "We should live on the edge of chaos." This sounded crazy to me. He referred to intermittent amounts of Eustress. Eustress can motivate us to act and achieve our goals. It can inspire us to work harder, be more pro-ductive, and take on new challenges. Exercise is a perfect example of this eustress; it has many physical components of stress, such as an increased heart rate, blood pressure, and glucose.

Before the hotel was sold and that job ended, I began studying epi-genetics and lifestyle medicine. It led me to wellness coaching and writing a book. One of the chapters discusses thriving. During my studies, I realized the power of positive psychology, the scientific study of human flourishing.

Recognizing that personal responsibility is a key component of well-being and a key factor in promoting individuals' ability to thrive. Positive psychology explains that individuals who assume personal responsibility for their lives are likelier to experience a sense of control and autonomy. These attributes are essential for well-being. We can direct our lives toward our goals by taking responsibility for our thoughts, emotions, and behaviors. We can become mindful and intentional about our choices with work or play. I began to experience greater satisfaction and fulfillment. Taking personal responsibility, adopting a growth mindset, and viewing challenges as opportunities for growth and learning made me better equipped to bounce back from setbacks and maintain a positive outlook—even in the face of adversity.

For me, combating burnout and understanding the proper levels of eustress became a focus.

When practicing mindfulness, or the act of paying attention to the present moment, I learned to reduce my overall stress and improve my well-being. I began to meditate. This accomplished various positive outcomes, including reducing the adverse effects of stress and focused me to be aware. By aware, I mean being intentional about what I do. I call this intentional thriving. I engage in actions that benefit me in the present and future. This starts with B.E.S.T. Living™. First, the art of breathing and slowing down. Meditating is one component. Second, understanding our genetic blueprint, eating whole foods, and being energetic with deliberate movement. Third, consistently sleeping 6.5 to 7.5 hours every night. And fourth, learning what activities make us thrive. What inspires us is our sense of community and family. Finding and pursuing a sense of purpose in life, whether through work, relationships, or personal passions, can increase meaning and fulfillment.

I welcomed challenges and have developed a few non-negotiables. I exercise in the morning, emphasizing strength training. I walk a mile at lunchtime whenever possible. I find beautiful places to hike and kayak. These activities give me the eustress I need. I sleep as close to 7 hours as possible every night with a consistent routine. I think about what things my future self wants to experience and learn and then work toward those goals. My future began to reveal itself as I learned to live in the now. It's important to think of your future self and take action to create the future you want. Sometimes that means stepping outside your comfort zone.

Ultimately, ask your future self how you want to live the last decades of your life. Take time to write it down. If the answer is vibrant and strong, then take responsibility now. It is in your hands. You have the ultimate choice, and it starts in this moment.

Rachelle Sweet ~ *Thank you to my parents, who inspired me to dream and believe.*

One of Rachelle's Favorite Quotes

If it is to be, it is up to me.

William Johnsen

BODY Commentary

By Coach Peggy & Dr. Markus

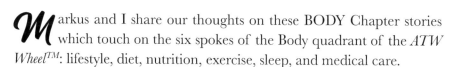

*M*arkus and I share our thoughts on these BODY Chapter stories which touch on the six spokes of the Body quadrant of the *ATW Wheel*^{TM}: lifestyle, diet, nutrition, exercise, sleep, and medical care.

Tanner, when you give 100% to the pursuit of talents and gifts, other sectors of the Wellness Wheel suffer. A hard reboot (pardon the pun) gave you the opportunity to balance your life again. After a life-changing injury you began focusing on your health and mindset. It started with baby steps, literally, and then to have fought an addiction along the way, kudos for serious grit. Thank you for this story. It will be a beacon of hope for many.

Evelyn, it is a major battle won when we come to realize how powerful we are. Turning the light on negative aspects of our life is difficult. To "make this work for me" is the next challenge. Involving help frequently shortens the time to resolution. You turned a loss into an opportunity to grow and help others. Thank you for these guideposts to win the battle. You are a leader by sharing your story about how grief can drive purpose, and your are helping connect the masses.

Cyndi, chronic pain is very difficult to live with. Your detailed account proves that. Medication is the easy, quick fix for some, but it does not address the root cause. It takes a lot of determination to reveal and deal with the "trigger event." You tackled the "monster" and found coping mechanisms that work for your migraines. It is so important to show chronic sufferers that there is a way out. Suicide is the only perceived resolution for some. Thank you, Cyndi, for saving lives.

Peggy Press On (Preston) is your new name from us. When we discussed the framework of this book, we never realized we would be connecting with a real-life soldier. Peggy, has become a resilient beast. War is the largest contributor to amputations, so your story will resonate with a lot of people who have not fought a physical battle yet have struggled with physical hardships.

Jesica. *"I feel your agony. I am a Nutella addict,"* says Markus. Once the switch is turned on, there is no reasoning. It is constant work to tone down the voices and identify triggers for any addiction. This is a topic that affects us all whether directly or indirectly. We just choose different substances. Admitting to an addiction is difficult. Dealing with it is even harder. Thank you, Jesica, for giving us the will to fight.

Michelle, you showed us that hitting rock bottom is one of the most significant triggers for people to change. She is not alone, and finding her new tribe makes the battle a bit easier. Acceptance and connection with others change lives. Motivation to change is hard to generate. Motivation to keep going is even tougher. COVID was a challenging experience when many people lost hope. She didn't give up or lose focus.

Carolyn, in the medical community, hypertension is also known as the silent killer. As you pointed out, we uncover a lot of penned-up issues that can express themselves in elevated blood pressure. This sympathetic overdrive indicates the parasympathetic system has to be activated more frequently for balance. You accomplished this. Thank you so much for sharing, Carolyn. I am certain, many readers will start the move towards medication independence.

Martiné, when the mind leaves before the body, caretaking takes on another dimension. Then there is the personal cancer issue on top. Your resilience is admirable. A lot of people refuse to help with elder care, even for their loved ones. You showed us how to negotiate all of the above with grace and gratitude. For that, we salute you.

Renee, you have put the spotlight on a topic many of us are facing. We are all aging, and who is going to care for us? Care-giving Especially for the terminally ill is very complex. It depletes you of energy in all sectors, mind, body, heart, and spirit. You also show how a huge heart, as is yours, can become exhausted and how it takes a toll when we "over" give to others. Breathing has really helped you out and we are hoping you continue to share your journey of helping others and how you are also helping yourself. A recharge regularly is necessary to be able to complete the mission. Thank you, Renee, for giving so many a dignified exit. I can only hope for a blessing like that for each of us.

Dr. Amadi, you showed us how trusting your gut and having the willingness to try something new may have prevented your daughter's blindness. We underestimate our own ability to predict. Trust thyself. And you have taken your experience and education into your field of practice. Thank you for sharing this personal experience with us.

Rachelle, the story you shared in our first book, *The Four-Fold Formula for All Things Wellness*, jumped out to us because of your transparency and determination. In this story you offer a path to a more balanced, harmonious, and happy life. All the way to the end. Literally. Most of us live on auto pilot more than 80% of our waking life, which represents a lot of time spent not being aware of what we are doing. The body is executing programs. This disconnect over time causes dis-ease. One year later, you have not only continued your journey, but you have created a new program to help others, written a book, and will be starting your own radio show. Now if you aren't an inspiration, who is?

The Coach and The Doc Battle Tips

*A*fter a combined 65+ years in our industries, Dr. Markus and I have been privileged to help thousands of people improve their health and wellness.

Because of this experience, we offer below a few observations and recommendations for each of the 24 spokes of the *ATW Wheel*™. You may want to jot them down on the back of your wellness wheel or on a separate piece of paper for quick reference. Don't forget to create your own tips and and be sure to email us your brilliant ideas so we can share them with others.

If you have not downloaded the wellness wheel, go to:

www.allthingswellness.com/ATW-Wheel-Worksheet

HEART Battle Tips

From the Coach:

Emotion: *Identify your emotions. Find the source.*

Frontier.org found 25 different categories of emotion we respond to—admiration, adoration, appreciation of beauty, amusement, anger, anxiety, awe, awkwardness, boredom, calmness, confusion, craving, disgust, empathic pain, entrancement, excitement, fear, horror, interest, joy, nostalgia, relief, sadness, satisfaction, and surprise. Whoa, that is a lot.

We all have the feels. A feeling is a reaction to an emotion. Have you ever analyzed who or what drives your emotions? Have you ever tracked how many positive or negative emotions you have in one day? Several factors affect our feelings and emotions, like colors, foods, exercise, geographic locations, people, conversations, situations, trauma, etc. If we pay attention to how and why our emotions and feelings are created, we can improve them or prevent a drastic pendulum swing.

For example, do you throw things or cuss if you are angry? What is the source of the anger? Is there a commonality such as work, work, work? What do you do when you feel pain or sadness? Do you cry or maybe you overeat? Again, what is the source of your pain or sorrow?

Tip: 1) Write down the 25 different emotion categories above, and for a few days (I usually recommend a week), track the emotions you feel, 2) Write down who or what drives each of the emotions you feel, and 3) Go a bit further. Write down the actions you took during and after feeling those emotions. Negative feelings, emotions, and actions affect you mentally, physically, spiritually, and financially. And who wants to feel yucky?

An example might be…You always feel angry. The source is your boss. The result is that you often binge eat.

When I have my clients complete this exercise, many things fall out. In order to reduce negative emotions and behaviors, many have restructured or ended relationships, changed their sleep patterns, improved their exercise, found a new job, etc.

I think about prescription medication when I think of this activity. So many physicians prescribe medications that treat the symptoms and never help patients determine the source of the pain or disease. Do not just "treat" the "emotional" symptom—identify the source. That is where you gain control.

Stress: *Identify the stressor. Find a solution.*

Researchers have linked weight gain to stress, and according to an American Psychological Association survey, about one-fourth of Americans rate their stress level as eight or more on a 10-point scale. There are three stages of stress: acute, chronic, and burnout. When in fight or flight, the chronic or burnout stage of stress, the adrenal glands work overtime. Under pressure, the hormone cortisol is released. Elongated periods of high cortisol will affect most spokes of your wellness wheel, such as appetite changes, lack of self-care, sleep, and more.

Identifying who, what, and why you are stressed out is one of the most helpful exercises you can do. This exercise is very similar to the emotion tip I shared above.

We unconsciously throw around the sentence, "I'm so stressed out." Let's see what the actual data is. The goal is to find healthier ways to cope, thus reducing your stress and improving your health. You can often manage stress simply by taking a few deep breaths between your feelings and actions. You might be glad you counted to ten before chasing down a kid who flipped you off.

Here we go. 1) Who or What are your top three stressors? Maybe finances, kids, and work. 2) What is your "current" coping skill (if you have one)? 3) If it is not healthy, write down a few you can try.

Make a list of your top 3-5 stressors. For the next several days, make the list as detailed as possible. If you do not have coping skills for specific stressors, write NA. The goal is to eventually create healthy coping skills to help you control your stress levels.

- ***Who or What*** *causes the Stressor: Children*

- **Why** does it cause stress? For example, their sports and school schedule, their disrespect and attitude towards others, lack of time with them, or maybe the financial struggle to provide for them.

- **Current Coping Skill:** I will go to the gym or call my mom.

- **Healthy Coping Skills:** Sit down and chat weekly. What are they stressed about? What can you all do to improve respect? Hire a babysitter once a week.

Coping Skills. *Dirty Dozen.*

Healthy coping skills change and save lives. A healthy coping skill finds the calm in the storm. It is a way to balance negative behaviors or feelings and gets you back on track to living a productive life. It is a temperature gauge for your tolerance.

Over time, most coping skills change. They work until they don't. Going to the gym to blow off steam may no longer be feasible now that you have twins. Now how will you get a grip when you are losing it?

Step 1: Make a list of coping skills that work for you right now. The goal is to have at least a dozen. This will bring attention to those you might need to tweak a bit or some you may have forgotten about. 2) Now is a fun twist. Make a list of at least a dozen you have not tried. And now you get to TRY THEM. There are many sources online to give you ideas of ways to cope with emotions, feelings, stress, workload, relationships, and more. I believe everything in life is about experiments. If you have not tried lima beans or Brussel sprouts, how do you know if you like them? If listening to meditation music no longer decreases your anxiety, what else might you do? It is especially advantageous if you find healthy coping skills for each of the 24 spokes of your wellness wheel.

From the Doc:

Self-Care/Self-Love. *What feels good or brings joy?*
Taking care of yourself is loving yourself right down to every cell in the body. This cannot come from the mind, so addictions are out. For smokers, the first drag off a cigarette feels great. But it is only erasing the symptoms of nicotine withdrawal, which causes your brain to tell you to light up.

Instead, the stimulus comes from the heart. You are on the right track if your heart "jumps with joy." This rarely happens to me, so a more settled indicator is a sweeping electrical sensation, like a wave flowing through the body. I focus on the harmonization of my cells. It is a great feeling to strive for. If you struggle with a self-care practice, start simple. Think about what truly brings you joy and do more of it.

Relationships. *Who is in your circle of trust?*

It is a lot of work to build and keep heartfelt relationships. I gauge my ability to forgive. In relationships, we all make mistakes. Sometimes, words slip out of my mouth that I wish I had not uttered. Others do the same to me. But remember, to forgive means never to use the incident against your spouse in a negative fashion. Too many people out there use personal information to harm others. As a result, people close themselves up. This is not good for the heart. We must find at least one person to trust and open up to. What I find amazing is that my children have formed tribes of kindhearted peers. Likewise, anyone reading this book is forming a group of like-minded individuals willing to move in a positive direction of living life with an open and kind heart. There is one line representing the relationships spoke on the ATW Wheel™. However, a great tip is to create three lines—one for intimate relationships (spouse, significant other, partner), a second for extended relationships such as in-laws or siblings, and then a third for social, friends or co-workers. Take a peek at all three categories and write down the names of those that warm your heart and those that are not aligned with you right now. The key is that if there is a possibility to improve your tribe, do so. Spend more time with those who have your integrity and values and less time with those who don't.

Integrity and Values. *Stay true to you.*

The value of freedom cannot be understated here, and it takes integrity to uphold those values. So, it is only appropriate at this point in our book to extend a heartfelt Thank You to our armed forces. Soldiers make the ultimate sacrifice to defend our country. Their integrity scores 100% in this sector of the wellness wheel. We recommend striving for a minimum of 80% in this area of the wheel. Stand confidently to your values and integrity, then make sure you walk the talk. We are mostly off-kilter when we are not living our own truth and values. Stay true to yourself, and your promises, and continue to be gracious in the process.

SPIRIT Battle Tips

From the Coach:

Creativity. *What sparks you?*

Solitude and quiet time are like using a magic wand. Poof, you're restored and centered once again. When we still our minds, we naturally become more observant internally and externally, ultimately lighting a fire and igniting our creativity. We also become more grateful. Taking a walk in nature will prove that. I am most sparked with creativity when I am in an environment I love or doing things that bring me joy, like kayaking, walking, or riding my bike. Ideas flow so rapidly into my brain that I am often scrambling for something to write on. Many of my exciting ideas also come to me during dreams. Keeping a dream journal can be so helpful. A quiet mind is an exciting playground. You can use the 6Ws here. Make a list of who, what, why, where, when, and how you can increase your creativity.

Rituals. *Stacking.*

To me, rituals have special power, especially if you connect them to something you enjoy and that is healthy. They can tie in your religion, relationships, traditions, beliefs, and more. I think of "stacking" when I think about rituals. If you are going to church every Sunday with your parents and then having lunch after with a friend, you made a routine/ritual out of your Sundays. My ritual right now is to get my butt down on the beach every morning at sunrise. It is my way to connect and center. Without it, I feel off-kilter and not whole. I have a friend who does yoga every day before coffee, and then she "earns" her coffee with her hubby. This is a deeper connection than just a habit. Yoga might be the habit but stacking it with other things gives it a bigger bite, and you are more apt to execute it.

Harmony. *Tipping Point.*

We all know when we are not harmonious with our body, mind, surroundings, purpose, etc. That is easy to feel, whereas finding true harmony might be more of a challenge. I lean on my gut and vibes—what makes me feel good and think clearly? Where do I find self-value and self-worth? For me, lots of Vitamin D, being in nature, connection to friends and family, proper nutrition, enjoying my work, listening to music, and…I could go on for days. I know my tipping point. Do you? What makes you balanced? Start a list. Writing it makes it real. When you can identify what makes you feel good, you will more quickly feel the vibe when it isn't.

From the Doc:

Purpose. *Sharing is caring.*

I will quote Pablo Picasso here: The goal of life is to find your gift. The purpose of life is to give it away.

My interpretation: when it comes to living a healthy and happy life, we must align with our cosmic blueprint, God's plan for us. Walking that path is blissful. Sharing that knowledge brings peace and harmony. Some are born knowing their purpose while others develop their purpose and passions over time. If you read our first book, The Four-Fold Formula, Peggy mentioned that purpose can often be that idea or feeling that bolts you up in bed at 3 AM. When you are overcome with joy or excitement, stop in that moment, and determine what the driving force may be… then seek more of it.

Talents and Gifts. *We all have them.*

1. *Explore life.*

2. *Find out what you like to do. Once you realize there is something you do with ease and joy, you have found your gift.*

3. *You will find others who are struggling to do the same thing you do. Be helpful and try to convey joy.*

Beliefs and Faith. *Tap in.*

I was raised in a catholic/protestant household. This gave me room to explore my own spirituality. Over the years, I began studying more about Eastern concepts and practices. That, along with quantum mechanics, helped me shape a new spiritual path. I now know we are all connected, and I strongly believe we can help humans rediscover their humanity. Our society is built on competition and survival of the fittest, but I see more and more people cooperating and loving each other. Why? Because it feels better than going to battle.

Expand your knowledge. Read more, watch videos, and communicate with others about their beliefs. Try it out. You will know when you align and when you don't. I continue to expand my consciousness and broaden my knowledge. You will be amazed by the positive changes that come automatically into your life. It's awesome!

MIND Battle Tips

———————— ★ ————————

From The Coach

Personal Awareness and Growth. *We can't fix what we cannot see.*

Personal awareness and growth tend to go hand in hand. As we become more aware, we have three choices: go backward, remain the same, or become a better version of ourselves. Awareness is not easy, and it requires becoming aware of your strengths and areas of improvement. I hate the word weaknesses because, to me, that word is not only negative but relative. Becoming more aware allows an opportunity for growth.

How do we improve our self-awareness? I encourage clients to tap into their feelings and emotions. Throughout your day, you have several opportunities to assess your feelings, especially if you try the emotion exercise, I recommended in the Heart Battle Tips. How do you react to people, things, events, etc.? Are there ways you want to improve your feelings or behaviors?

Being silent or journaling with the intent of becoming more aware is another great way to identify growth areas. Start with questions: What or who makes you happy or sad? What or who makes you want to run and hide? A few examples might be phone calls, your job, household chores, or specific people. After reviewing your answers to these questions, what might you do to improve how you feel about them?

Depending on your continued awareness, you might need to set new boundaries, which often makes some people fall away, or old habits die off. For example, if you become aware that your best friend makes you feel insecure or judged, you may need to spend less time with him or work with a coach or therapist to help you set boundaries.

1. *Check-in with how you feel.*
2. *Continue to educate yourself by attending lectures, taking classes, or learning a new skill.*

3. *Try new hobbies or learn a new language.*

Do you want to try another exercise? Yes, Coach. I personally completed this process back in 2016. Once I became aware, I left Corporate America, and moved to another state. I pivoted, and it changed my life.

You can do this with any area of your life such as your relationships or even where you live. Let's see how satisfied you are with your professional life. Pros and Cons. At the top of a piece of paper, write your current job title (Executive Director, Police Officer, Nurse, etc.). Include things like being a mother or domestic goddess (DG. Love that). Those are jobs, too! Then make two vertical columns under the job title. On the left, list the Pros of your job—your responsibilities/tasks, the people, the location, etc. On the right, list the Cons. Do not forget how you feel about the organization: mission, vision, values, leadership, communication, continued education opportunities, co-workers, etc.

Once you are done, sit back and take a peek. Set your emotions aside and ask yourself how satisfied or dissatisfied you are with your job and the people you work with daily. You may discover it just isn't that bad, or this exercise might reveal it is time to take responsibility and make changes which just might include finding another job.

Become more aware and find areas to grow.

Organization. *External chaos causes internal chaos.*

Time to make some cash. What can you donate or sell? Facebook Marketplace is a great place to start, especially if you are not interested in organizing a yard sale. Look at your books, clothes, toys, extra sets of plates and utensils, and holiday decorations. As they say, a disorganized environment most often means a disorganized mind.

A secondary plus to downsizing is the ability to create income from doing so. Turn it into a game. How much can you and your family make? What would you spend it on? A trip? A new couch? Getting rid of what you do not want, what is broken, or you no longer need, is an excellent start to becoming more organized.

Habits (Approaches, Strategies, Routines). *Find what works.*

What are your cues? Just before you execute a behavior, there was a cue. Cue review. Just before we execute an action, your brain has told you to do so. AND there is a reason your brain shouted the command. Cue: You feel hungry. Habit: You go grab a snack.

Cue: You feel hungry. Pause. Before you take action, count to 10. What cue prompted you to grab the bag of Doritos mindlessly? Was it a TV commercial? Are you tired, hungry, bored, or maybe a certain time of day triggers you to snack? If your action is unhealthy, it is time for a rewire. Rewiring your cues becomes easier when you are aware of what they are. Walking during your work break instead of hitting the vending machine or going to bed early might avoid snacking or feeling depressed.

Many people beat themselves up wondering why they cannot embed healthy habits. Trust me, if you identify The Cue, you will be able to emotionally and physically respond more healthily to the trigger.

From The Doc

Home Environment (organization and planning). *Our home is our castle.*

My home environment must feel comfortable. To achieve this, I find my home in the sweet spot between filth and sterility. The gray zone is wide, and your sweet spot may lie closer to one extreme or the other. If you find yourself uncomfortable in your own home, plan for a battle to find your comfort zone. Our mind is strong, and the willingness to change the status quo is difficult to generate. Once the feeling of ease, security, and safety take over, it is much easier. The signals come from the heart and settle the mind. This way, it is much easier to deal with changes around the home.

Planning ahead also helps my home operate more smoothly. I remarried a few years back. The transition from a single household to life with my fabulous wife and three kids was not easy. Leading by example is difficult with kids. Open communication and sharing responsibilities are requirements that need to be reinforced constantly. From my perspective, a recharge or timeout is required to maintain a cool head. I use my bedroom as the "man cave." Sometimes I am the one that needs the timeout. Do you have a recharge location for your timeouts?

Work Environment (time management, finance, education, and job satisfaction). *Does your job make you unhealthy?*

Job satisfaction is the most important driver to combat stress. A few years back, Peggy and I conducted a Destress the Stress pilot project. One of the most common drivers of the participants' stress was their job and finances. Depending on the study you review, about 65-70% of working-age adults are working full-time, and about 65% of workers are happy with their profession. Most of their happiness is based on their relationship with their co-workers, learning new things, and feeling appreciated.

According to https://www.apollotechnical.com/job-satisfaction-statistics/, only 20% of workers are passionate about their jobs. Most people work to pay the bills. Many try to like their job, but nobody can get around their subconscious mind. If you are unhappy, no matter how much you suppress it, it will bubble up. Many of us have been forced into a job we do not like, but I ask you to dig deep and see if there are ways to make it more satisfying. If we do not pursue our purpose, "dis"ease will set in. Chronically, this may lead to serious diseases such as a heart attack, cancer, diabetes, and many more. We are responsible for investigating how happy and satisfied we are and determining what needs to change. For many, a change in jobs is necessary, but they do not make a shift unless something catastrophic happens, like their health.

By finding a job you enjoy, you could improve your positive state of mind by 30%.

Mindset (thoughts and beliefs). *Is your heart or your mind in charge?*

Question: are your thoughts mostly negative or positive? Is the glass half full or half empty?

As science proves, electric charges affect each other. Ideally, there is a balance between negative and positive attractions. When the mind is boss, it can take over and lead you one way more than the other. Check in often to see if you hover more in a positive or negative field. This is not easy, but only "mind-heart coherence" will help with balance and improving more positive energy. How do you do that? I use the heart-math device I mentioned above. Once the heart and mind communicate, stress is replaced by calm bliss. Once felt, the desirable aspects give the heart more room to eventually govern the mind. I place affirmations in my mind. I begin my day with: I love myself, and I love my life. Slowly, over time, my inner critic, the mind, slowed down its chatter. I strive for joy and happiness of the heart, and the mind simply follows because it feels so good.

BODY Battle Tips

From The Coach:

Diet. *What's the plan, Stan?*

Instead of trying to follow a meal plan that works for others, experiment, and design one that works for you. A diet is a "plan" such as keto, Mediterranean, etc. A diet consists of rules such as what to eat, the time to eat, and portion. Depending on whether you are an emotional, habitual, or passionate eater depends on what plan might work for you. For example, if you are a passionate eater, you are attracted to diversity: lots of colors and a variety of flavors to entice your palette. If you are a habitual eater, you will follow your plan more closely if it is simple, and you are able to set consistent timeframes to eat.

Try different meal plans. Track how each plan you try makes you feel. Does your stress increase? Is your sleep the best it has ever been? Are you so grumpy that no one wants to be around you? Has your cholesterol doubled?

Your "diet" should consist of foods that your body needs and those that make you feel your best. It is important to also align your diet and nutrition with the goals you are trying to achieve.

Nutrition. *An apple a day keeps the doctor away.*

A few quickies to begin improving your nutrition is to strip your meals and snacks back. Take off the crap! Get naked as I say—your food, that is. Reduce consumption of condiments and salt. Bake versus frying. These baby steps can make a big difference. By keeping your sodium under 2400 mg a day (1500 for diabetics), you might lose several pounds in water weight. Big results for small actions. The average American consumes about 3500 mg of sodium daily. Leaving the salt shaker alone and reducing the amount of salt you cook with are great starts.

Look at those labels. Foods free from dyes, additives, antibiotics, pesticides, condiments, or unhealthy spices (again— naked foods) are healthier. Look for ingredients that are real and whole foods: carrot, almond, and chicken are three simple foods whereas words difficult to pronounce such as Butylated Hydroxy anisole and Butylated Hydroxytoluene are artificial chemicals used in potato chips. We find healthy foods often have one-two syllables max. I dare you…spend this week tracking your sodium, consuming more naked food, and reducing all foods in your house that have ingredients that are not real food. I damn near guarantee you will feel better, reduce inflammation, and lose a few pounds in the process.

Lifestyle. *Way of living.*

A healthy lifestyle is one with a balanced ATW Wheel™. All four quadrants (heart, spirit, mind, and body) are in harmony. Are you satisfied with the way you live your life, your relationships, finances, nutrition, beliefs, integrity, etc.? When in our 20s, our lifestyle might involve eating out daily, dancing on Friday and Saturday nights, and rooming with a buddy. In our 30s, we might settle down, have a few kids, and focus on our careers. If you think about where you are in life and where you want to be and go, what improvements can you make that align with your health and wellness?

From The Doc

Sleep. *The secret ingredient.*

I cannot state strongly enough how important sleep is. I regard sleep as the base of our existence. Without proper sleep, we cannot have a functional life. I suggest downloading a sleep app. Consistently review the hours of sleep and find out how much you need. Try to achieve that goal every night. You will feel refreshed waking up when you do it just right.

Usually, the free apps go even further. You can determine if you snore, cough, or even stop breathing (sleep apnea). Sleep hygiene is a vast topic. For many people, poor-quality sleep can be improved by shifting certain behavioral habits, such as reducing anxiety and stress, especially before you shut down at night. For some, using meditation music or fans helps. I enlisted others to win this battle. As a scientist, I dug deeper into the sleep phases and cycles and their importance. Unfortunately, one has to spend money to get better data. There are also "sleep labs" which take this topic to the cutting edge.

Medical. *Sooner rather than later.*

Western medicine has its place. And regular physician visits allow us to help you. In my specialty of endocrinology, I focus on metabolic function and diabetes. Learning that your thyroid is not functioning properly requires seeing a physician, addressing the problem, or dying. I know that sounds dramatic, but your thyroid helps regulate your metabolic system and controls many bodily functions. As medical doctors, we are trained to help you with your health problems.

Unfortunately, many humans have problems they do not know about until something breaks, and a disease is established. At that point, people give up their autonomy. Instead, they take a "Doc, fix me" approach.

Casting physicians as pill pushers is demeaning and perpetuates animosity. It also causes noncompliance which can be dangerous. By attending annual physicals, you can identify illness and proactively combat it. For example, let's say during your regular checkup, it was determined that you have high blood pressure (BP). You might take a few steps: 1) begin taking a medication to lower the BP, 2) modify your behavior and achieve positive results or 3) try a combination of numbers one and two.

These choices can improve your health or even save your life. However, you may have missed your high blood pressure altogether without a regular checkup. You might suffer a stroke if you do not visit a physician regularly. You would then live the rest of your life with permanent damage. So why not try a medication to decrease the risk of a devastating event while simultaneously working to improve your lifestyle? Under a physician's care, the pill will be tapered by your doctor as you lower your BP on your own. And if you can improve your numbers entirely independently, excellent job. We want more of you in our offices.

Being proactive requires finding out the information, to begin with. Make every effort to see your dentist, eye doctor, and family physician at a minimum annually.

Exercise. *Building strength prevents injury AND illness.*

Beware! If you do not use it, you lose it. Muscle mass is critical, especially in the elderly. I prescribe "functional exercises" to help them maintain strength, balance, coordination, and bone density to avoid disastrous falls.

But even youngsters these days have a poor muscle-to-fat ratio. According to a recent Harvard article (https://www.health.harvard.edu/exercise-and-fitness/age-and-muscle-loss), we lose 4-6 pounds of muscle every decade without strength training.

Young or middle-aged people risk developing type 2 diabetes if they do not retain their strength. Due to more sedentary lifestyles and unhealthy diets, they will continue to lose muscle mass. This is why we begin with prescribing diet and exercise. We know that patients who improve their muscle mass and lower their body fat content can REVERSE diabetes, even if using insulin at the beginning of their lifestyle change.

Here is a helpful link for functional exercise:

https://www.spartan.com/blogs/unbreakable-training/best-exercises-for-functional-strength

Summary

———— ★ ————

To be prepared for war is one of the
most effectual means of preserving peace.

George Washington

Some wars are won, and some are lost. Some battlefields leave remnants of destruction and defeat, while others bring about a cause of celebration—the Win.

Failing, being frozen, or spinning are wellness whispers telling you there are areas of improvement. You are now trying to let go of that 4/10. Going for the B and mastering 80% of every component of your life is more impressive and healthier than averaging 40-50%.

Remember to Break up with Perfection and Win.

Crawling, walking, or running is the only way you will improve any area of your life. Standing still is no longer an option, nor is complaining. You own this.

It is hard, work and war when working on your wheel. Some spokes may improve more quickly for you, whereas others feel like you have been stuck in the mud for years. Either way, it takes self-discovery, preparation, planning, and action to keep your wheel in balance before your Wellness Wagon ends up in a total collision.

Walking away from any battlefield can be extremely graphic and even deadly. Do not wave a white flag in defeat.

It might not feel like it, but when you are winning those small battles, you are winning the war. You are now armed with data to improve punctures below 50% (5/10). You are on your way. Your Wellness Wagon wheels are filling with air, and you are getting back on track.

You have earned a medal of honor because you are still reading this book. If you do the work, you will earn that new pair of jeans, cut the ribbon of your new home, or step off the plane in Bali.

Don't give up. Don't quit the gym if it is working for you; maybe just rearrange your schedule so you can go more often. Don't divorce your high school sweetheart; maybe try counseling or start date nights. Don't leave college in your junior year; maybe move a class to the next semester or get a tutor. We often quit because negative emotions pop up or we simply need support or a new perspective. Then, defeat starts to rain on us, and we run. Don't run!

A win is a win, and a loss is a lesson.

Welcome both the win and the crumble. What? That is ludacris! No, it is not. In our failures and victories, we find areas of improvement and growth. After one battle (goal) is lost, another is right behind it, whether you know it or not.

Remember the words hard, work, and war? These words have followed us everywhere since the beginning of humankind and will continue to do so until the end of time. Neanderthals hunting buffalo to feed a family of six was hard. It was work. It was a war. Though we no longer need to hunt buffalo, improving our health and wellness can feel just as monumental.

What did you learn by completing your 6Ws and filling out the *ATW Wheel*™? Take the time upfront to fill out these tools. Do not run to your goal if you first need to crawl and walk.

There are smoking guns in your health and wellness journeys. Most often, there is concrete proof right before your eyes. You know why things worked or why they didn't. Do not ignore your gut or your personal history and data. There are answers there. Embrace them. Dissect the hell out of them. You know why you avoid certain situations or people. You know why you come up shy on your goals.

There will always be obstacles, landmines, or logistics to go over or around. Preparing for the unexpected is as important as designing a plan to move forward. Not everyone can see into the future, but we can prepare for many things ahead of time. What can you control or not control? I certainly cannot control the weather and predict when a hurricane will head for us, but we can prepare as much as possible in case it does.

The ability to adapt to stressful situations or a crisis can change your life dramatically. We must pivot when faced with unexpected challenges, and by developing healthy coping and communication skills, your health and relationships benefit greatly.

What are your smoke and mirrors? Have you obscured the truths of your success or failure? Do you avoid change? Do you fantasize about results without even taking a baby step? Look at the real you; wipe the fog off that reflection. *Deal with the Real.* We want you to take responsibility and move into action instead of just fantasizing or blaming others because you are not as healthy and happy as you can be. Take responsibility for your own health and stop blaming physicians, big pharma, and "genetics."

When you complete the *ATW Wheel*^{TM} by using the prompts, the *6Ws of Wellness*, some of our battle tips, and doing your own research and experiments, how you can improve your health will magically appear.

Do what you do with passion. Find that sparkle. Make your dreams come true by making your dreams come true! When taking responsibility in the 24 areas of your life, you will continue to *Win the Wellness W.A.R.* by assessing and re-assessing your health, wellness, and lifestyle. You are on the front line—the leader of your own infantry, marching forward and bearing a rucksack loaded with strategies and tools that work for you. Carry on, soldiers.

Inward, Outward, Forward

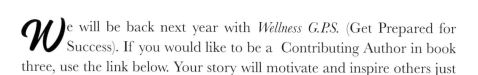

*W*e will be back next year with *Wellness G.P.S.* (Get Prepared for Success). If you would like to be a Contributing Author in book three, use the link below. Your story will motivate and inspire others just as the stories in this book have hopefully affected you.

Thank you for being a part of our journey. Together, we will *Win the Wellness W.A.R.*

Reserve your spot for book three:
www.allthingswellness/authors/wellness-gps

Download your free *ATW Wheel^TM:*
www.allthings.wellness.com/ATW-Wheel-Worksheet

Purchase the *ATW Wheel^TM Assessment and Improvement Plan:*
www.allthings.wellness.com/ATW-Wheel-Assessment-Improvement-Plan.

Win the Wellness W.A.R. Story Teasers:
www.allthingswellness.com/authors

All Things Wellness YouTube
https://youtube.com/@allthingswellness1718

Additional Recommended Reading

12 Rules for Life by Jordan Peterson

A New Earth by Eckert Tolle

All About Love by Bell Hooks

Anatomy of the Spirit; The Seven Stages of Power and Healing by Caroline Myss, PhD

Atlas of the Heart by Brené Brown

Atomic Habits, by James Clear

Boundaries: When to Say YES, When to Say NO, To Take

Control of Your Life by John Townsend and Henry Cloud

Breath: The New Science of a Lost Art by James Nestor

Change Your World by Dr. John C. Maxwell

Conversational Intelligence by Judith Glaser

Daddy, Are You Proud of Me? by Sean Smith

Daily Gift of Gratitude by Teresa Velardi

Eating in the Light of the Moon: How Women Can Transform Their Relationship with Food Through Myths, Metaphors and Storytelling by Anita Johnston

F*ck Feelings by Michael Bennet and Sarah Bennett

Girl Wash Your Face by Rachel Hollis

Good Moms Don't by Alysia Lyons

Heaven is for Real by Todd Burpo and Lynn Vincent

Homecoming by John Bradshaw

Hunger, Hope, and Healing: A Yoga Approach to Reclaiming Your Relationship to Your Body and Food by Sarah Joy Marsh

Inward by yung pueblo

Marinka by Marinka Melanie Hunter and Lily Star

No Drama Discipline by Tina Payne Bryson PhD and Daniel J. Siegel

Ready Player One by Ernest Cline

Sound Mind, Sound Body by Kenneth R. Pelletier

Serpent Rising by Victor Acquista

Tease by Brandy Wilde

Ten Years Behind the Mast by Fritz Drammer

The Energy Bus Field Guide by Jon Gordon and Amy P. Kelly

The Field by Lynne McTaggart

The Go-Giver by Bob Burg and John David Mann

The Gift of Giving: Living Your Legacy by Jim Stovall and Don Green

The Inner Landscape by John O'Donohue

The Moment of Lift: How Empowering Women Changes the World by Melinda Gates

The Power of Now by Eckhart Tolle

The Power of One More by Ed Mylett

The Power of Your Subconscious Mind by Dr. Joseph Murphy

The Success Principles™ -How to Get from Where You Are to Where You Want to Be by Jack Canfield

The Tao Te Ching by Lao Tzu

The Universe Has Your Back by Gabby Bernstein

There is No Plan B for You're A-Game by Bo Eason

Think and Grow Rich by Napoleon Hill

The Tao of Pooh by Benjamin Hoff

The Untethered Soul by Michael Singer

Three Feet from Gold by Sharon L. Lechter and Greg S. Reid with the Napoleon Hill Foundation

Vagina: A Re-Education by Lynn Enright

Vibrational Medicine, The #1 Handbook of Subtle-Energy Therapies by Richard Gerber, MD

We Should All Be Feminists by Chimamanda Ngozi Adichie

Whole Brain Living by Jill Bolte Taylor PhD

Why The Jews by Dennis Prager and Joseph Telushkin

You are a Badass by Jen Sincero

You are a Goddess by Sophia Bashford

You Are The Brand by Mike Kim

Frank Zaccari's books *When the Wife Cheats, From the Ashes - The Rise of the University of Washington Volleyball Program, Inside Spaghetti Bowl, Five Years to Live, Storm Seeds, Business Secrets for Walking on Water, Business and Personal Secrets of Avoiding Relationship Landmines, Business and Personal Secrets of Getting Stuck, Business Secrets from the Battlefield to the Boardroom*

Book Club Talking Points

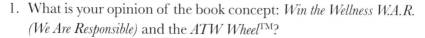

1. What is your opinion of the book concept: *Win the Wellness W.A.R. (We Are Responsible)* and the *ATW Wheel*™?

2. What are your thoughts and feelings when you hear the words hard, work, battle, and war relating to your health and wellness?

3. What are your thoughts about:

   - The descriptions of each book section: Heart, Spirit, Mind, and Body?

   - The *ATW Wheel*™ tool and how to use it?

   - The *6Ws of Wellness* and how to use them to define your goals clearly?

   - The Co-Authors' Commentary at the end of each chapter?

   - *The Coach and The Doc Battle Tips?*

4. What stories in each of the four Chapters: Heart, Spirit, Mind, and Body, resonate with you the most?

5. Are there any standout sentences or scenes for you?

6. Did reading the stories of this book impact your opinions of specific subjects? Which ones and why?

7. What surprised you most about the book?

8. If you could ask the Co-Authors anything, what would it be?

9. If you could ask a Contributing Author anything, what would it be?

10. Are there lingering questions you are still thinking about from the book?

Meet the Co-Authors

Peggy Willms

Peggy has been a certified personal trainer, sports performance nutritionist, personal and executive health, wellness, and life coach for over thirty years. Peggy is an entrepreneur, author, and host of The Coach Peggy Show. She is also the executive producer of Coach Peggy Real Time, a transformation docuseries. Peggy hosts wellness retreats and is a featured contributor for BizCatalyst360, an international online magazine. She spent over twenty years in corporate wellness and has managed multi-million-dollar medical clinics. Her unique business and work-site wellness programs have earned her multiple awards. She has two sons and two grandsons. She loves all things beach and sunshine and lives in Florida with her better half.

Linktr.ee/coachpeggy

Markus Wettstein. MD

Dr. Wettstein has practiced endocrinology for nearly thirty years. He is a diabetes, metabolic, and stress management specialist. He also works in energy medicine as a Licensed Bio-Well practitioner. He assists clients in improving their health and wellness by measuring their energy field, stress level, health status, and energy reserve via electro photonic imaging. He lives in Colorado with his wife, has three children, and enjoys skiing and hiking.

mwettst@gmail.com
https://www.facebook.com/groups/281480796353365
www.linkedin.com/in/markus-wettstein-0a2037b4/

Meet Hassan Tetteh, MD

Dr. Hassan A. Tetteh is a US Navy Captain and Associate Professor of Surgery at the Uniformed Services University of the Health Sciences and adjunct faculty at Howard University College of Medicine. Currently, Tetteh is a Thoracic Surgeon for MedStar Health and Walter Reed National Military Medical Center and leads a Specialized Thoracic Adapted Recovery Team in DC.

A native of Brooklyn, New York, Tetteh received his BS from State University of New York (SUNY) at Plattsburgh, his MD from SUNY Downstate Medical Center, his MPA from Harvard's Kennedy School of Government, an MBA from Johns Hopkins University Carey Business School, and an MS in National Security Strategy with a concentration in Artificial Intelligence from the National War College. He completed his thoracic surgery fellowship at the University of Minnesota and advanced cardiac surgery fellowship at Harvard Medical School's Brigham and Women's Hospital in Boston.

Tetteh is the founder and principal of Tetteh Consulting Group, creator of *The Art of Human Care*™ book series, and best-selling author: *Gifts of the Heart*, *Star Patrol*, and *The Art of Human Care*. Dr. Tetteh is also a TEDx speaker.

He's an alumnus of the Harvard Medical School Writers' Workshop and Yale Writers' Conference and lives near Washington, DC, with his wife, son, and daughter

Meet Our Front Cover Contributing Authors

————— ⭐ —————

Angi Currier is an author and medical Patient Access Representative. She has three biological children and a granddaughter. She hopes to inspire others with her triumph over addiction. Angi feels like she has lived two lives. The first life involves physical and emotional struggles, and the second is living in gratitude, acceptance, and confidence. ajhinkle5@yahoo.com
www.facebook.com/angi.hinkle

Alexxa Goodenough is a serial entrepreneur, starting at age nine. Her passion is creating change and making the world better. She is a polymath, business strategist, and Multi-Modality Holistic Healer and trauma specialist. Her education includes; MSW (master's in social work), Bachelor's in Management, and is an Executive MBA candidate. Certification as Elite neuro-transformational coach, Advanced EFT (emotional freedom technique/tapping practitioner, numerologist, and professional doula. She is an author, speaker, trainer, advocate, consultant, grant writer, event retreat and conference planner. She is a self-proclaimed foodie, Aquarius, ruling number 5, loves Karaoke, and is an INFP-A (The Mediator).
www.linkedin.com/in/AlexxaGoodenoughdot.cards/Alexxa (case sensitive)

Alysia Lyons is a mom first, an entrepreneur, a life coach, and an author second. She is passionate about helping women live their lives with more joy from the inside out. She has her Bachelor of Science in Business Management and is a certified Master Neuro-Transformational Life Coach. Alysia guides her clients through long-lasting neurological shifts to help ease their guilt and increase their emotional freedom. She is the author of the blog The Mom Support Coach, which focuses on relationships, mom guilt, communication, and lessons she has learned throughout her daily life.

info@alysialyons.com
www.alysialyons.com
www.facebook.com/momsupportcoach

Christine Hersom graduated from Franklin Pierce College with a bachelor's degree in accounting and a minor in social science. She has owned a daycare for 25 years. Self-professed hater of cold climates. She is an author and blogger for *All Things Wellness* and BizCatalyst360.

christinehersom@yahoo.com
www.facebook.com/chersom1
www.linkedin.com/in/christine-hersom

Cyndi Wilkins has practiced the art and science of therapeutic massage and energetic bodywork for 20 years. She believes in co-creating health, reinforcing mind, body, and spirit to explore the root causes of discomfort and disease. She is an author, blogs for *All Things Wellness,* and a featured contributor for *BizCatalyst 360°,* and. She lives in Marblehead, Massachusetts, with her wife, their beautiful daughter, and ‹pandemic pets› Keena and Luna.

cyndiwilkins12@gmail.com
www.cyndiwilkins12.wixsite.com/website
www.linkedin.com/in/cyndiwilkins/

Evelyn Knight Evelyn Knight is an engaging speaker and leading expert in Early Childhood Education (ECE). She specializes in helping leaders navigate the business of childcare while making sure the children come first. Evelyn is the CEO and founder of Child Care Business Professionals, which has helped hundreds of ECE leaders find success. She is the host of The Child Care Business Coach podcast and has been a successful childcare center owner for over a decade. Additionally, Evelyn was a full-time nurse to her terminally ill husband while running her two companies. She is deeply passionate about elevating the ECE field.

   https://linktr.ee/evelynknight

Faith Pearce is a single mum with an adult daughter. Faith has worked in Banking & HR. She spent 10 years working for a private medical company in Quality management, reviewing, updating, and issuing all company documents, and departmental onboarding. After a career change, she is retraining in Pharmacy. Faith loves animals. She is an author and blogs for All Things Wellness. She loves art, photography, and getting creative in the kitchen. Her favorite place is the beach. She is passionate about self-development and empowering others to discover their own potential through a holistic approach. She dreams of traveling the world.

   Fancyfaith1234@icloud.com
   www.facebook.com/faith.miller.90
   www.linkedin.com/in/faith-miller-79ab1131

Jacki Long is a certified Jack Canfield Success Principles™ trainer. A Master Coach for Sean Smith, Jacki was a featured trainer and mentor for Sean's advanced coaching certification programs. She is a speaker, author, and Neurolinguistic Programming (NLP) practitioner. Jacki spent 20 years in the corporate world, owned and operated a mystery shopper company, and achieved success in direct sales. With over 30 years of leadership, training, and mentoring experience, Jacki customizes coaching and training programs for clients, helping them achieve their professional and personal goals.

coachjackilong@gmail.com

www.facebook.com/CoachJackiLong

www.linkedin.com/in/jacki-long-02ba6415/

https://wa.me/13174405655

Jesica Henderson has a bachelor's degree in audio engineering. She is an executive producer at The Transformation Network and for The Dr. Pat Show. She's been a lifelong creative and musician and hosts her own radio show: *The Possibility Perspective*. She enjoys exploring the mountains, paddling on Lake Washington, or learning/practicing new songs on the fiddle, guitar, clarinet, or ukulele. Still passionate about learning, she continues to further her career and self-development, always pursuing opportunities to create, learn, and grow.

jesica@thedrpatshow.com

www.thepossibilityperspective.com/

www.facebook.com/thepossibilityperspective

Lara Scriba loves exploring new places, and whether she's sailing the world with her family or discovering the nuances of her inner world, her curiosity always leads her to look just below the surface. Her passion to support others to heal through a holistic lens has been nurtured by her background in nursing, work as a Reiki practitioner, Yoga Teacher specializing in stress resilience, ayurvedic habits and eating disorder recovery, and Numerologist. She delights in co-creating an experience with others to reignite their inner spark, shine a light on the wisdom that already exists, and cultivate a deep sense of connection and trust with one's self.

k2kyoga@gmail.com

www.kitokaizenyoga.com

Renee Gideon is a wife, mother, and roofing contractor with 30 years of experience in commercial and residential roofing. In her spare time, she enjoys spending time with her grandkids, cooking, gardening, traveling, and deep-sea fishing.

Sophia Long graduated from Carmel High School in 2019 with an honors diploma. She has dedicated herself to her passion for activism and equity. This scholar has been through several life experiences that have allowed her to grow personally and professionally, including mentorship from the author of The Success Principles, Jack Canfield. She is an undergraduate student studying at Indiana-University Purdue-University Indianapolis (IUPUI). She will graduate with a bachelor's degree in an Individualized Major with a concentration in Women, Gender, and Sexuality Studies, a bachelor's in Sociology, and a minor in Communication studies in 2023. She currently lives in the Midwest with her fiancé and two cats.

sophialongwrites@gmail.com
https://linktr.ee/authorsophialong

Tanner Willms is an author, logistics specialist and spent six years in the oil and gas industry as an NDT inspector. After a tragic motocross accident, he spiraled into alcohol addiction. He is focused on sobriety and raising a family. He and his wife, Brittney, have two sons, Crew and Dutton. As an accident survivor and recovered alcoholic, he hopes his story will inspire others to keep fighting.

Meet Our Other Contributing Authors

⭐

HEART Chapter Contributors

Anita VandenBerg graduated from Ferris State University and has been a dental assistant for 37 years. She loves spending time with her husband biking, hiking, and playing pickleball. Being by the water and in the sun brings her peace and happiness.

Gina Lobito is an author, Transformational Coach, and Energy Intuitive with a background in Bodywork, Shamanism, and Healing Arts. She worked in Law Enforcement for 14 ½ years. She has advanced studies in Self Mastery, which led her to create Soul-Inspired to guide others through their transformation and Ascension Process. She hosts a radio show, has a sheepadoodle, and loves the beach.

gina@soulinspiredreflections.com

www.soulinspiredreflections.com/

Keith Zygand, aka **Ziggy Salvation,** is a husband, father, and Master Barber with over 20 years of experience. When he is not behind the barber chair, he spends time with his family, takes day trips to Legoland with his wife and kids, and live streams video gameplay on Twitch.

ziggysalvation@gmail.com

twitch.tv/ziggysalvation

Phillip Williams worked for Merrill Lynch for 23 years as an operational leader with human resources accountabilities. He studied business and human resource management and development at the University of Phoenix and Villanova University. He holds a Bachelor of Science and a Master of Science degree in Human Resource Management and Development. Phil is currently a PhD scholar at Northcentral University and resides in the greater Atlanta, Georgia, area.

Philgs400@gmail.com

https://www.linkedin.com/in/philliptwilliams61/

SPIRIT Chapter Contributors

Mark Reid inspires independent thinkers on his *Zen Sammich* podcast. He has an MA from Florida State University in philosophy and religious studies and graduated from Syracuse University of Law. He is an attorney and professor turned Washi (Japanese paper) Maker. Mark is also an award-winning contributor at BIZCATALYST 360.

website: zensammich.com

https://www.linkedin.com/in/zen-sammich/

Victor Acquista has become a successful international author and speaker following careers as a primary-care physician and medical executive. He is known for "Writing to Raise Consciousness." His current focus is on embodying a soul-centered presence and awareness in daily life.

https://victoracquista.com/

https://www.linkedin.com/in/victor-acquista-md-bb540917/

Allison Kenny is an author, speaker, Belly Dance teacher, and the creator of Bellydance Meditation® - a movement modality that combines Pilates, Yoga and Bellydance with a feminine twist! A former professional belly dancer and performer, Allison is a certified Subject Matter Expert by the Yoga Alliance.

https://www.linkedin.com/in/allisonbrynkenny/

MIND Chapter Contributors

JoAnna Baanana is a mother of two wonderful little humans, a marketer, an insatiable learner, a writer, and an avid reader. She is grateful to work at O'Brien Communications, where she has learned the restorative craft of writing. JoAnna is also a self-acknowledged survivor.

> linktr.ee/joanna_baanana
> joanna@obriencg.com

Sylvie Plante is a former Human Resources Sr. Director with over 40 years of international experience in the Software, Engineering, and Professional Services industries. She holds accreditations and certifications in Leadership. She teaches Human Resources at the University level and coaches individuals who want to get to the next level and reinvent themselves.

> Sylvie.plante@createalifybydesign.com
> www.Sylvie-plante.com

Ashley Romero aka Lana Montreese is an entertainer, multi-city producer, and international burlesque and drag king sensation based in Portland, Oregon. They/Them are the owner and creative mind of Banking on Burlesk, a newly launched show on the Transformation Talk Radio Network, focused on telling Lana's story about how burlesque saved their life.

> lanamontreese@gmail.com
> instagram.com/lana_montreese

Marshall Townsend II has a bachelor's degree in history from California State University and attended Boise State University. He is a certified executive and business coach, keynote speaker, and US Army Veteran.

> mtownsend@MT2Leadership.com

BODY Chapter Contributors

Carolyn Lebanowski worked in the corporate environment from retail to becoming a senior-level executive in strategic development, organizational communication, and executive coaching. She is a Strategic Business Leader for nonprofit spiritual institutions. She writes, focusing on raw, authentic experiences drawn from real life. Carolyn champions connection, integrity, and radical positivity.

 https://www.linkedin.com/in/carolyn-lebanowski
 https://www.facebook.com/carolyn.miller.1806

Dr. Hepsharat Amadi is a native of New York who graduated from Bronx High School of Science in 1974, Harvard University in 1979, State University of New York at Stoney Brook Medical School in 1987, and Bronx-Lebanon Hospital Family Practice residency in 1990 and moved to South Florida where she graduated from the Community School of Traditional Chinese Medicine in 1998, has been in private practice since 2001 doing holistic healthcare, including Quantum Bio-Feedback and Bio, Identical Hormone Replacement Therapy. She is married with three children.

 www.greatnaturaldoctor.com
 www.dramadi.com
 www.facebook.com/DrHepsharatAmadi
 YouTube: @hepsharatamadi4494
 LinkedIn: Hepsharat Amadi

Michelle McDonald is a Mental Health Therapist who wants to help people spark change in their lives and relationships. I am a lover of Summer and all things water. My greatest joy is being an auntie to many nieces and nephews. I love to embrace life!

 Instagram @MY.SHELL.23
 www.facebook.com/michelle.mcdonald.731

Peggy Preston works in the Foodservice Industry specializing in Bakery and Desserts; North American Category Manager for Gordon Food Service in Grand Rapids, Michigan, as an amputee and hopes to inspire the amputee community to get active. She lives in an RV with her husband. Mom of two boys and two Havanese pups.

https://www.facebook.com/peggy.m.preston/

https://www.linkedin.com/in/peggy-preston-5b9a8788/

peggypreston21@gmail.com

Dr. Rachelle Sweet's background is in Neuropsychology, Health Coaching, and Genetics. She evaluates epigenetic blueprints to guide stressed, tired women, to achieve more energy, and clarity, and helps them wake up confidently to rock their day. She maximizes client results by using genetics as a guide and understanding biological individuality. She is the author of *Expressive Origins*.

coach@DrRachelleSweet.com

linktr.ee/CoachRachelle

Meet Our Media Partners

Dr. Pat Baccili is the owner of *The Transformation Network*-Live Streaming TV/Broadcast Company, an International award-winning radio host, *The Dr. Pat Show* – Talk Radio to Thrive By, #1 *Positive Talk* in Seattle several years running, reaching millions of people broadcast on hundreds of AM/FM/Digital networks in 165 countries. She is a TV commentator, Keynote Speaker, Certified Career and Belief Coach, award-winning Author/Researcher-Broken Promises, and Founder of Street Smart Spirituality.

https://linktr.ee/thedrpatshow

Eileen Bild is the CEO and Executive Producer at OTELproductions, ROKU Channel Developer and Talk Show host for OTEL TALK. She is an author and internationally syndicated columnist for BizCatalyst360, Life Coaching Magazine, Women's Voice Magazine, and NSAEN. She is also a Breakthrough S.P.A.R.K. Coach.

https://linktr.ee/eileenbild

Dom Brightmon is a top-rated Podcast Host of Going North, ranked in the Top 10 of all self-help podcasts worldwide for three consecutive years. Author and certified Self-Leadership Trainer inspiring others to create their own piece of immortality. https://sarklink.com/dombrightmon

Martiné Emmons hosts *Transformation with Martine'* on *Transformation Talk Radio* (Compromise Nothing, Conquer Everything), best-selling author, certified Transformational Life Coach, mentor coach, and virtual executive assistant for coaches and therapists. She is your girl if you want to set up a TEDx Talk. Martine' loves staying active in all areas of her life and finds travel, especially to ocean destinations, the best thing ever! She lives in Michigan with her husband. https://linktr.ee/transformationwithmartine

Christine Innis is the Editor and Chief, Corporate Escapist, TV and podcast host, 4x #1 International Amazon best-selling author, keynote speaker, and educator, hailing from Australia. Mission: share 1 million stories by 2027.
hello@thecorporateescapists.com
https://www.linkedin.com/in/christineinnescoach/
https://www.thecorporateescapists.com/

Dennis Pitocco is the Founder and CEO and Reimaginator of 360° Nation, encompassing a wide range of multimedia enterprises, including *BizCatalyst 360°* - an award-winning global media digest; *360° Nation Studios* - dedicated to reaching across the world to capture, produce, and deliver positive, uplifting messages via blockbuster global events, including *HopeFest 360°*, *BucketFest 360°* and *GoodWorks 360°*—a pro-bono consulting foundation focused entirely on providing mission-critical advisory services to nonprofits worldwide. Dennis is also a contributing author to the Best-Selling Book *Chaos to Clarity: Sacred Stories of Transformational Change* and *The Four-Fold Formula for All Things Wellness.*

https://linktr.ee/dennispitocco

Christopher Rausch is an author and debatably the world's most effective and impactful UNSTOPPABLE "No Excuses" coach, speaker, workshop facilitator, and retreat leader. With a Master's Degree in Organizational Management and over 30+ years of experience, he has personally and professionally applied his education and life experiences to build a thriving coaching business. Catch his RAW & UNSCRIPTED Show on YouTube.

www.ChristopherRausch.com

christopher@christopherrausch.com

Andy Vargo is a Podcast host, *Own Your Awkward*, Best-selling Author, and creator of the *Awkward Journal series* and *Own Your Awkward Life Changes*. He is a motivational speaker, business and life-change coach, and comedian. He lived the first forty years of his life feeling "awkward." Coming out of the closet at forty doesn't define him, pursuing his passion to help others does. Having changed everything about his life, Andy leads others as a motivational speaker and helps people live their fullest lives as a business and life-change coach. At night you can find him working stages around the northwest as a comedian, making light of his journey with the gift of laughter. Awkward is not only his brand but his style as Andy encourages us all to 'Own Your Awkward' and be true to your genuine self.

https://linktr.ee/OwnYourAwkward

Teresa Velardi is a Radio Host: *Conversations That Make a Difference* on DreamVisions7Radio. She is the founder of Authentic Endeavors Publishing. Multi Best-Selling Author, Speaker, Potter, and Transformational Life Coach.

teresavelardi@gmail.com

www.authenticendeavorspublishing.com/

www.facebook.com/teresavelardi57

www.linkedin.com/in/teresavelardi/

Frank Zaccari served as a military medic in the U.S. Air Force before spending over 20 years in the hi-tech industry. His education includes UCLA Anderson School of Business and California State University at Sacramento. His experience includes senior positions with Fortune 50 organizations before turning around several small and midsize companies. His path has helped him learn a great deal about business and life. Frank is a bestselling author who has written and published seven books about life-altering events.

frankzaccari@gmail.com

www.frankzaccari.com/

www.linkedin.com/in/frankzaccari/

www.instagram.com/fzaccari53/

References

Introduction

https://www.smule.com/song/toby-keith-american-soldier-karaoke-lyr-ics/198955714_133449/arrangement

https://bit.ly/AmericanSoldierMeaning

HEART Chapter

https://www.health.harvard.edu/staying-healthy/why-stress-causes-people-to-overeat

SPIRIT Chapter

https://en.wikipedia.org/wiki/Flow_(psychology)

MIND Chapter

https://eh.net/encyclopedia/hours-of-work-in-u-s-history/

https://educationdata.org/college-enrollment-statistics#:~:text=1.69%25%20of%2040%2D%20to%2049,are%20enrolled%20in%20postsecondary%20education.

https://www.npr.org/2022/01/12/1072057249/new-business-applica-tions-record-high-great-resignation-pandemic-entrepreneur

https://eh.net/encyclopedia/hours-of-work-in-u-s-history/

https://www.freshbooks.com/hub/productivity/how-many-hours-does-the-average-person-work

https://www.theguardian.com/lifeandstyle/2022/jan/01/marginal-gains-100-ways-to-improve-your-life-without-really-trying

[1] https://www.hipaajournal.com/hipaa-history/

[2] https://www.bls.gov/news.release/pdf/work.pdf

[3] https://www.statista.com/statistics/1258612/global-employment-figures/

BODY Chapter

https://parade.com/986848/nancy-henderson/types-of-diets/

https://www.health.harvard.edu/blog/4-essential-nutrients-are-you-getting-enough

https://blogs.scientificamerican.com/observations/vanishing-nutrients/

6Ws of Wellness

Int J Exerc Sci. 2009; 2(3): 191–201. Published online 2009 Jul 15. PMCID: PMC4241770 NIHMSID: NIHMS594583 PMID: 25429313

Battle Tips

https://kids.frontiersin.org/articles/

Coming Soon

You are invited to submit your story for book three
of the *All Things Wellness* series
Reserve your spot now!

Wellness G.P.S.

(Get Prepared for Success)

www.allthingswellness.com/wellness-gps

Made in United States
Orlando, FL
14 April 2024

45791294R00239